MW00667922

FOUR FAVORITE TOOLS
Fantastic tools selected by 150 notable creators

**Produced by Claudia Dawson,
Mark Frauenfelder, and Kevin Kelly**

Designed in California

Published by Cool Tools Lab, an imprint of KK*

ISBN-13: 978-1-940689-03-6

About This Book

Creative people tend to accrue a nifty set of tools. Great tools enable efficiency and further creativity, and sometimes inspire whole new ways of working. For the past five years, we (Mark Frauenfelder and Kevin Kelly) have interviewed leading creative people, asking them to enthuse about four of their favorite tools. The tools range from classic handtools, to state-of-the-art laser cutters, to perfect pencils. Each pick is a surprise and a lesson. We've taken these interviews, which were originally broadcast as a weekly Cool Tools podcast, and extracted the best parts for this book. Claudia Dawson, the manager of Cool Tools, did the hard work of distilling the essence of the reviews, laying them out on a page, designing the book, copyediting, and overseeing the production. The result is 300 pages of concentrated goodness and tool fandom. Each tool recommended in the following pages represents a possibility — a potential power, service, product, object, pathway, or opportunity for you that may not exist without the tool. There is no need to purchase every tool described here; just knowing it exists and can be easily purchased is often enough to spark a possibility.

This book's format encourages browsing. If you want to find a particular tool mentioned, you can of course Google it. If you are reading this in a paper book, we have provided a QR code that links directly to a retail site for the tool, usually on Amazon. (*We use Amazon for maximum reader convenience, and because we get a small sliver of revenue if something is purchased there.*) Many modern smartphones will read a QR without having to load an app. If you are reading this as a PDF, the blue links to each source are clickable.

As always, we are interested in hearing about tools that are better than the ones recommended here. If you are familiar with a superior tool, write us a note with why it is better and how you use it. Email it to editor@cool-tools.org. We pay for any reviews that we publish.

Who else should we interview about their four favorite tools? If you have a suggestion for a guest you'd like to hear on our podcast, write us via the same email above.

About Us

We are Claudia Dawson, Mark Frauenfelder, and Kevin Kelly. Claudia is a poet, a production ace, and website manager. Mark is co-founder of BoingBoing, a popular website, and also editor of Cool Tools. Kevin is a co-founding editor at Wired magazine and founder of Cool Tools.

In addition to the Cool Tools podcast, we also produce a weekly one-page email that gives you six very brief recommendations of great stuff. These are personal recommendations about handy apps, great things to listen to or watch, the best stuff we are reading, places to visit, tips, tricks, and life-hacks. This short newsletter, called Recomendo, is free and is shared with about 30,000 subscribers. You can get back issues or subscribe at recomendo.com.

And every weekday since 2003, we post a user-written review of a cool tool on our website Cool Tools. These tools can be anything super handy, from a neat little-known implement, to an inexpensive introductory device, to a premium lifetime tool. Our reviews are independent, personal, and make outright recommendations. Thousands of current and past tool reviews are available at cool-tools.org.

Additionally, we publish a weekly newsletter highlighting everyday carry tools, called "What's in My Bag."

Finally, on YouTube, we offer a series of video tool reviews that compare similar tools and select the best tool to get. Our Cool Tool reviewers methodically go through each candidate to show why this particular tool is the best.

For the full menu of our independent, user-written tool recommendations go to Cool Tools at cool-tools.org.

Our favorite tools to make this book

All 150 interviews were recorded remotely using Zencastr. Mark, Kevin, and the guest were each recording in a different city, yet with Zencastr we could record a conversation with near studio quality. Each participant's speech is recorded locally on their PC and then automatically uploaded to a Dropbox folder as separate audio files. That means there is no loss of quality over crackly phone lines or stuttering VOIP. While participants may hear low quality voice from distant participants, in reality, Zencastr is only recording what it hears from the participant's own nearby microphone.

It's super convenient for guests. No one needs to sign up for an account, and there's nothing to download. You send someone a web link, they add their name, and off you go. Overall it works as advertised, although occasionally some guests have technical issues with their mic or storage area on their laptop. Zencastr is free for minimal use and has paid levels (which we use) for more frequent use and additional features.

We use Rev to transcribe the audio files we download from Zencastr, and those transcriptions were used for the product descriptions in this book. We pay $1 per minute for professional transcription because it is more accurate than automated transcriptions. Files are usually returned within 12 hours or less.

InDesign is the default layout tool used by almost every book, magazine and brochure designer. Built

to do complicated jobs with many bits of text and images. It is one app in Adobe's expansive (and very expensive) network of media tools called Creative Cloud. Still, it's worth it.

We use Amazon's print-on-demand service Kindle Direct Publishing (KDP) to print paper copies of this book. We upload a PDF of the finished book to KDP. The book is listed on Amazon. When someone (perhaps yourself) purchases a copy, Amazon prints the copy at that moment and sends it to you. That means no copies are inventoried – we don't have any books — so there is no sunk investment. KDP charges us $9.65 to print and mail this book in B&W. With a cover price of $13, we make $3.35 per book sold. (*Color books cost us $37.80. We earn even less — $2.15 per book.*)

We hired the proofer to proof the text in this book on Upwork. We use Upwork whenever we need to hire a freelancer to do a short-term job such as proofing, masking images, designing pages, and the like. The freelancers generally offer world-class expertise, but because they often live in places with cheaper living costs than the US, they have lower fees. They can also work fast.

shutterst.ck

The image on the cover was found on Shutterstock. The image was created by Eka Panova, an artist based in Russia. It's one of hundreds of thousands of wonderful illustrations of all types available on Shutterstock. We paid a license fee of $14.50 to use it.

Cool Tools Show Guests

Larry A.
Engineer

Larry A. is a longtime subscriber to Cool Tools and an occasional contributor. He's an engineer who loves technology, and who sees things differently and in more depth than the average consumer.
(Published 08/17/18)

Staedtler 2.0mm Mechanical Pencil

I was looking for a reliable pencil for marking wood and drywall, using a straightedge, during a recent home improvement project. I learned about this 2mm lead holder on ToolGuyd. This is a smaller pocket-size version of a draftsman's lead holder, which is the size of a wooden pencil. If you enjoy using a wooden pencil to draw or draft, you should consider the lead holder. It marries the advantages of a traditional wooden pencil — variable line width expression and a large range of lead grades — with the convenience of a mechanical pencil. And that sums it up. It combines the best of both worlds.

Wireless Remote Plug

I use this remote-control plug to power my router and cable modem off and on (reboot) in order to re-establish my internet connection whenever I

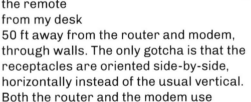

experience a slow-down. I can go for weeks or months without a problem, then, all of a sudden, my connection slows. It is solidly built and it works the first time every time. I can use the remote from my desk 50 ft away from the router and modem, through walls. The only gotcha is that the receptacles are oriented side-by-side, horizontally instead of the usual vertical. Both the router and the modem use large and bulky wall-wart transformers which are oriented at 90° to each other, making it impossible to connect both of them at the same time into the two receptacles on the unit. I have to use a Single Outlet Grounding Adapter to extend one of the receptacles. A simple $0.69 solution.

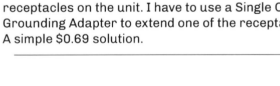

GraphicRiver Pencil Sketch Photoshop Action

This is my exciting new "toy," I mean tool. I used this Photoshop set of actions to compose the sketch for my headshot. I wanted something unusual but I wasn't satisfied with Photoshop's Filter Gallery results, so I tried to find a way to transform a photo

PENCIL SKETCH ART

PHOTOSHOP ACTION

into a pencil sketch. I kept on finding remarkably realistic pencil sketches online, made using the Pencil Sketch Photoshop Action. This is quite an amazing tool for $7. You load an image in PS, load the included brushes and patterns, load the action set, create a layer mask, select the area of interest on the layer mask, and hit the action's 'play' button. It goes through thousands of actions — the exported action set had over 3,800 lines of code, creating and deleting layer upon layer, applying filter upon filter, and finally giving you the finished result. The result is so good, it really looks hand-sketched, including hatch marks, guidelines, and a paper texture. It organizes all the layers it creates into folders of several categories, so you can easily tweak the image by deselecting which layers you want to be invisible. The author must have spent lots of time developing such a polished product. There is a video tutorial that shows you all you need to know to use.

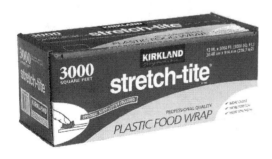

Kirkland Signature Stretch-Tite Food Wrap

I can't say enough in praise of this product. It is the best cling wrap my wife and I have ever used. From its heavy duty, static-resistant thickness that allows handling it without it clinging to itself until you want it to, to its safe, easy-to-use slide cutter. Its great price. It's convenient dispenser box is designed for economical practical use by commercial establishments and home users alike. Although 3,000 ft. seems like a lifetime supply, this lasts us about a year, a year and a half. We keep the box hidden in the pantry right next to the kitchen island. When we need a piece, we just zip off the right length, using the "optional" slide cutter (which is mandatory if you don't want to end up with jagged, uneven pieces, and/or scraped knuckles). The cutter cuts effortlessly using one finger to slide it in either direction. We "float" the piece over to the nearby island without it wrinkling and sticking to itself, and place it onto a container, bowl, plate, or chicken cutlets for pounding.

OXO Good Grips 3-Blade Tabletop Spiralizer with StrongHold Suction

Lately my wife and I have embarked on a low-carb, low-fat, low-meat, small-portion diet consisting of mostly vegetables. I found out there was this tool called a spiralizer, which shreds vegetables into noodles, and it interested me because it sounded like vegetable noodles would be a healthier alternative to carb-laden pasta. It has turned out to be a great investment for $40. It is made of a solid, quality plastic. The whole thing packs up into a compact "cube" shape. The suction base holds so rock solidly, it is actually a bit of a challenge to get it to release. It is easy to use and it works well, producing long, consistent noodles. I can make noodles from many different vegetables, the best being squashes such as zucchini, calabacitas, Asian fuzzy squash, and butternut squash. We serve the vegetable noodles with marinara sauce and grated cheese, or mixed into a stir-fry. They are delicious and very healthy and nutritious. It takes about 5-10 minutes to clean to like-new condition.

Scotty Allen
Strange Parts

Scotty Allen is a nomadic engineer, entrepreneur, adventurer and storyteller who orbits around San Francisco and Shenzhen, China. He runs a YouTube channel called Strange Parts, a travel adventure show for geeks where he goes on adventures ranging from building his own iPhone in China to trying to make a manhole cover in India. (Published 05/18/18)

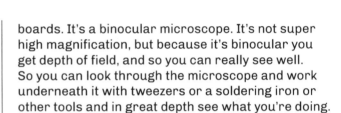

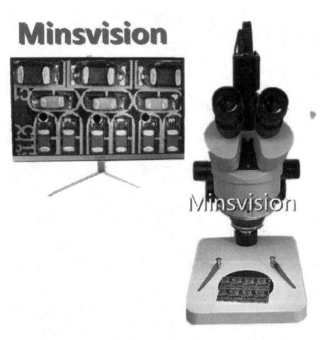

boards. It's a binocular microscope. It's not super high magnification, but because it's binocular you get depth of field, and so you can really see well. So you can look through the microscope and work underneath it with tweezers or a soldering iron or other tools and in great depth see what you're doing.

1080P HDMI digital camera video microscope

One of the things that I have gotten an outsized amount of value from over the past year has been this microscope that I bought here in the electronics markets in China. It's a no-brand-name microscope that I got from a little tiny microscope booth in the market, and it's really been this incredibly high-leverage tool for me, and I didn't realize how much I was missing out until I bought it. It's been really great for doing detail work. And I use it for really small soldering work on iPhones and related circuit

Frame.io

Frame.io is an online tool that I use for collaborating on the videos I'm making. And it's a really simple tool. The short version is that you can upload a video to it, and then you can share that video privately with other people, who can then go in and leave comments. You can even draw things on a specific frame of the video using some drawing tools. And then you can have threaded conversations on each of the comments you leave, and multiple people can leave comments, etc. And that, at face value, is super simple, but it really allows remote collaboration on videos in ways that there really aren't very many other good tools for. In fact, I don't think I've found any other good tools. I come from a software engineering background, and we have some great tools there now that have been built over the past 10 years for doing things like code review where you can do something similar, where you can go in and leave comments on a particular line of code on a change someone wants to make. And so I come from that. I come from running a remote software team prior to doing Strange Parts, and so I was really hungry for all of these tools that I'd used as a software engineer. And so Frame.io is one piece of that. It's sort of that feedback piece of, "Hey, I did this thing. Can you give me feedback on it in a detailed way that's sort of context-based on the part you're talking about?"

TV-B-Gone Universal Remote Control

The TV-B-Gone is a universal television remote with one button, and the button turns any TV off. So this is a cool thing made by a close friend of mine, Mitch Altman, who I know from Noisebridge hackerspace, and I actually owned one long before I knew Mitch. It was given to me as a stocking stuffer at Christmas one year, probably like 10 years ago, or something like that. For the first long while that I owned it, I didn't really use it very much, but now it has become indispensable because I'm traveling a lot more, and when you're jetlagged and you're in an airport on a layover in the middle of the night in Russia and there's a blaring TV in the corner that nobody's watching, the TV-B-Gone is a great way to solve that problem. So in short, you press the button,

it takes up to 15 seconds, and it will cycle through all of the off codes that are programmed in it for all of the different televisions. So you just point it at the TV, and it's great for just sort of calming an otherwise unbearable airport lounge.

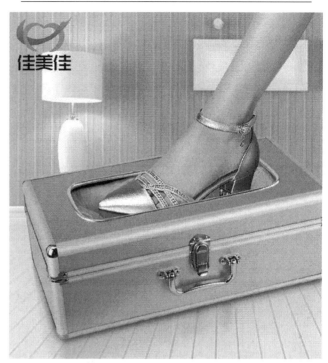

Shoe Cover Dispenser

The one I have kind of looks like a suitcase. It's maybe two-feet-by-one-foot by like six-inches tall, and it's that silver metal that they make briefcases in the movies for carrying large amounts of cash in sort of look. It's got a handle. And on top, it's got an oval-shaped hole that is slightly larger than your average foot, or your average shoe, and the idea is that you stomp your foot down through the hole and it applies a shoe cover over your shoes automatically. You don't have to touch anything. You just step in it and then step out, and now you've got a shoe cover on your shoe. I ran across it on a factory tour. I visit a lot of factories here in Shenzhen, and I was at an LED factory that was making LEDs. They were trying to keep dust down, and one of the ways they do that is by having everybody wear shoe covers. So there are a number of factories that will do this, and you can tell how fancy the factory is based on whether you have to bend down and put the shoe cover on yourself, or whether you have one of these automatic shoe cover machines. And so this LED factory was the first time I'd seen this, and it blew my mind. It was a special purpose thing that was so clever and so well made.

Chris Anderson
3D Robotics CEO

Chris Anderson is the CEO of 3D Robotics and Founder of DIY Drones. From 2001 through 2012, he was Editor in Chief of Wired Magazine. Before Wired, he was with The Economist for seven years in London, Hong Kong, and New York. He's the author of the New York Times bestselling books The Long Tail, and Free, as well as Makers: The New Industrial Revolution. Chris is also the founder of the site Geekdad. He lives in Berkeley, California with his wife and five children. (Published 05/10/16)

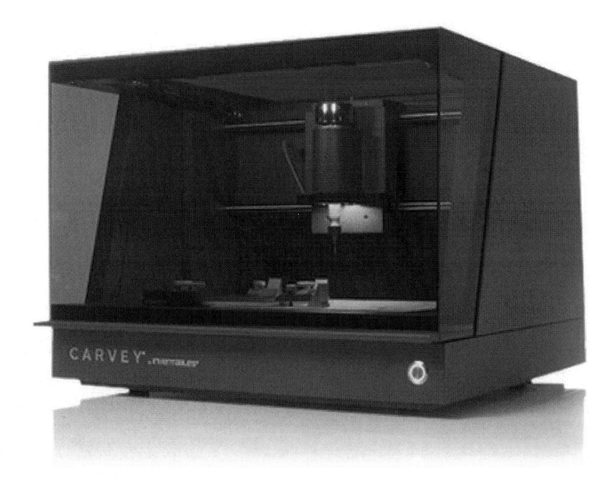

Carvey CNC Machine

CNC machines are subtractive. 3D printers add plastic but CNC machines cut it away. The Carvey is the first one that really feels like it belongs in my workshop and on my desktop. It's beautiful. It's quiet, it's got a cover, hydraulic hinges, etc. It's the perfect replacement for a laser cutter in that it does 2D quite easily. It can actually do limited 3D, which is to say give depth to stuff. Think of it right now as the kind of thing you would use for carving wood and plastics of various sorts.

Cricut Explore Air Machine

The Cricut is a CNC paper cutter and plotter. It's sold on places like Home Shopping Network as a crafting tool. It's actually just like the Carvy, but rather than having a rotating bit, its got a knife like an exacto blade. It cuts rather than burns away as you would with a bit. It's also beautifully made, and looks like a small paper printer. Exactly like the Carvy, you pick design, create a design, or scan a design and then you press go. In this case it will be cutting out of paper, maybe different layers of paper, different colors, or it'll cut out of vinyl so you can stick it. Or it'll cut out of thicker material like poster board or thin leather.

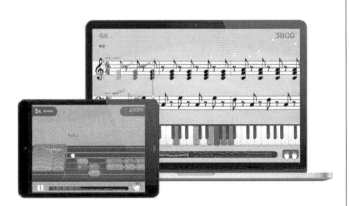

Yousician

Yousician is an app that teaches you how to play guitar or keyboards or ukulele. What I love about it is that it combines the fun of Guitar Hero with the incredible instructional power of apps these days

with videos. What really does it for me is that it has an acoustic engine in there that listens to you playing, it can pick out individual notes in a chord, and it grades you and corrects you as you go. We play with an acoustic guitar, and it listens and it can tune the guitar for you. It's basically the best music teacher ever, great lessons, great feedback, and they have real songs like Guitar Hero.

Kikkerland Leuchtturm Notebook

This is a notebook that has a nice hard cover and inside lots of blank pages. This one turns out to be the perfect one to do math homework with kids. It's like a lectern, I guess. The key thing about this, is not the nice cover or design. The key thing is that it's larger than 8 1/2 X 11, because when you're doing math homework together, you're not sure how much paper you're going to need so you want more space. Second of all, because it's big you can actually share, so you can spread it between two people. It's legal-size but when you open it up it can be sitting on two laps. And the key thing is the grid of dots, if you have to do a graph it's really easy to do it, if you need to eyeball spacing for geometry that's really easy to do, if you need to rotate points that easy to do as well, and if you just need to write equations or math, the dots don't get in the way.

Andreas Antonopoulos
Bitcoin expert

Andreas Antonopoulos is an acclaimed author, speaker, educator, and one of the world's foremost Bitcoin and open blockchain experts. Andreas makes complex subjects accessible and easy to understand. Andreas is also the author of one of my favorite books about bitcoin and blockchain technology called The Internet of Money. (Published 12/22/17)

Bose QuietComfort 35 Noise Cancelling Wireless Headphones

One of the reasons I love these noise-canceling headphones is because if I want to sleep I can't really tolerate earplugs for too long. Like, I can do it for an hour, but if I have earplugs in my ears for eight hours, I get really sore. The thing about a properly designed over-the-ear headphone is that it shouldn't touch the cartilage of your ear at all. It should cup on your skull basically, all the way around your ear, so your ear is completely inside and not touching anything. These are very comfortable to wear, to where I can sleep in these for hours and hours. They charge through a micro USB port, and the charge lasts for 10 – 12 hours easily.

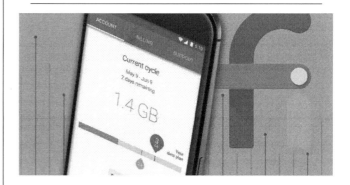

Google Fi as an International Phone Plan

Google Fi has worked beautifully. I get 4G in dozens of different countries so far. I mean I've tried it in 15 or 16 countries just in the last year, and have gotten 4G service. With one or two exceptions, like they don't support Vietnam yet. Google Fi is basically primarily a data service. They also do voice and messaging and it's free for National, but you know, who uses a phone as a phone anymore? I don't. So for me, it's only data, that's all I care about. It works in the US, 4G, LTE — everywhere with no problem.

Atmosphere

There's an app called Atmosphere, which you can get on pretty much every platform, that plays

Immerse yourself in different environments

various background sounds — white noise, fans, babbling brooks and rain sounds and things like that. You can just pop in the Bose headphones in an eight-hour flight and sleep and not even notice you're wearing them.

TP-Link AC2600 Dual Band Wi-Fi Range Extender

My background is in security, and one of the things that I handle in my life, in my professional life, but also in my personal life, is managing risk and understanding risk. And what risks are important and what risks are not important. I don't let my security be anybody else's business but mine. So, the funny

conversation you always have at an Airbnb is, they say things like, "And our router password is ..." And I'm like, "Oh, thank you dear. I will not be using your router." I don't know where that router's been. Also, it's probably badly configured, and keeps dropping packets and I need communications here. So this gets plugged in directly to the back of their internet, or wherever I can get a hard connection, or piggy backs off their provider's router, and then it's my communication network. And it includes VPN technology in it, but so do all of my devices.

Danielle Applestone
CEO of Other Machine Co.

Danielle Applestone is a material scientist, co-founder and CEO of Other Machine Co., the leading manufacturer of high-precision desktop CNC milling machines. Formerly, Danielle ran a DARPA project to develop digital design software and manufacturing tools for the classroom. Danielle's team took that technology and launched Other Machine Co. in 2013. (Published 03/20/17)

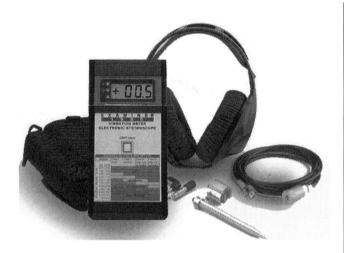

Monarch Instrument Examiner 1000

I came across this electronic stethoscope as part of our manufacturing process. We would get motors from a manufacturer that looked balanced and met a spec, but once we put the whole machine together, sometimes a machine would have a lot of vibration and we didn't know how to quantify that vibration or know what was good or what was bad. There's a lot of intuition when you're putting something complicated together like "Well, it feels right," or "It doesn't feel right." That's really hard to do, so we found this amazing thing which cut a ton of time out of our manufacturing process and now we have beautiful graphs of everything. We know exactly what things vibrate and which ones don't. You can use it on musical instruments. It's an amazing tool. Once you have one you realize how much you needed one in your life.

Bicycle inner tubes with holes

I came across bicycle inner tubes with holes in them through a friend who had made a sail boat that was attached only with these bicycle inner tubes — it was a catamaran. The reason why they're so important is they are waterproof, they stretch, and you don't have to tie them in knots, so you can latch things together really quickly and then undo them and make a new configuration. They're used a little bit like a bungee cord, but bungee cords are really expensive and you have to make do with the hooks. Whereas if you take a long inner tube that has a hole in it — you're not going to use it anyway — slice it up into strips, and it's like a variable length bungee cord, but it also doesn't have the hooks so you can just wrap it around itself and tuck it under and it'll stay put.

The Encyclopedia of Country Living

This is a great tool. This is so comprehensive for every little thing. I moved out into Kentucky and lived on 1,200 acres for a while and didn't have much. It was the go-to for, "Okay, we need to build a shanty for chickens. We need to learn how to clean a chicken." It has everything, like "How to bury your own dead." The thing that's magic about this book is it has the right level of detail, just enough to get yourself in trouble. It's just enough to get you going and then you can kind of DIY the rest. I still use it. The pages are all rained on, and moldy, and whatever, but it's well loved.

X-ray Photoelectron Spectrometer

This is the highest tech thing I've ever laid my hands on. What's great about this tool is it's super useful for telling what's on the surface of materials. I used

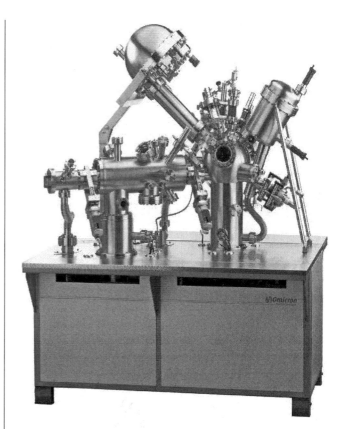

to be a material scientist and I worked on lithium ion batteries. The surface is where all the action is. There's not a lot of techniques out there that are nondestructive. Usually, if you invent a material, you have a sample, you have to crush it up or put it on a slide, you have to do something to it that mixes the surface in with the bulk. Sometimes, you don't want that. The X-ray Photoelectron Spectrometer is amazing because you can just put a sample in and it's nondestructive. How it works is you take a beam of x-ray, so you shoot photons at the surface of your material, and those photons have enough energy to pick off electrons. A photon goes in, ejects an electron, and then there's a collector that collects that electron and measures the kinetic energy, measures how fast it was moving. Then, if you know the energy of your x-ray going in, and the energy of that electron that you caught, you can just subtract and figure out how tightly bound was that electron to my surface. What's cool about that is if you know how tightly a molecule was hanging onto it's electron, you can tell what that molecule was. Whether it was a sulfur dioxide, or sulfur monoxide, the electrons that are swimming around those molecules will be held differently depending on what those molecules are. The place that I used one was at The University of Texas at Austin. They're quite common, but they're usually at universities or national labs. They're millions of dollars.

Madeline Ashby
Science Fiction Writer

Madeline Ashby is a futurist and science fiction writer living in Toronto. Her most recent novel, Company Town, is available from Tor Books.
(Published 03/2/18, 02/8/19)

Lancome Bienfait UV SPF 50+

Everyone should wear more sunscreen. This is an SPF 50. It's a broad-spectrum sunscreen. There are chemical ingredients as well as physical sunscreen ingredients within it, but it's a liquid, which means that, unlike a lot of sunscreens which are really creamy or heavy or oily, or kind of sticky and tacky and make your skin kind of feel weird, or make you feel kind of gross, this is a liquid. You shake it vigorously. It pours out into your hand like a liquid or like it's water-based. And because it's a liquid, it absorbs into your skin really quickly. You don't have to stand there sort of rubbing and rubbing trying to get this into your skin. It just sinks right into the face and doesn't cause breakouts and doesn't feel sticky or weird. I was in Palos Verdes and wore it every day. I was standing outside in the sun during the afternoon. Had no ill effects. It was a real surprise. And I only had to apply it once a day, which really says a lot.

Intelligent Change Productivity Planner

This is the productivity planner from Intelligent Change, and it's a company that makes only a

handful of planners. And what I really like about the productivity planner is that it allows for a weekly format as well as a daily format. It's unnumbered. You number it yourself. It streamlines some of that work for you, and it asks you a really important question. Right at the beginning of the planner, they sort of explain their philosophy — and this really changed how I thought about getting things done — because what they explain is your most important task of the day, which is how it's labeled at the top of every page, they ask beneath it, "If this was the only thing you did today, would you be satisfied?" And crucially, when they talk about how to find that out for your day, how to prioritize your tasks, they ask you at the beginning of the book, "What is the thing that you're afraid of doing? Do that first, and then everything else will follow." Their philosophy is basically if you do the thing that you're scared of right away, you will go into the day with more confidence, generally, and I've found that to be true.

Sabatier 200 Series 10" Knife

This is the Sabatier 200 10-inch knife, and it is probably the best knife that we have ever owned in our household. It goes really well with vegetables. It also slices through meat and fish really well. There are a few really interesting things about this knife. One is that it comes from a family business that has existed in France for the past 200 years. There are eight generations of this family that have made this same knife. And it's also made with the thinnest and lightest steel that they could find. It's loaded with nitrogen. They use cryogenic tempering to get the hardness of it. It has an ultra-fine grind, and it is the lightest knife that I have ever, ever used. It feels dangerously light in your hand. It's like it whispers through herbs and through vegetables. Suddenly, it's like they disappear under the chopping edge of this thing. It's so light that you almost feel you almost have to retrain yourself in how to use it. But it means that the cuts can be very fine and that you can break down things a lot more quickly. It's not like a big, heavy Santoku knife or a big cleaver or a dollar knife, obviously, that requires a lot of extra brute force. You don't have to exert extra foot pounds of pressure to get through things. It's so light and really so sharp that it's just amazing.

Travelon Set of 7 Packing Envelopes

I use the Travelon Clear Packing Envelopes both for packing, both for travel, and for just everything in my house. There are clear packing envelopes all over my bedroom. I have a couple I carry with me in various bags that I might be using. I'm a big bag full of bags person because it allows me to change bags really easily. It's like "Oh, this is the cosmetics bag. It goes in here. This is the bag full

of cables and dongles. It goes here. This is the bag that's full of stickies, and stationary, and pens, and it goes here. And do I need the pens bag today? Yes. Do I need the cosmetics bag today? Yes, or no. And the clear packing envelopes really help with that, in that they can get you through security a bit faster and help you find stuff more quickly.

Clarisonic Mia

The Clarisonic is a device that uses the same technology as something like a Sonicare toothbrush and other ultra-sonic cleaning devices to wash your face. It's a device that has a brush on one end of it and basically vibrates across your face at a certain frequency and vibrates the bristles on a brush head to exfoliate your face, and it works like a dream. And I've owned one for about four years now, and it has yet to die, which I suppose I'm jinxing myself. But all of those four years have been wonderful. I bought it when

I turned 30 as a gift to myself because I wanted to actually start taking my skin seriously, for once. And I've found that, much like a Sonicare Toothbrush, which I also have, having the device forced me to be more mindful about what I was doing and encouraged me in a good habit, which was washing my face in the morning and at night. The logic behind the Clarisonic is that, because you've exfoliated with this device, anything you put on your skin, like serums, or sunscreen, or anything like that, will actually go deeper into your skin. I don't know about the actual science of that, but I do think that anything that actually helps you wash your face is probably good for you in the long term.

Andy Baio
Technologist and Blogger

Andy Baio loves making things online. He's written waxy.org for the last 13 years, helped build Kick Starter, and organizes XOXO — an independent art tech festival in Portland. His upcoming projects include the XOXO Outpost, which is an experimental workspace opening this January, and the reboot of the collaborative event calendar, upcoming.org. (Published 03/28/16)

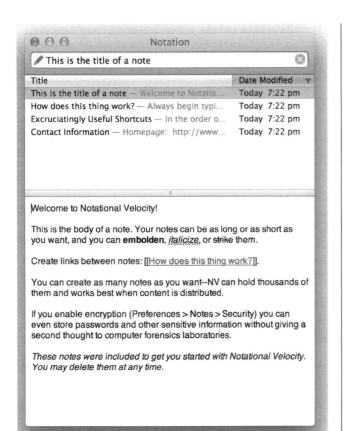

Notational Velocity

This is a free Mac app and it's open source. It has search and auto-complete built in. It's so dead simple. There are no folders or anything like that. You just start typing and it creates a new note. Anything you're searching is just a full-text search. For me this becomes a dumping ground for project

ideas, interviews I do, SQL Queries, to-do lists, anything, and everything will go in there. I have thousands and thousands of little notes, some are stubs, like a wish list. Because it's full text search, I don't have to remember what I called something or what folder it's in, or how it's organized. I just start typing and it retrieves all of the notes that match those keywords. It's just great.

Pomodoro One and StayFocusd

Pomodoro for those who aren't familiar is a technique for helping you stay focused on your work. It's a timer where you take 25-minute stretches of work, working on

Shouldn't you be working?

Have you found StayFocusd useful? Please make a $10 donation!

Donate

work collaborative tools. It has all the little playful things like third-party integration with animated GIF tools, emoji picker, emoji reactions, it does an incredible job of unfurling links you paste in. It's just a very natural place to collaborate and throw ideas in and get work done. So much of what I would have previously used email for I now do in Slack.

a single task, then a five minute break. After four of those, you take a longer break of 15 minutes. This has been one of the only things that has worked for me. I'm easily distracted, I'm constantly flitting around the internet looking for interesting things. When I actually need to work for an extended stretch, a pomodoro timer keeps me moving and keeps me more likely to fall into flow. Pomodoro One is a free utility app. It's dead simple. It has a start button, and that's basically it. It'll do the 25-minute timer and then it'll do an alarm, then five minutes. It's configurable, there are things you can do with it, but that's how I use it, it's dead simple. The pairing with that is StayFocused, which is a Chrome add-on inspired by a FireFox extension I used to use called LeechBlock. For Safari users, there's a similar add-on called WastenoTime. StayFocused is a timer that keeps you from time wasting websites. You define a list of sites that you're likely to fall into, whether it's Twitter, Facebook, TVTropes, Meta-Filter, whatever your community is that you fall into. You add those to a list, then it watches those as you're using your browsers and it will give you warnings, "You've got 5 minutes left, then I'm going to block them." If you keep going, it blocks the website. At that point you've set up these goals for yourself and it's trying to protect you from yourself.

Belong.io

This is an example of where I'm always looking for interesting new projects. I built this site and what it does is essentially streams the Twitter feeds from 2,300 people. Everyone who has ever attended XOXO. Then it ranks them. It grabs just the links they post. It tosses out everything that is just a Tweet, and it grabs just the Tweets that have a link in them. They're saying, "This is a new project." Grabs those links, expands them if they're short URLs, then ranks them based on three factors: popularity, freshness — When was the last time it was seen in the database? How many days old is it? — The third factor looks at the complexity of the URL. The idea is I am favoring shorter, simpler URLs over longer ones. It's a bit of a flawed technique, but it generally works to favor projects over blog posts, news articles, and so on.

Slack

For those not familiar, Slack is effectively a incredibly well designed chat-room. I think the thing that separates it from everything else is it has a sense of whimsy and fun to it. You don't see that in

The Lonely Work of Moderating Hacker News | The New Yorker
oddly moved by diannaelenerʼs profile of the Hacker news mods ⇒

Science Hack Day San Francisco 2019 (the 10th Annual) Registration, Sat, Oct 19, 2019 at 9:00 AM | Eventbrite
This year we are putting together our 10th and last Science Hack Day in San Francisco. Please come geek out with us and make things! No ... ⇒

Harry Reid to Dems: Kill the Filibuster to Tackle the Climate Crisis
Listen to Harry Reid. ⇒

How to Make Preserved Lemons in the Workshop - YouTube
This is some extreme yak-shaving. ⇒

When It Comes to Mass Shootings, It's the Misogyny, Stupid
Read me on what we keep forgetting to mention when we talk about these mass shootings. ⇒

Ben Baker
Owner of Cigar Box Nation

Ben "Gitty" Baker fell in love with the idea that anyone, anywhere can build their own musical instrument and make music on it. His company was founded to spread that message all around the world. (Published 09/6/17)

dent wood. Having a little more, shall we say, gentle method of persuasion, is handy at the work bench. I always find myself reaching for one of these.

CigarBoxGuitar.com

This is a website that I created and have built up full of free how-to information related to cigar box guitars and other homemade instruments. We've got how to build them, how to play them. We've got modern plans and blueprints. We've got historic plans and blueprints. We've got photo galleries of famous celebrities holding and playing cigar box guitars. So, my goal with that was to make it the one-stop resource and knowledge base for the entire homemade instrument movement, and it's been a work in progress over a few years, but there's a lot of great stuff on there.

12-ounce Brass Head Dead-blow Fretting Hammer

I got to thinking, "What tools am I always reaching for when I'm there at the bench, building a new cigar box, guitar or other instrument?" This little hammer is a dead-blow hammer, which means the head is filled with a metal shot. So when you strike something, it doesn't have that bounce and recoil that a standard hammer will. One of the heads is brass, and the other head is kind of the molded plastic that the rest of the hammer is, and it's great for more gentle tapping or hammering. Most people have a hammer of some sort, but with that hardened steel head, you can dent softer metals. You can

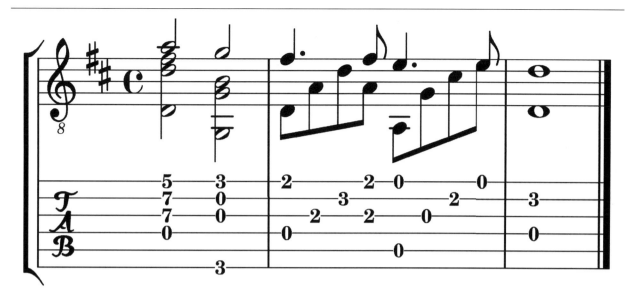

Tablature

Tablature is a way of depicting where you put your fingers on a fretted instrument neck to play your particular tune. So, usually there are horizontal lines that represent the strings on an instrument, and then there are numbers that get placed on those lines that indicate what fret you place your finger on to play a particular note. And the number of horizontal lines depends on what instrument it's written for. So, a conventional six-string guitar will have six lines. A three-string cigar box guitar will have three, and so forth. It's a much easier and more approachable and accessible way for a beginner to start playing recognizable music. They don't have to learn musical notation, they don't have to know what all the notes and lines and everything mean. It's just pretty much a way of displaying "Put your fingers here and you'll get a song out of it." So, I like it as a very accessible, kind of like an on-ramp, to playing a musical instrument.

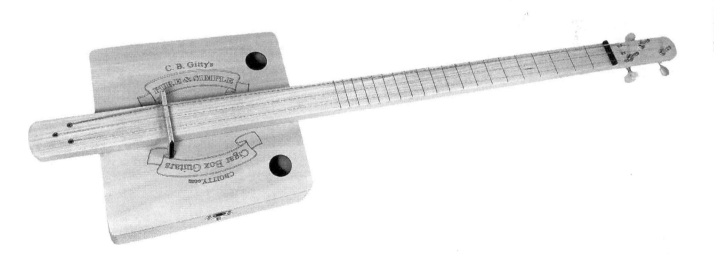

The Cigar Box Guitar

My favorite tool of all is the cigar box guitar. Because it's both a tool that you make yourself, and it's a work of art that we use to make more art in the form of business. Or, business in the form of music. And there are very few other tools that you can say that about.

Danielle Baskin
Product designer

Danielle Baskin is an entrepreneur, painter, and performance artist based in San Francisco. She's created internet jokes, like Custom Avocados and Drone Sweaters. She's also the founder of Inkwell Helmets, a custom bike helmet company, the co-founder of Your Boss, a voice-chat based productivity app, and has started many other companies. (Published 07/20/18)

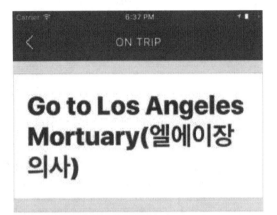

OffBot — Randomly Go Places

OffBot is an app that sends you to random destinations that are taken from Google Maps, like restaurants, parks, bars, or any place. You can choose what kind of place you're looking for, and it will

just select for you at random. I use this to make decisions for me to save mental bandwidth. I also use it to discover interesting places spontaneously and to have unexpected experiences either locally or in new city.

Matterport Camera

This is a 360-degree rotating camera with an infrared depth sensor that can capture interior spaces and turn them into high-fidelity 3D models. It's meant for real estate tours, but I've been borrowing one to document abandoned spaces or soon-to-be-bulldozed buildings for virtual preservation.

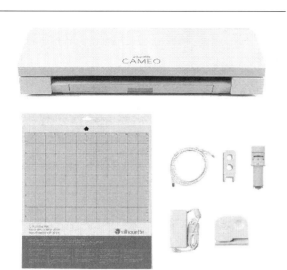

Silhouette Cameo Electronic Cutting Machine

This is an extremely useful vinyl die-cutter I've had for 6 years. I use it for so many projects: putting logos on fruit, making decals for my helmet company, making masks, custom stickers, labels, and signs. It also cuts paper and fabric — and if you swap the blade with a pen, it's an automatic drawing tool. There's just so many uses for it. It was definitely worth buying.

Cardd

This is a beautifully-designed, single-page site builder, and host to many of my domains. I'm somewhat of a domain hoarder, but I try to put content on most of my sites. Cardd is great for quickly getting content online and making it look sleek,

without spending the time custom-coding something — which is often unnecessary for certain projects and experimental ideas. Carrd also lets you export your code, if you wanted to turn the site into a larger project later on.

HP Latex 110 printer

I was actually a beta tester for it, so that's why I have one. I can print my own custom Pantone colors on vinyl. It's a vinyl and fabric printer.

You've been invited to a phone call from Your Boss.

Pairs you randomly in a one-on-one voice chat!

Your Boss

I'm working on a peer-to-peer voice chat network for people with creative side projects. It's an accountability network — a way to get a boss for a project when you otherwise wouldn't have one.

Carl Bass
Former Autodesk CEO

Carl Bass has been designing and making buildings, boats, sculpture, and machinery for the last 40 years. He is the former CEO of Autodesk and now spends his time researching the boundaries of digital fabrication in his shops in Berkeley and with a number of companies he's working with. (Published 10/5/18)

Shinto Saw Rasp

I've spent a lot of time sanding, and grinding, and filing, and rasping wood, and then sometimes you just come along the perfect tool. In this case, my Shinto rasp. It's an inexpensive, cleverly made tool, and it works perfectly. The cool thing about it is, it's got like a coarse and a fine side, and they really are different, and it's sharp as could be, so it actually cuts wood. Compared to all the crappy files, which mostly are made for metal that people use, and all the rasps that aren't really sharp, this thing really cuts wood. I just used it on this canoe I'm building, for soft wood. I'd used it before on this gigantic sculpture I did out of ash. If anyone's ever tried to carve ash and particularly the end grain, it's really hard and this thing was perfect.

Decimal Tape Measure

I found a decimal inch tape measure. It is like the bridge for me between my world of computer control tools and the world that I normally live in. Over the last decade, more and more of my tools are either numerically controlled or computer numerically controlled. For example, in my wood shop, I have a planer where I press in 2.35 inches. I'd like to be able to measure that as opposed to going 0.0625 is a 16th of an inch or whatever it is. So, this is a nice thing. There's not many of them out there. I just bought a handful of them because they really are this perfect bridge between the digital world and the analog world.

Dewalt Trigger Clamps

These squeeze clamps are made by DEWALT. They have them in Home Depot in a variety of sizes, and what I really like about them, they do two things. One is you can use them as just a clamp — and for plastic clamps with just a metal rod — they apply a surprising amount of pressure. The second thing that they do is they're easily reversible and you can use them to push. People first go, "When do you need a clamp to push?" I just finished planking a strip canoe and most of the job there is actually pushing as opposed to pulling things together. You get a hard surface and you push against it. So, I use it on planking this whole canoe. I have a water jet where I often do it. When you want to push things apart, it's good for that. So these DEWALT clamps, they're reasonably priced but they are totally versatile and useful.

Plastic Center Finder

This is a very specific-purpose build tool. This tool helps if you have a cylinder or a circle and you want to find the center of it. There are number of ways to find the center of a circle that you already have.

So imagine, a three-inch round cylinder. With this tool you just hold it up to it and you draw two lines, kind of a right angles. The point where those two lines intersect is the center of the circle.

Homemade metal 3D printer

A couple of years ago, I started looking at metal 3D printing. I printed a bunch of stuff in plastic, but generally I wasn't interested in more plastic crap, but I had a lot of need for more metal. I was doing more and more things with crazy organic shapes, and a bunch of us had this idea that a MIG welder is really just like FDM 3D printing machine. It puts down liquid metal and then it solidifies, and that if you were able to control it, you could actually use it as a 3D printer. So I built a machine, kind of a gantry with a bunch of servos in a computer, and I can now print things out of metal. The point is you have a welder that just runs around and lays down material and builds forms, but the more general principle is in this age in which things like motors, and servos, and microprocessors are relatively inexpensive, people should start thinking about not just building old fashioned jigs and fixtures, but you can start building things where you have microprocessors controlling them for any of the things you want to do. I think we still rely on doing things the old way and in some case it's good, but there are lot of things you can go out and make way more precise easily.

Joshuah Bearman
Epic Cofounder

Joshuah Bearman is Epic's cofounder and CCO and has written for Wired, GQ, The New York Times Magazine, Harper's, and is a regular contributor to This American Life. Josh has written about meteorite hunters, deranged private investigators, jewel thieves, surfing smugglers, and the metaphysical implications of being the world's greatest Pac Man player. He was a finalist for the 2014 National Magazine Awards, and his work has been anthologized in various Best American series. The movie Argo was adapted from Bearman's 2007 Wired article, "The Great Escape." (Published 05/10/19)

Adios Email Scheduler

I suffer from the tyranny of the inbox like everyone else. And I try all these various systems to manage it right — like, "Okay, I'm going to be an inbox zero person," which I did achieve once. The paradox of it was that it was satisfying to know that there was not much email in my inbox at any given time; however, it requires this constant maintenance. So I was like, "I wonder if there's a way to set it, so that it only sends you email every so often. So that you basically unwire your neurological pathways to seek the constant influx." Because I feel that over time, your brain gets rewired to be looking for a certain kind of stimulus. And then that sort of affects concentration and also identifies a certain constant input into this machine that you're sitting at. This is Adios — you can log it into your Gmail accounts, and then specify times you want to receive mail, and you can set as many times as you want. Then you don't have any email until the appointed time, and the

effect is very quick. Within 48 hours, you just forget that there's email coming at you all day, and your quality of mind sort of returns. Then all the email shows up at once and you dispatch it in 15, 20 minutes and deal with everything and that's it. And also by then, half of those emails are just threads, so that by the time you're seeing them everything's been resolved. This has become a very effective concentration tool.

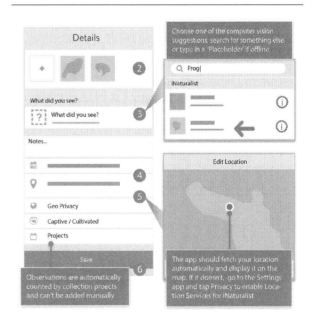

iNaturalist

This is an app, and I got into this because I was on an artist residency, and I was out in the woods and it was late summer, and there were wild flowers everywhere. And I was like, "What are these flowers?" I always fancied myself as the type of person who knows Arboriculture and horticulture and can pick out Queen Anne's lace from across the meadow or something, which now I can, thanks to iNaturalist. You just use the camera, go over take a picture of the petals of a flower or leaves, and then it searches a database. It is probably using some kind of machine learning algorithm to recognize this in relation to all the other flowers. And then it gives you a suggestion and says, "I think it's probably this." And for the most part, it's correct. It also identifies birds and insects, which is exciting.

Kuretake Zig Cocoiro Letter Pens

This is a Japanese pen, and it's sort of the modern version of a felt tip pen, but it's not a ballpoint. It's got a very narrow tip or nib and stylist. This came about because I started keeping a written journal. So I experimented with a lot of writing pens. I also had really bad handwriting — my crazy chicken scratch. This pen makes it a little bit more legible. And they're also refillable with a little cartridge. And they're pink. At least the ones I have are pink. Although I didn't really realize that because I'm slightly colorblind. A lady was like, "I love your pink pen." I was like, "Really? I thought this was tan." I had no idea I was doing a performatively, adolescent girly thing like writing in my journal with a pink pen. The Zig pen, it's just a great little writing device.

This Is Ground Bags

This Is Ground is just one of the many, many, many, many companies nowadays making leather doodads and bags. There's sort of a proliferation of these, where it's toiletry kits, and the tech place for all your cords and a little clasp for your iPhone, headphones

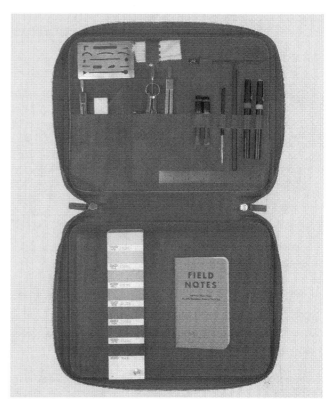

and all that stuff. I have a bunch of the Dopp kits. When I'm traveling, what I do is I have one that has everything in it, like doubles of all of my cords and stuff and it's just sitting there in my bag always, so that I don't have to remember to take it. I also have a little briefcase, but that's for my iPad Pro, and inside are all these little slots for the stylus and notebook and all those little things. I really like things that have pockets where everything goes in its place. And This Is Ground bags are those types of bags. It's kind of like the Wall All of the '60s, where it was like this plastic thing on the wall that has all these little pockets that you put all your stuff in.

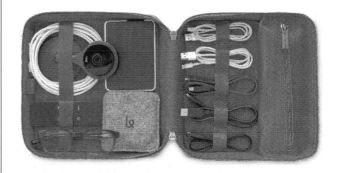

Donald Bell
Maker Project Lab

Donald Bell creates tool review videos for Cool Tools. He also hosts a weekly YouTube show called Maker Update, which collects interesting projects, news, tips, and tools for the Maker community. You can find him on Twitter, Facebook and Instagram @makerprojectlab. (Published 04/19/19, 06/29/17)

Flexible Silicone Neon-like LED Strip

The first place I came across this was on the Adafruit site, and they still have kind of the best selection of color options for this. It's an LED strip that takes 12 volts, which is a little unusual. It is the most realistically neon alternative I've come across. This really is geared toward people who want to make a neon-style sign or replacement signage without all the mess and hassles of really using glass neon tube. You can bend it in half. It's very flexible, you can cut it. John Park did a whole guide on using this stuff to make a neon-style sign in his workshop. His is cooler than mine. His will animate. He's got like a thunderbolt going through a robot or something like that, and they kind of alternate. You can cut it to length, just like an addressable LED strip, to get exactly the length you want, or also to bridge between different sections of it. It's useful, it's not cheap though. Adafruit has a meter of it for about

$14. I'm also starting to see it now on Amazon. I just bought a batch of it today on Amazon to see if this other brand is going to be as nice a color as what Adafruit is able to provide. You can do all the same tricks you would do with a regular neon sign. You can duck it behind another color of the same style of strip, or you can black out sections. Or you can really use it the same way a sign maker would use neon, but it's not delicate. It's weatherproof. The way I found to mount mine — and I haven't really seen anyone else do this before — but it was the first thing that occurred to me, was to get a piece of plywood and use a router to just route out a shape using like, maybe it's like a quarter-inch routing bit, just like a flat bit, just to dig in enough of a groove that I could fit the LED strip into the shape that I put in with the router. Then run a cable out the back and plug it in.

Kai Chan Cardboard Cutter

This one is kind of a call back to my obsession with these Canary-style cardboard cutter knives. I've gone through a few of them. There's the yellow-handled one. There's a green-handled one that I found last year that's retractable. Now recently, there's this pink-handled one that has a little nub of a knife that sticks out. Maybe about an inch out from the handle. About as much as you'd think like a utility knife would extend. It's really just made to open up boxes. It's just long enough that you can rip open a box. Anytime someone signs up for Amazon Prime, this should come in your first package. It's not sharp; you're not going to stab anyone with this thing. It's deliberately made to be a little blunt at the top so that you're not cutting into

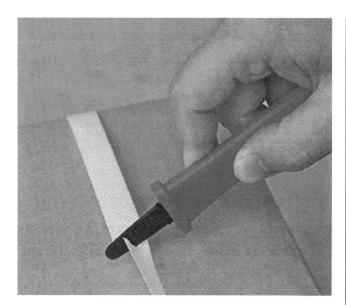

the thing that's in the box. The sides of this knife are serrated in this very fine way that just loves to go through packing tape or the paper-based Amazon type of packing tape. It can cut through cardboard really easily. I love grabbing this thing. When a box arrives at my doorstep, I know that I've got just the right little tool to kind of get through it, and make quick work of opening it up.

Manfrotto 143 Magic Arm Kit

This one actually I learned about from Becky Stern, Make alumni. But before I started working at Make, when I was doing how-to projects for CNET, I was

trying to figure out the easiest way to take those great shots of your work, like an overhead view of your workbench, while you're working on a project. And I've never been able to do that easily with a standard tripod. The Magic Arm will clamp onto your table and then kind of cantilever out over the workspace so that you can position the camera looking straight down. It's been a good tool for me to film project videos or be able to document projects as I go, and for taking photos and putting them on Instructables and documenting projects.

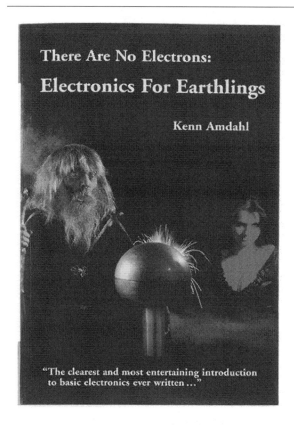

There Are No Electrons: Electronics for Earthlings

I think of this book like if Stephen Colbert wrote a book on electronics and describing how electronics work. It's just a really funny, whacked perspective on trying to understand how electricity and electronics work. It's not a lightweight text in terms of backing away from teaching you everything you would want to know about circuitry and hobby electronics. It covers all the bases, and more. I mean, there's actually stuff I learned from this on mutual inductance that either wasn't taught to me in other books, or I just glazed over it at that point in other texts. But it made its impression from this perspective, and I'm grateful for it.

Tory Belleci
Mythbusters

Tory Belleci is best known as the daredevil of MythBusters and can build just about anything. He has worked with Industrial Light and Magic on films such as: Star Wars Episode I: The Phantom Menace and Star Wars Episode II: Attack of the Clones. The Federation battleships and podracers are some of Belleci's pieces. (Published 12/8/15)

GoPro HERO4

GoPro has been an important tool for our show and our new show. Kari and I are doing a new show on Travel Channel and we're riding roller coasters. They don't let big, giant cameras on the roller coasters so they have to put GoPros all over the ride for them to get the shot. I feel like GoPro has really changed the playing field for video making or filmmaking. You can shoot 4K. The video never degrades. You can project it and it still looks amazing. You can shoot broadcast-quality video and the great thing about it is you can fit it pretty much anywhere. When we're doing shots when we're in a car, if you had a big giant bulky camera, you can't sit that camera on the dashboard. With a GoPro, it slips right in and you get an amazing shot where years ago, you just didn't have that option. It has a microphone built in and it is decent. From time to time, what we'll do is we will actually stick a separate mic in wherever the GoPro is. If you want to get higher-quality sound then you just slate it, but for the most part, for simple filmmaking, the GoPro is a compact perfect little camera.

Canon EOS 5D

If this camera had existed when we were in film school, it would have been like, "We have no excuses now — let's go make film," because you have this compact camera that's very affordable, and the quality that you get is pretty mind-blowing. With this 5D camera, you can get gorgeous pictures and if you don't like it, you just erase the disk. When we were making films, you really had to pick your shots and you really had to rehearse it and make sure everybody was on point because as soon as you start rolling that film, that was money going through the gate, but with digital 4K technology like this, you can just put a button on and let that thing roll for as long as you want. If you don't like, you wipe it or get a new card.

DJI Phantom 3 Professional Quadcopter Drone 4K

There's a lot of controversy about drones right now because of the FAA and privacy issues and safety issues, but having a drone and attaching a camera to this drone and getting these shots, the production value is astronomical. Before, if you wanted to get an aerial shot, you had to hire a pilot. You had to hire a helicopter and those guys could charge $1,000 an hour. With the drone, you instantly turn your production into a professional-looking production. The footage comes back and you're just like, "It looks like we had a helicopter.

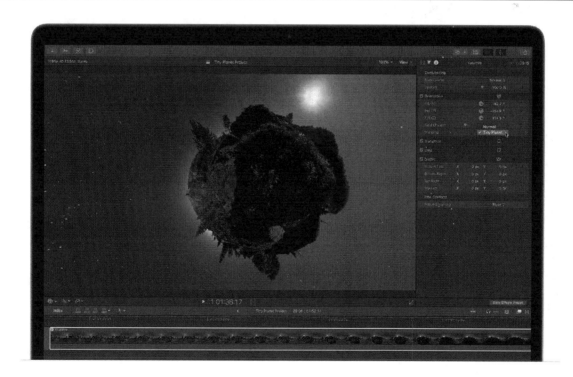

Final Cut Pro

Now that you've got all this footage and amazing shots, what do you do with it? You take it into Final Cut Pro and now you have a professional post house in your laptop. It's the most incredible tool for a filmmaker because you can quickly make changes and you can try different combinations of stuff to see what works, and if it doesn't work, you just erase it and start over.

Jim Beloff
Musician

Jim Beloff is the author of The Ukulele: A Visual History, and with his wife Liz publishes the popular Jumpin' Jim's series of ukulele songbooks, including The Daily Ukulele, one of the best-selling ukulele songbooks ever published. (Published 11/10/17)

Kent The Handmade Comb

I was was reduced to buying the same old ACE comb at a drugstore that used to be unbreakable, but is no longer unbreakable, because as you can imagine, if it's unbreakable then you don't resell a lot of them. I just got really tired of them breaking and I thought there's got to be a good pocket comb, and lo and behold, I found one. They're made in England by a company called Kent, and I think, just based on some really quick research, I think they've been in business for 300 years. They say it's handmade, it's kind of like tortoiseshell, and it says saw cut, and the code on it is R7T, and it fits perfectly in my back pocket. It hasn't even got any kind of usage marks on it whatsoever, and I've been using it for the last six months, and I'm just happy as can be that I found a really good kind of lifetime comb now.

Penguin Woven Elastic Leather Belt

This is in the same category as the comb. I've lived at least half a life, or more, and I have just resigned myself to the idea that you just have to kind of burn through kind of mediocre belts with holes that are not always where you want them to be. Then I just recently stumbled upon a belt made by Penguin. They're just a brand name, they make a lot of sort of sportswear, but they make this weave belt, and the key to this thing is that it doesn't have holes. It's just an elasticized belt, and the beauty of it is that you can put the prong anywhere, so if you're feeling a little more relaxed, you can loosen it by the tiniest amount, or you can tighten it by the tiniest amount if you're on a diet. You don't have to be a slave to the holes. They're inexpensive, so it's like a trifecta: it works, and it looks good, and it's cheap.

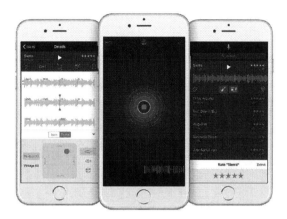

Music Memos

I think now it's been maybe two years since Apple introduced Music Memos, and this was just a gift. It sort of dropped on our doorstep at some point; they announced it and there it was. It was kind of the answer, at least for me, and I imagine for a lot of songwriters or composers who were always on the hunt for an easy app to just capture musical ideas on the run, and this was by far the easiest. First of all, it's free, it's from Apple, and the presentation could not be simpler. You just push it on, and there is this sort of beautiful little blue signal in the middle, and you just push that and you're recording and you're off to the races.

Enjoy Sudoku

This is my deep, dark secret. My nephew about 10 years ago, curse him, he introduced me to Sudoku and there was no turning back. You would think after 10 years I would have gotten even a tiny bit better and I have not, but by far in a way this Enjoy Sudoku, which is an app that you can find in the app store, I have found to be the cleanest,

easiest Sudoku app that I've ever played with, and if you so choose, it will help you, and give hints, and suggestions, and teach as well. It's just a great game, and it's challenging, and Enjoy Sudoku is certainly the best one I've found.

Jim's book of palindromes

The way I describe this is that these were my sleep aides, meaning that when I would wake up in the middle of the night for no reason necessarily and had a hard time falling back to sleep, I found that it was restful to think about sentences that can be read the same in both directions. Maybe that goes to sort of the same mathematical part of me that likes Sudoku, I don't know, but anyway, I've been thinking about them and collecting them for at least 30 years, and always with the idea that I'd love to publish some of my favorite ones. I chose a palindromic number, I chose 44 of them, and the title of the book is Ones Reverses Reverse No, which is of course a palindrome. It's got some short ones, like, "Same nice cinemas" or "Retro porter". One that I'm actually somewhat known for and has been published in other wordplay books is, "Lapses order red roses pal", and "Eli began a motel bible to manage bile," and they get kind of odd as they get longer. "No no is I've let a television on." It's a limited edition, a number set of 250, and I'm not offering it for sale on our website, so the only way people can get it is if they email me at Jim@FleaMarketMusic.com, and it's $25 a copy plus shipping.

Oh, who is as selfless as I? Oh, who?

Dan Benjamin
Founder of 5by5

Dan Benjamin is a podcaster, writer, software developer, and ex-corporate stooge. He is the founder of 5by5, a podcast network where he hosts a handful of shows. He is the author of baconmethod.com and hivelogic.com, and has written for A List Apart and O'Reilly. Dan lives in Austin, Texas with his wife and their children. (Published 05/24/16)

Staedtler Mars Mechanical Pencil and Rotary Action Lead Pointer

This could be called an architect's pencil or a draftsman's pencil or a lead holder is the name that I've always used for it. What's nice about it is it's lightweight, but it's got that nice metal grippiness to it. Instead of being like a regular mechanical pencil where you click the end of it and it advances the lead millimeter by millimeter out, this you can control. When you press down the button end of it, as much lead as you would like to slide out can slide out. A supplemental item is the Mars Rotary Action Lead Pointer and Tub, which allows you to put the lead holder in there. It presets how much of a point you want

based on these two little holes that you adjust it to, and then you spin it. I encourage people to write and draw with a pencil. It's the most fun thing in the world.

Telefunken M82 Dynamic Microphone

I started podcasting back in 2006. This is my microphone of choice these days. I have used so many different microphones over the years. I care a lot about the microphone. This was maybe the fifth or sixth microphone that I'd tried. When I try one, I tend to try to use it for several months. This one I've been using now for about a year, and I just love it. It really meets with my voice I think really well. What's nice about it is, it was originally designed as a kick drum mic. If you were mic'ing up a drum set, you would put this microphone in front of or even inside of the kick drum. As weird as that may sound, some of the most widely used microphones for voice in broadcasting actually were originally designed or designed in part to also be kick drum kind of a mic or a mic for a drum.

Vitamix 5300 Blender

I started getting into the idea of making smoothies in the morning for breakfast and I said to my wife, "I think I want to try making them at home." She says, "Well, you know we have a blender that could do that." I said, "You mean like the one we got when we got married, like a million years ago?" She's like, "No. We have a really nice blender. It's a professional-level Vitamix blender." I'm like, "Where is it?" She's like, "It's in the box in the garage." I'm like, "Why is it out there?" She's like, "It was so expensive that I was going to return it. I just bought it not long ago and I felt like there's no sane reason I should have spent this much money on a blender." I said, "All right, let me try it." I tried it and the smoothie that I made — the world stopped and everything went dark and a spotlight went down on the smoothie. It was the best thing in the world. I was full. I was full all day. I had energy. I lifted a car off of a fire hydrant in the garage. It was amazing what I was able to do. I said, "Don't you dare return. I'm keeping this thing." She's

like, "All right. We can keep it." A week later I've been making smoothies all week long. It's been the most amazing thing. Anything blends in this.

Steelcase Series 7 Height-Adjustable Desk and Mat

I got this desk is because years ago I started dealing with chronic lower back issues. As a result of that, my doctor said, "One thing you should really consider doing is instead of spending most of the day sitting, you could spend a significant part of the day standing. " I went with Steelcase because at the time that I got it that was the desk that you get. Now there are lots of other alternatives for sit-stand desks, but I still really like the Steelcase one, because it's just made so rock-solid. The motors in it are super, super solid and strong. You can have your big, fancy monitors up on top of it. In my case, I even have a rack with a whole bunch of audio gear on top of it and a screen. It lifts us up and down, no problem.

Rob Beschizza
Managing Editor of Boing Boing

Rob Beschizza is the Managing Editor of Boing Boing and the founder of Txt.fyi, an effectively invisible publishing platform and low-key internet cult.
(Published 07/19/19)

Vortexgear Tab 75 Mechanical Gaming Keyboard

With mechanical keyboards — the appeal is in the old-fashioned key switches which have a more tactile, more clicky feel to them — and there's all sorts of different types that you can get depending on your preferences. It's just great for people who type a lot who just don't like modern keyboards or who are getting sick of butterfly keyboards from Apple. I think for anyone who listens to a tech podcast or is familiar with the cult of mechanical keyboards, a big part of the appeal is you can swap out the keys, so there's a cottage industry of key caps and sorts of different color schemes and styles. You can have a keyboard that looks like an old typewriter or one that looks like a very specific 8-bit computer that you had 30 years ago, or that looks like a nuclear missile launch silo console. Vortex is one of the brands and its thing is that it makes offbeat sizes and includes Bluetooth, which is a relatively rare feature in mechanical keyboards. They make these tiny little 40-key keyboards that will fit in a shirt pocket, or you

can get these huge, sprawling hundred-key keyboards with a condensed or otherwise bizarre layout. This one has all the keys that you get with the 10 kilos keyboard, so it doesn't skimp and make you learn weird shift levels or anything like that. There's no spaces at all between any of the keys, including the arrow keys and the page up/page down stuff. It has this extremely compact layout, not much larger than a Magic Keyboard, but you get all of the benefits that you would get from a mechanical keyboard. You can have it with clicky keys. You can have it with tactile keys. You can have it with linear ones that gamers like, and of course, you can make it look any way you like.

Logitech Vertical Wireless Mouse

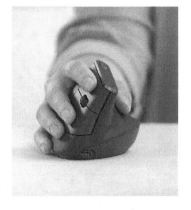

I have a little bit of repetitive strain-type trouble in my right hand, and the trigger has always been using a mouse. If I was smart, I would probably adopt better posture, hold the mouse in a more ergonomic way, but why do that when I can just buy something?

The idea here is the mouse is in a peculiar shape, which means it's almost like a handshake posture rather than a hand flat on the table posture. I tried a cheap one, I don't know what brand it was. It stopped working after two weeks. Logitech has muscled in on this field in the last year or so and it has all the features and the stylish look of the brand, so I'm giving it a go. The big problem is it just seems very difficult to be as precise with it, at least for me, but I'm giving it a go and it has instantly made all the pain go away without sending me to a trackpad or a stylus or some other control system that I don't want to use. I want to use a mouse, so I'm having a good time with it.

Gyokucho Ryoba Saw

This saw has a long, thick blade with two sides, and one side has teeth for rip cuts and the other side has teeth for crosscuts, so for going against and with the grain on a piece of wood. The way it's designed, you apply pressure on the pull rather than the push, and this means that its flex is always straight rather than threatening to bend. It doesn't require expert technique the way Western saws do to actually get quality results. A complete idiot can do fast, accurate cuts with one. It was a revelation to me. I've got a baby son who is now almost two years old, and he got to the stage where he's running crazy around the house constantly and he managed to headbutt our ancient Victorian-era radiators. He was okay, but it was immediately obvious the design of these radiators with the metal sharp edges was absolutely lethal, so I decided, "Okay, I'm going to get radiator covers." They have to be custom made to whatever size your radiator is, and they cost $200 or $300 each. I've got a house full of these things, so I thought, "I'm just going to buy the wood at the lumber yard and get a decent saw and cut everything into rudimentary, straightforward runs

myself." It was so difficult to get precision. I was getting frustrated. It was slow going and someone told me, "Just buy one of those cheap Japanese saws off of Amazon. You'll be amazed." I was. I was absolutely gobsmacked. Suddenly I'm doing all these fancy cuts and making radiator covers that look really nice rather than just boxes.

2006 17" iMac

I think these were only made available to schools, but they're widely available on the internet. If you write a lot and you're not very good at focusing, maybe have a little bit of the attention deficit about you, which a lot of us writers do have, especially when the writing is on deadline, you want something which lets you focus but which isn't completely ridiculous. There's a whole cottage industry, almost like the keyboards, of gadgets for focused writing, and likewise there's all sorts of apps to help you do focused writing. I don't think the apps work because you can just close the app and go back to YouTube. I don't think the gadgets work because they're all really expensive and just hinky, weird things that encompass an idea but don't really have much to them. An old 2006 17-inch iMac is a nice, small computer which has all the useful features of word processing software, some basic internet access if you need to look things up, but which is too slow and too primitive to do anything with but write. I don't think it can even play YouTube videos because you can't install software with the new codecs and all that stuff. It's great. It's the focused writing machine you've always wanted if you're the person who's looking for a focused writing environment.

Nick Bilton
Special Correspondent for Vanity Fair

Nick Bilton is a Special Correspondent for Vanity Fair and author of three books, including Hatching Twitter and his latest, American Kingpin, which chronicles the rise and fall of the Silk Road and the Dread Pirate Roberts. (Published 06/12/17)

Epson R-D1 Rangefinder Camera

This was one of the first digital Rangefinders, and it's so cool because it has these physical dials that pop up like you're manning an airplane from the 1920s or something like that, it's pretty neat. The Rangefinder actually has a viewfinder that you look at, and then it has a different viewfinder that the lens looks at. Almost like mirroring two images on top of each other, you have to put these images on top of each other, and that is essentially what you end up taking a picture of, but the photos are so crisp. All the Magnum war photographers use these old Rangefinder cameras.

Macbook Air

I know this is a totally lame tool. It's like, "Oh a MacBook." It's like saying an iPod or an iPhone, but the thing is, I do 90% of my work on my computer, it's all writing. The thing with the MacBook is it's got two holes. It's got one for the power cord, and one for your headphones, which I don't even want anymore because I have the AirPods. I love that there's nothing you can do with it, other than just use it to write. Of course, you can use it to surf the internet, but I just love the simplicity and how tiny it is. I always ask people what their desert island device is, if you had to take one device, it would probably be my MacBook.

ENA Micro 9 Coffee Machine

I, like every nerdy coffee person in the world, have been through 4,000 different versions of different coffee machines and things. I have found, and I am sure there are hardcore coffee drinkers out there that will be sending me hate mail when they hear this, but I found that the machine doesn't really matter as much as the beans. Now, I have this coffee machine. My brother-in-law had one that he bought for work, and it was too small for his office, so I got a good discount on it for a few hundred bucks. You put in your beans in the back, and you press a button in the morning to heat it up, you press rinse after about 12 seconds, and then you press the coffee button, and in a matter of about 30 seconds you have a nice, hot cup of coffee with a nice little crema on top, and that's it. On my desert island, if I were allowed to bring a second device, as long as there were coffee beans, I would bring this coffee machine.

Miyabi Paring Knives

I've been through my fair share of cheap knives, and my wife bought me one of the Miyabi's for Christmas, and it's amazing. You can chop a cherry tomato by just resting the knife on the edge of the skin. The only problem is, I hate doing dishes, and you can't put it in the dishwasher, you have to clean

these knives because they've got an old Japanese wood handle that expands if you put it in the dishwasher. It's fine, I can handle cleaning a couple of knives. It's amazing. The texture of the blade kind of looks almost like fire. These are basically hand forged, hand crafted. It's a really beautiful knife and it's also really an impressive tool. You don't buy a lot of these things, they're like $100-$200 each. I think I have two: one's the paring knife and one's the six-inch chef knife. This is the thing though. I see all these knife kits, and you don't need all those knives. You just need one good knife, maybe two if you're going to make some meats and fish. You only really need one good knife in your life. I think one of the most enjoyable things for me, after a really long week of work, is chopping vegetables into cubes. You have to pay attention to when you need to sharpen it, because if you don't sharpen a good knife it can start to get brittle on the edges and then your knife is done. So, you've got to take care of it, you've got to keep in a little protective case, in case your two-year-old gets their hands on it. But, it's worth it.

Matt Blum
Editor in Chief at GeekDad

Matt Blum is a dad, a geek, and a software engineer who's been writing for and editing the GeekDad blog for almost 11 years. He foresees the day soon when he'll need to buy a new house just for his books, games, LEGO sets, and Funko Pop! Vinyls.
(Published 04/5/18)

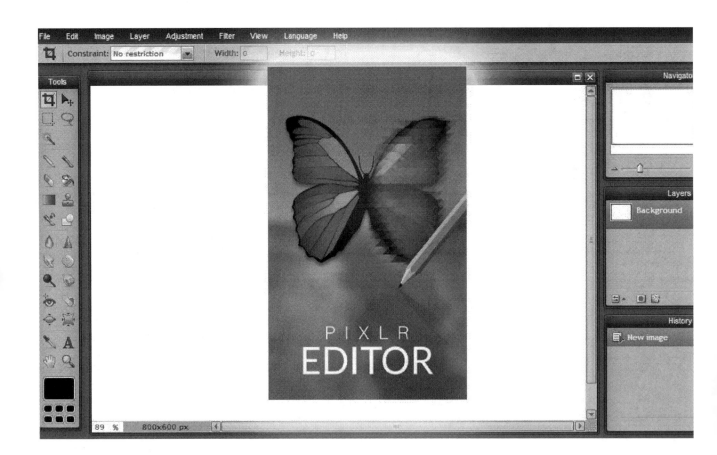

Pixlr Editor

Writing for and editing a blog, I need to do a lot of image manipulation here and there. Pixlr will never replace Photoshop, but it does the basic things that you usually need to do to graphics. You can crop, you can resize, you can tweak the color balance, you can stitch pictures together. You can even do things with layers if you really want to. What's great is that whatever computer I'm at I can do it, and I don't have to worry about booting up some extra program. And it's just dead simple.

AfterShokz Bone Conduction Headphones

The idea is that rather than having to stick buds in your ears, these don't actually go in your ears at all. They just kind of wrap around your head, and they sit just in front of your ear. And they use your skull, essentially, to conduct the sound, and you hear it just as clearly as you would over regular speakers. It's a little different, but you get used to it very quickly. And the very nice thing is that your ears are still free, so you can still hear things around you, which is designed for people who go jogging so that they can hear somebody if a car is coming or they can hear if somebody is approaching them for safety. I find it's really useful in my office if I'm programming or if I'm writing, because I always found if I wore earbuds or over-the-ear headphones, inevitably somebody would come up and tap me on the shoulder and it would just completely startle me, or I would miss something that other people were talking about that might've concerned me because I had the headphones on. This way, you get the best of both. You get your music or your podcast or whatever, but you can also sort of hear the stuff around you.

Hiku Shopping Button

This is a marvelous tool for any family, particularly those with teenagers. It's a wifi-enabled button that magnets to your fridge and can scan barcodes of things you're using the last of, or you can talk to it. It all goes to a list on a server which you can get on your mobile device. So then you just pull up the app in your phone, and you have your list there. It categorizes things by where in the store you're likely to find them. You can change information, you can add information, add categories. You can have

multiple different lists for different stores, and as you get things you can just swipe, and it'll check it off on your list, and then once you confirm that you actually are buying all those things, you can clear them off so that they'll disappear. But it updates immediately, so if anybody else is also attached to that list, they'll see it getting checked off, too. So it's really convenient.

Rugged Geek Portable Car Jump Starter

This is a device nobody with an automobile should be without. This way you don't have to depend on a stranger or wait for AAA if your car needs a jump-start, or if your tire is losing air. And it works as a power brick for mobile devices, too.

Ruben Bolling
Cartoonist

Ruben Bolling is the author of the award-winning comic strip, Tom the Dancing Bug, which premieres each week on Boing Boing. (Published 01/19/18)

Bose QuietComfort 20 Acoustic Noise Cancelling Headphones

I think of headphones as being the big bulky things that you put over your ears, but the cool thing about these is that these are just the ear buds. A friend of mine showed them to me and I didn't think they could really work because I thought most of the noise cancellation of these things comes from these big cushions that you put over your ears. I was really amazed. You switch it on, and all of a sudden, the volume of everything else, boom, just floors. My wife got them for my birthday and they're just awesome because they really just fit right into your ears. They really do work. You can put your head down in bed and go to your side and you don't have these big bulky things on. I used them on the airplane on the way to Tokyo. That was awesome. These things are essential on airplanes.

Apple Music

Of course, everyone's heard of Apple Music. There's no revelation. I sort of was interested in my reaction to it because this was a gift that I gave to my daughter because she really wanted it. And I'm a guy who, I love my music collection and it's in my iTunes and it's curated and it's organized and I'm really careful about what goes in there and what I get. She wanted this so we got it and it's just so weird, that I can't wrap my head around the fact that I can listen to literally anything ever recorded any time I want to, wherever I am. I have to remind myself, I hear something and I'm like, wow, I'd like to hear that. I wish I could. Then, once I do hear it on Apple Music, I still have this instinct or this impulse to say, "Hmm, now should I get it? Do I want it for my collection?" It's like a totally alien concept to my kids. They're just like, why do you want to have it? You can listen to it any time you want.

Citi Bike

This is an app that you have on your phone and it tells you where all the docking stations are, where the bikes are kept, and whether there are any available bikes at those docks at this time. And also, where you're going, whether there are any empty docks to put your bike. Instead of owning a bike, you just go and put a card into a slot and then you get a bike for an hour and you drop it off somewhere else. I pay an annual fee of a hundred and something. There's the helmet issue so it's hard to do it spontaneously. Sometimes, I bend that rule. The first time I used it, I just took out a bike and I'm

riding along and I see someone I know and I wave to them on my bike and it was like I was 10 years old again. Ringing the bell, it was just amazing. It's really a great service and a lot of fun.

SodaStream

I don't use the flavors with the SodaStream, I only use the seltzer. I think seltzer is a regional thing. I think it's in the Northeast where you can actually buy seltzer. When I travel and I go to a CVS or a convenience store, I find that they don't even have seltzer, whereas in New York and New England, they have lots of options for different brands of seltzer: plain seltzer, flavored seltzers. Making it at home with this Soda Stream, you just sort of put a bottle in there and press the button a few times and it makes the water into seltzer. It's environmental because we used to buy these big bottles of seltzer, with all the plastic and transportation. I love this. I usually drink a whole one with dinner.

Michael Borys
Interactive Design Director

Michael Borys is a designer who creates experiences for the entertainment industry. He is currently the Vice President of Interaction and Game Design at 42 Entertainment, a Magician Member of The Magic Castle, and his immersive magic show is called The 49 Boxes — which is not to be missed. (Published 04/13/18)

The Book of Codes

This is a treasure trove of every single type of language that is used for encryption from the dawn of man to now. Of course, you've got braille and Morse and things like that. There's even Klingon. It sort of teaches your brain to look at the world differently and see language in everything. For example, the way that binary works, as you know, it's all ones and zeroes, and binary isn't just on-off like that. It can be birds sitting on a fence, and if a bird has his wings up that could be a one, and if he's got his wings down it can be a zero. Even a hem of a dress, if it has stitching that changes from time to time, you can embed information even with stitching that way. I'm looking at Page 19, for example. It gives you versions of how information was decoded in the hems in garments during times of war, for example, and so across enemy lines. This is called steganography, by the way, the hiding of information. Soldiers were given information that were kept in their jackets. And so when they would go across enemy lines, if they were captured their captors wouldn't know that they actually had this information, but if they did get to where they needed to go the information could then be parsed, and that could win a war or lose a war. Hundreds and hundreds of these different ways of thinking that just become part of your rote memory, and so it makes you, as you travel, as you work, as you meet people and see things in a curio shop, you'll realize that information is being hidden everywhere without anybody knowing it. It's exciting, actually.

The Puzzle Keyring

I wish I had this at every escape room that I tried to solve. Because it would be a tool to both — make puzzles, think about things differently, and to solve things really quickly. It's great. It is a plastic-coated booklet, so you can dump it in water, and it'd still be fine. Unrippable, and it's on a metal keyring so that you can have it on your keys if you wanted to during the event. It's too bulky to have it with you every day of your life, but, boy, is it convenient. It's durable, and it's very, very useful.

BLACK+DECKER Impact Screwdriver

Because my show travels, all my tools have to travel, and a lot of times I don't have time to be delicate with the stuff that I have. This particular Black+Decker drill, I've charged it one time in two years, and darn it, it is great. Whenever I need it, it is ready. It has a light at the head of it. It seems unbreakable. I have a few different ones because I have a couple different sets of screws on many boxes that I have to undo and do during the show. This thing has been a lifesaver. You're probably expecting, well, specialized tools, but this is the best drill I've ever had in my life. It was like 70 bucks, but again, it has fallen 20 feet to the ground and it's never shattered, and it's just always been there for me.

Mag Hand Workstation

This is the greatest for me because what this is is a platform that has magnetic trays — and it's heavy, which is good — that I can keep the tiniest screws in and the tiniest washers, and because I'm always working with these tiny boxes and building things and making things tighter than what they probably were designed for, things fly all over the place, and how many times have you lost eyeglass screws? This thing, I can tip it upside down and all my screws and washers stay in one spot. I've knocked it on the ground and things have been fine. And there are also these posable arms with clips on the end of them, so if I'm ever painting something or I'm staining something that's delicate, I won't have the stain or the paint on my hands, because this thing will hold objects in place for me so I won't have to worry about that. It's great. It's a multipurpose thing that keeps me sane.

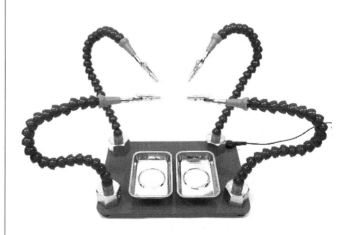

Gareth Branwyn
DIY Technology Author

Gareth Branwyn has been writing about DIY technology, media and culture for over three decades. He's the former senior editor of Boing Boing, a founding contributing editor to Wired, and the former editorial director of Make. He's the author of eight books, including his most recent, Borg Like Me, a memoir and best-of collection. He's currently writing two books, a shop tip book for Make, and a book on magic and role-playing games, which he's co-authoring with author Peter Bebergal.
(Published 01/5/18, 01/8/16, 07/10/14)

20 Bin Medium Portable Parts Storage Case

I just reorganized my office/workshop/ studio and created a multi-functional workstation that has mostly a clear desktop and all of the tools, materials, and supplies in labeled bins above the desk (general electronics, robotics, mail art, crafting, rubber stamps, etc.) in these cheap Harbor Freight storage cases. To work in an activity, I just take down the bins I need, place them on the rolly tool cart that sits beside the desk (which houses additional tools and equipment), and off I go. These cases are somewhat cheaply made, but since this is occasional, light-duty use, I traded durability for features. This system has all removable trays and the bins stack and lock together.

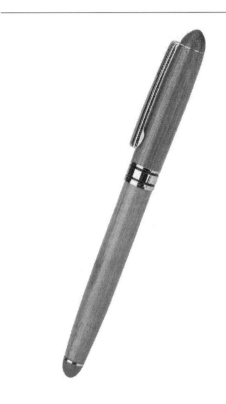

Calligraphy Art Fountain Pen

For years I have exclusively used Varsity Disposable Fountain Pens. I was talking about these on Facebook and a kind and generous friend (thanks, Michael Pechner!) sent me a Pilot Metropolitan Fountain Pen and a bottle of ink. I really liked it, but I still preferred the Varsity's flow rate and smooth travel (the Pilot's nib is a little scratchy). Then, another lovely friend sent me one of the bamboo fountain pens that can be found for around ten bucks on Amazon. I like the flow of this one better than the Pilot and have now adopted it as my regular pocket pen. I find that I really love the ritual of filling it and I really love the cool packaging and cut-glass designs of the ink bottles.

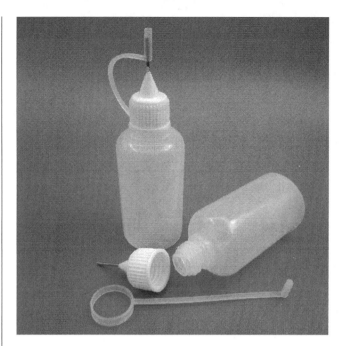

a needle applicator. I bought ten of these needlle-capped bottles (30ml) on Amazon. I put glue in one and kicker in the other. And lived happily ever after.

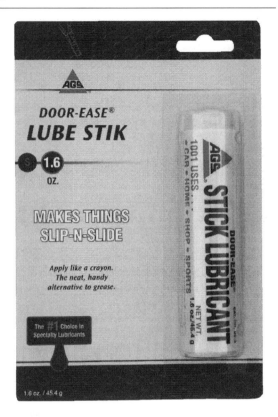

Door-Ease

There's this thing called Door Ease, which is a stick of wax for unsticking drawers, and I looked at those things and thought, "Oh, that's cool," and then one day five years later I had a sticky drawer and I thought, "Wait, I have the technology!" So I went downstairs and got my Door Ease and it hasn't stuck since.

Needle Tip Glue Bottle Applicator

I watch a lot of videos on scale modeling and miniature modeling for tabletop gaming. I often see modelers using the capillary gluing technique. Here, rather than gluing along the edge of a part and holding it to another part until it dries, you hold or clamp the two pieces together and then run a bead of CA (or other) glue along the seam. Capillary action draws the glue into the seam. And if you follow the glue bead with a bead of CA accelerator (aka Kicker), you can very quickly and precisely assemble your project. To do this, the best application method is

Empty Touch-up Bottle

We've been painting all the rooms in our house and when we finish I save a small container of it, like a cup's worth, in a little jar and then just stash it in a drawer of whatever room we painted in, so that way if you drill a hole or remove a painting and pull a nail out, you can spackle it and paint it over with that paint rather than leaving a big jar somewhere rusting away.

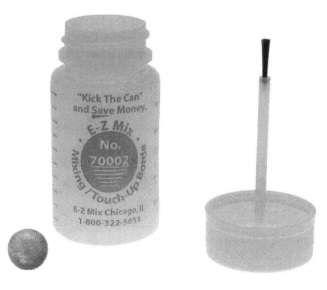

Anne Briggs
Anne of All Trades

Anne Briggs grew up in Montana and spent a lot of her young life abroad because her parents are missionaries. She majored in Chinese and Business hoping to become an international business mogul, but quickly realized that working in the tech industry wasn't a life she wanted to live. So she started a garden and built a workshop in her spare time. One thing led to another and now she's a farmer, woodworker, blacksmith, musician, and full-time content creator. (Published 11/30/18)

Knipex Cobra Pliers

This has been the single most awesome tool I've come across in the last like year and a half. One of my buddies is a contractor, and he always had them in his pocket when he was helping me build my shop out back. And I found myself borrowing those things so often that I ended up just picking up a pair myself. For some reason, I'm not quite sure why, but the person who owned the property before we did here on the farm had insisted on using different-sized nuts and bolts to fasten literally everything, like to a ridiculous degree. Everything is nutted and bolted together, but with never a consistent size, no differentiation between metric or imperial. And so having those little pliers in my pocket has been pretty much the best thing since sliced bread, because previously I would have to walk all the way up to the shop, rummage around, find something that I thought might work, and then walk all the way back down into the field or whatever. I absolutely love those things. They come in super handy. If I'm driving a tractor and I have to just twist something really quick, it's really fantastic to have that.

TanTan Smart Plugs

My husband was nice enough to set up Amazon Alexa in every room of our house, in the barn, and in my shop. And then everything is actually connected to smart plugs. And so those use a wifi signal. I just have to tell Alexa to turn on this or to turn on that. And the one thing that has been super indispensable for me is that he wired it up so that the well on our farm is connected to Alexa. So I just have to tell Alexa to turn on the well or turn off the well. And that allows me to automate different areas of the irrigation in my garden, but also fill up the watering things for my kitchens and for my livestock. It's a wireless plug. So you just plug it into your plug. And then you plug whatever you want into that plug.

Quickloader Straps

Recently someone turned me onto Quickloader straps, which is an automatic, self-reeling ratchet strap, which is just a huge game changer. I mean, when it comes to pulling fences or strapping stuff onto my tractor or putting stuff in the back of my truck, they are so fantastic, because you never have to tie down the extra strap that's hanging off. But then also, your straps are never tangled, because they self-reel. They reel themselves up. They are amazing.

Bouton Safety Glasses

My safety glasses are just cheapo safety glasses except because I do so much random stuff like with metal work and just in the wood shop in general, I really love having those vintage shades on the side, which keep my eyes so much safer than if they were just not there. And one of the most asked questions I get on my feed besides what sweatshirt I wear is where to get my safety glasses. The reason that I like these is because I feel like they cover more real estate. And so you just have more real estate protected.

Maldon Sea Salt Flakes

If you want your entire cooking game to be changed, you should get some Maldon flake salt. It's not cooking salt. You put it on your food after it's cooked, and it's these delightful little sea salt flakes that will change your life. And that's all I have to say about it, because it's only $5, so just give it a shot. It gives it a very nice salty crunch, plus you can look super, super fancy when you pull out the salt. And bonus, if you have a lathe or a chisel, you can make yourself a little salt bowl and then toss that on the table, because salt shakers are for peasants.

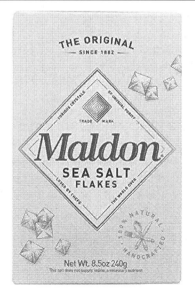

Susie Bright
Feminist and Author

Susie Bright is a pioneering, preeminent feminist sex writer and legendary audio producer. She's also reached peak satisfaction as a guest editor of Boing Boing and early member of The Well. Susie is one of the world's most respected voices on sexual politics, as well as an award-winning author and editor who's produced and published thousands of the finest writers and journalists working in American literature and progressive activism today. (Published 09/6/19)

Gingher Craft Scissors

One of the most important tools that I use every single day of my life is the Gingher craft scissors. Having good scissors is priceless. Really priceless. It's like having a decent knife on your belt. But these particular scissors are not as big as a scissors that you would imagine — usually like eight-, 10-inches long with the long sheers. These are short, and one of the things that is remarkable about it is that the points — the very tip of the scissors — are vicious. When you need to get to the very end of something and have a perfect complete cut and you cannot have one scintilla out of place, these are the scissors. I've had these scissors for 15 years and I thought I would eventually take them to one of those knife sharpening places and get them spruced up, but they're magic, they never get dull. They feel good in your hands. They're so small and they have this little leather pouch that the tips go in so you don't accidentally hurt somebody. Even the leather pouch

feels like supple, lovely leather. They have never gone cheap on these scissors. This is one of these companies where I made the effort to write them a fan letter and say, "I can't tell you how much it means to me that you've kept the quality of this going even though everything in capitalism tells you not to, that you insist on your craftsmanship."

8.5" (21.6 cm)

Palomino Blackwing 602 Pencils

This pencil is simply the creamiest, smoothest, most perfect texture-on-texture experience I've ever had in my life. It doesn't matter whether you're making a mark on some shitty little receipt that you got out of a parking machine or whether you're using linen paper, this lead is just the right smoothness and composition that it makes writing a whole new thing. Since the advent of keyboards, my handwriting has really gone down the toilet. I went to Catholic school, I used to get As in handwriting, and now I can't even write, "I love you," without some screw up as I'm using my hand. This pencil brought me back. The moment you place it on anything and you start to move, you have this effortless charcoal experience that is just heaven.

People are fanatics about Blackwings. You meet someone who's using Blackwings, you're in the cult. There are people who will tell you about the 1990s when these things went out of business and people were paying $40 per pencil on eBay to get one of these. That's how crazy it was.

Original Magic Wand

The tool that I am the most associated with is the very one that I have probably sold more of myself than anyone on earth and that is the Hitachi Magic Wand. This simply is the magic machine that has turned more women onto the experience of a real live screaming orgasm than anything. It's remarkable. The first time I encountered it, I was in San Francisco, it was I guess 1980 and a friend of mine said, "Yeah, there's this therapist who has a feminist vibrator store down the street in the Mission." She wanted to have a place where women could get a vibrator where you didn't have to go to a dirty bookstore and you could get something that worked, so I toddled on down there, I met Joani Blank, the owner of Good Vibrations, she was this philanthropist who started working in her therapy practice with a lot of women who, like everyone who read the usual propaganda, were naive. Well, after I met Joani Blank, I start working at Good Vibrations, and I remember women would come in and they would be feeling so sad. Some of them would say they were there because their doctor had told them to. It really is a consciousness-raising experience when you feel like sexual satisfaction is elusive to you. You feel like everyone else understands something about themselves and that you don't. I sold thousands of these and to this day, I'll be somewhere talking about completely different subject, I'll be talking about immigration reform, and somebody will come up to me and say, "You sold me my first magic wand. You changed my life. I'm so grateful to you. I feel like you should be up there with my first lover or something." And I know what they're saying. I felt the same way. I felt that grateful.

Heavy Duty Commercial Potato Ricer

I am an Irish Catholic socialist, so nobody expects me to make classic Eastern European latkes. But in fact, all of my friends, no matter how they were raised, bow down before me and say, "It's sad but true; Susie makes the best potato pancakes in the whole world and we do not know her secret." Well, now they know my secret because I have told on myself. When I first made potato pancakes, I was really disappointed with the results. I was like, these are watery and weak, they aren't flavorful. What am I doing wrong? And it took me some experimentation, but I realized that potatoes are watery and usually in a recipe book, they'll say something like, you should let them sit for a half an hour or you should salt them and let the water seep out. Well that doesn't work. Maybe if you have 14 days to let the water drain out, but no, it's time to make Laktes. So what you do is, you get the industrial ricer. There's a lot of crap ricers. The only ricer I want you to get is the one that I gave you the link to. It's great because you can put it on the edge of your sink and just use torque to press all the water out. You grate your potatoes, stuff a bunch of them in the ricer, a couple of handfuls and then you press down and kaboom all the brown water expresses itself. You then take your nice, expressed, fresh, crispy-fried potato leavings, put them in a bowl, add the matzo meal and the onion and the egg, and all of a sudden you are the most popular person in town because your pancakes are the best.

Brian Brushwood
Host of Scam School

Brian Brushwood is the creator and host of over 400 episodes of Discovery's "Scam School," with over one million subscribers on YouTube. In 2015, his first full season of "Hacking the System" debuted on the National Geographic Channel (now available on Netflix). Brian has performed thousands of live stage shows (appearing in every state in the continental U.S.), headlined 3 years at Universal Orlando, and recorded two Billboard #1 comedy albums with his "Night Attack" co-host, Justin Robert Young. (Published 06/8/16)

Southwest Airlines Rapid Rewards

One of the most important tools in my entire career has been the Southwest Airlines Rapid Rewards program. Everybody's got their own frequent flyer mileage program, but Southwest Airlines' is unique, because if you hit a certain level you get to have a second person that you designate as your companion pass holder and everywhere you go that person gets to go for free. Southwest Airlines has a very, very generous baggage policy. Right now, if you were to book me for a stage show, I would book a single person ticket just for me that would include me and, of course, my carry-ons, but also, thanks to the companion pass, I would be able to bring an assistant and all of us would have four 50-pound trunks that we'd be able to fly for free. Whereas normally travel alone would be like $1,000 or $1,200. We could do a show on a Friday night and come out to Albany, New York and with my rewards it only costs us $400 total.

Rakuten Super Logistics

This is cloud-based fulfillment for eCommerce retailers. One of the weird parts about being a content producer in a new media age is that you not only have to create the media, but you have to figure out a way to monetize it. An important part that I think a lot of people neglect or at least neglect to optimize is the retail side of things. The problem, of course, is when you ship T-shirts or whatever it is that you're selling, if you were to get 10,000 orders at once, it's obviously a big bummer when you're the one who's asked to stuff a bunch of T-shirts into mail packages. With Rakuten Super Logistics, all of a sudden, we were in a position to where now, when we woke up in the morning and there was a bazillion orders we were able to say, "Cool. That's someone else's problem, not ours." Basically you stop playing the game in terms of tomorrow I have to send out so many items and I have to picture them in my hands or whatever. Instead, it becomes an abstract idea and you realize you're playing, essentially, a roller coaster tycoon only with items that you happened to label, and come up with names for and marketing. That ability to pull yourself out of the equation, the ability to look at everything from a thousand meters up is incredibly valuable as far as making the smartest decisions for reaching out to your audience.

99designs.com

I was utterly astonished with how powerful this was. Let's say you wanted to make a deck of cards. The way you would do it is by hiring an artist, describing all the things you want, and then they show up with some comped up designs. Then you would explain why this isn't really what you wanted and then they would argue with you for a long time. Then eventually you'd write them a check anyway. The beauty of 99designs is every morning you wake up and you get some of the most talented artists and graphic designers on the planet putting together concepts and ideas for you to decide whether or not you like them. There were so many ideas that I was like, "Well, yes, I'd be perfectly happy with this, but I'm seeing something even more awesome." You get to pick the winners and then out of those winners, we were able to say, "Hey, we loved your design for the back, for the box, the best. We'd also like you to design the face cards, we'd like you to design this." At that point, you know who speaks your language. You know who you're going to connect with conceptually. Once you get to that point, it's amazing how easy and excited you can get about following things through to completion.

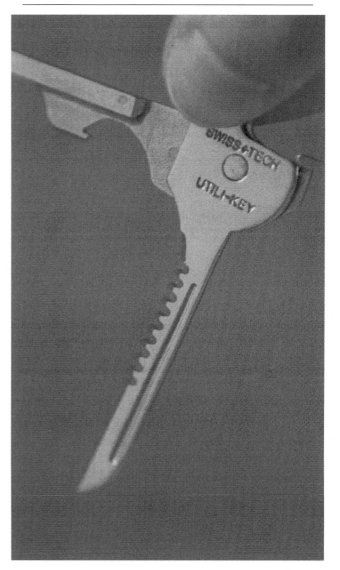

The Utili-Key

The Swiss Tech Utili-Key is a 6-in-1 multitool. It looks like a key that just sits on your key chain. That's important if you're somebody who travels a lot because it means that the TSA may or may not be inspecting those and may or may not notice whether or not it goes through. Basically, it's a key that splits in half, bisect the key vertically and imagine grabbing the two legs of it and splitting it open. When you split it open you have a straight edge, you have a serrated edge, you have a Phillips head screwdriver, a flat head screwdriver, an eyeglass screwdriver and a bottle opener, a 6-in-1 tool that sits on your key chain. In my last 15 years only once has it ever been confiscated. That's the best part. It's like $10 or $14 a piece, it's like whatever, just get it confiscated once every 10 years.

Jordan Bunker
Former Tech Editor for Make:

Jordan Bunker is a freelance engineer, designer, artist, and prop-maker based out of Oakland, California. He's also a former Make: magazine technical editor and BattleBots robot builder. You can find him on Twitter and Instagram at @TensorFlux. (Published 08/23/19)

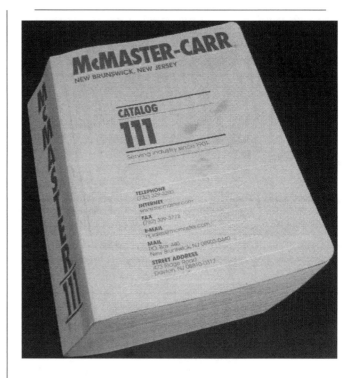

Dykem Steel Blue Layout Fluid Spray

When working with metals, it's useful to be able to make clear, precise lines on the surface to be worked on. Layout fluid is typically applied to the surface and allowed to dry as a colored film, and then a scribe is used to make light marks in the film. Many home-shop machinists know about the brush-applicator type of fluid, but this particular product is a spray, which makes applying the fluid a lot faster. There's lots of different companies that make layout fluid, but Dykem is kind of the go to company for a lot of machinists and fabricators. I typically use blue or red. I think it's just easier to see things in blue and red.

McMaster-Carr Catalog

MCMaster-Carr is one of my go-to companies for just about any kind of material or hardware needed for a project. Of course, you can search for what you need on their website, but being able to physically page through their catalog can often reveal the existence of hardware that you didn't even know existed. They only make a limited number of these catalogs, and they aren't available for purchase on their website, but I've heard that if you order often enough from them, they'll send you one. You can also request one from them, but I've never tried, and I find it's easier just to buy one from eBay for about $30 or $40. It's not color. Everything's in black and white, but there's a photo — they're actually beautiful illustrations. I'm not sure how exactly they're generating these illustrations. They look kind of like product photos that they've converted to line drawings, but everything's in black and white. Mine's actually doubled as a coffee table book, just because I find it so useful.

look for is Aramid fabrics. It's kind of a class of fabrics or fiber — Kevlar is one of them, Nomex is another, they're kind of brand names — but they're specifically formulated to be temperature, chemical and abrasion resistant.

Hot Air Rework Station

Most of the prototyping I do requires electronic design as well, and if you're working with surface-mount components, a hot air station is pretty vital. Usually when people think of soldering, they think of a soldering iron and that's great for what are called through-hole components. Well, if you're doing anything surface mount where there are no holes in the board, you're just sticking a component right onto the surface, and getting your soldering iron right there is a little tricky. So, a hot air station, what it does is it blows hot air out of the tip of this sort of wand and directly onto your parts and kind of melts all of the solder right around the area where it's heating up. So that's really useful if you're doing very small surface mount parts. And a lot of times if you go to look for a hot air station, they can be pretty expensive. A lot of them have lots of fancy bells and whistles and you're paying two or 300 bucks for these things. But this model is around $40 and doesn't really have any fancy options or anything like that. You can dial up the temperature and you can change the air pressure — the force of the air blowing out. But it's great to have it on the bench, Even if all you do use it for is heat-shrink tubing, which is where mine gets most of its use.

Air Force Jumpsuit

In my shop, I do a lot of welding, grinding, and working with chemicals. I found that I needed some kind of covering that would protect me, and found that military jumpsuits are a great option. Our tax dollars went into developing these suits, and they manufacture them by the thousands, so they're easy to get ahold of online or at a military surplus store, typically for about $20 – $30. They come in a variety of sizes (just as recruits do), and are made of a temperature-resistant, chemical-resistant, and abrasion-resistant material. I've been using mine for years, and have yet to put a hole in them (unlike several of my shirts and jeans). What you want to

Bonnie Burton
Pop Culture Author

Our guest this week is Bonnie Burton. Bonnie is a Los Angeles-based author who writes books and comics about sea monsters, Wookiees, mean girls, crafts, magical things, robots and aliens. Her books include Live or Die?: Survival Hacks; J.K. Rowling's Wizarding World Movie Magic: Amazing Artifacts; Crafting With Feminism; Star Wars Craft Book; Draw Star Wars: The Clone Wars; Girls Against Girls; Pros and (Comic) Cons; Womanthology and more. She's on Twitter at @bonniegrrl. (Published 3/8/19)

On Writing by Stephen King

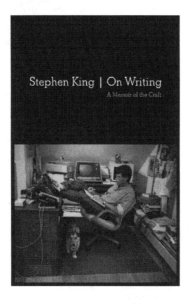

Stephen King wrote a great memoir about his career and how he struggled as a writer. I think it's immensely helpful and illuminating to any writer at any skill level. Because he shares his experiences and his habits and his thoughts all throughout all of the books he wrote. He even talks about his childhood, where he wrote kind of an underground zine at his high school, and almost got kicked out for it, because it was just making fun of teachers and stuff. But it was all the stuff that they wouldn't print in the regular high school newspaper. He kind of got his start as an underground writer. Then it talks about all of his struggles. But it also is very candid about his alcohol and drug abuse, and how his wife really kept him grounded, and how he still struggles with things like writer's block and impostor syndrome and all of that. For me as a writer, I re-read it once a year to remind myself I'm not a hack. It's funny too because it's not just about writing. It's also about what do you do after the book is published? Because I'm on my 10th book, and every publisher is different. Every marketing plan is different. You're still doing that hustle as an author. You still have to do all your own marketing.

Yellow Legal Pads

This is as old school as you can get. It's yellow legal pads. I do all my first drafts and outlines on yellow pads. You don't have to do yellow pads. I just prefer them because they're long, and they're yellow so they're easier on the eyes if you're writing late at night. I do it just because I am such an ADHD person. I get distracted by everything. If I don't have a yellow pad and I'm working on my computer, I guarantee you I'm checking Twitter at least 80,000 times before I get my first paragraph written, and that's a problem. I know some people just say, "Turn off your internet," but I can't do that. That's like turning off life support. I can't turn off my wifi connection. I would be horrified if the apocalypse hit and I'm just hanging out in my apartment writing. I think for me specifically as a writer it's just good because it slows me down a bit. I don't get distracted. I don't zone out. I notice when I type sometimes I zone out.

When I hand write I don't have that problem. Also, I can go back to these journals, where sometimes when you switch out laptops, or even though things are in the cloud they're not where you think they are. Or things get deleted. Or you don't have the right drafts. When you write something down physically, that's not going anywhere unless you physically put it in the trash can. I've found scripts from college that I'm reworking now as original screenplays, that in college would have been on a Mac classic, or a floppy disk or something. I probably wouldn't even be able to retrieve it. At least on a yellow pad it's old enough technology that you can find it again. You don't need some sort of software to reconfigure it to read it.

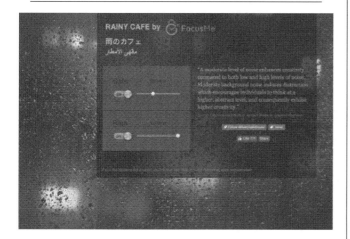

Rainy Cafe

This is a website that plays ambient café noises. Like the clinking of mugs, espresso machine noises, and just the kind of hushed conversations you would hear in a coffee house. It also has the option to have the sound of rain. Guillermo del Toro has a writing room in his Bleak House office museum that, it's just a room where it looks and sounds like it's raining outside. Even though it's not. He had it all set up to have fake rain sounds hitting the pane. Because that helps him write. For whatever reason, that's his litmus test. This you can run on any browser, in the background. I have it on my computer while I'm writing on my yellow pad. It's like, I'm getting the best of both worlds.

Soil Moisture Sensor Meter

I have a zillion houseplants and I constantly kill them. If you're like me, there's a tool called the soil moisture meter. They're usually under $10. You can get them at plant stores, grocery stores, hardware

stores, Amazon. Wherever you like to shop. I work from home so I like to have houseplants around me, because it gives me a sense of calmness. It also provides extra fresh air when I'm hyperventilating over a deadline. It's always good to stare at your succulents and ferns and spider plants when you start panicking. I also talk to them a lot. What this does is, it's a moisture meter. It's super simple looking. It's just a metal rod with a detector on the top that says the soil is either dry, normal, or super wet. It's great because you can poke it in the soil, and you don't have to do the finger test. Because usually they say just poke your finger in soil and you can tell. Yeah, that doesn't work. I've killed so many plants doing that. At least this goes all the way down, so you know if there's too much water at the base of your plant, or if there's not enough, like if you're a light waterer. Or if you soak it too much. All plants have different requirements, so it's good to just Google your plant name to research what watering they need first before you do all this. But it's a great tool, and it's a great procrastination tool. You feel like you're doing something productive when you go and measure over 30 plants in one sitting with your little soil moisture meter.

Live or Die?: Survival Hacks

My new book Live or Die?: Survival Hacks comes out this year. In it I explain how to find water and food, start a fire, and build shelters in tough terrains with everyday stuff. The book comes with a magnet to make your own compass. It'll be available at Scholastic Book Fairs in 2019 and at bookstores in 2020.

Kari Byron
Mythbuster

Kari Byron is best known for her role as a host on Discovery's flagship show Mythbusters. Since then she has gone on to host and produce shows spanning several networks, from White Rabbit Project on Netflix to Thrill Factor on Travel Channel to Positive Energy on Nat Geo. She just released her new book Crash Test Girl: An Unlikely Experiment in Using the Scientific Method to Answer Life's Toughest Questions. (Published 05/11/18)

Electric Matches

So I am an artist. That's how I got into Mythbusters in the first place; I wanted to do special effects and I started to work for Jamie Hyneman. I've learned a lot through being on Mythbusters. One is the uses of explosives or ignitions. The electric match is something that you can buy on eBay. I'm pretty sure it's legal, because they sent it to me, but you can get them on eBay. I think they're mainly for fireworks, so that you can light fireworks at a distance. I think possibly reenactors use them for cannons and such. But what I use them for is I attach this long

Black powder painting made with electric matches

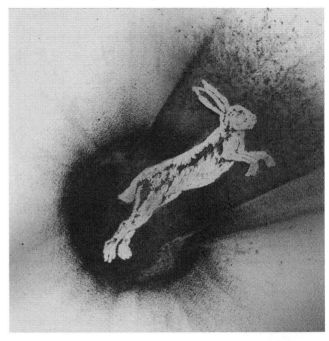

Leatherman Skeletool

I feel like with the Skeletool, because it is so lightweight and small, I can carry it easily, and I can also clip it on the top of my leather boots, which is also really an easy way to carry it. You've got your basics. You've got a sharp knife. You have got the players. You've got a screwdriver. For me, it's about the convenience of not having to go find a tool if it's just right there on my belt, or my boot.

wire that has a small charge at the end, I attach the wire end to some stereo cable. I go to a safe distance, and then I touch it to a drill battery, and I can ignite small amounts of black powder to create pieces of artwork. The detritus left over from the black powder, which leaves smoke marks, and burnt paper, and black markings, I can use to make things that look like planets. Or if smash clay into a picture, and blow up black powder above it, I can scrape off the place and have a negative space to create some sort of artwork.

Dremel Cordless Rotary Tool

The Dremel tool is just a rotary machine that has attachments that allow you handheld to grind, or sand, or cut. I find it's useful for so many different things, for creating things, for destroying things. In college I did entire sculptures out of wood using the sanding heads at the end of the Dremel. I've used it to dislodge screws where the heads have broken off, and I was in a bind, and used the cutting tool to make a new area that I could throw a screwdriver into. I find it extremely useful, and it's something that I have in my house.

My Talking Pet

A while ago a friend of mine introduced me to this app called My Talking Pet, where you take a photograph, and then you can alter the photograph

so a mouth opens and closes to your voice, so you can make your dog say things to you. If you have to, say, nag your husband or something, it's a lot nicer coming from the family pet, and it's also hilarious, so maybe it won't be taken quite as deeply. But I also found with that app, is that you can apply it to your human friends as well. So some of my cohosts, like Tory, I've been able to make him say weird things and send it out on Twitter, whatever. I find it to be a really fun application for those moments when you're a little bored.

Also mentioned:

Crash Test Girl: An Unlikely Experiment in Using the Scientific Method to Answer Life's Toughest Questions

This is a memoir. My life methodology is the scientific method, which is a tool for critical thinking that I use to break down all of my mistakes or opportunities I've created for myself over the years. I share how I got onto Mythbusters and some behind-the-scene stories, but mostly the book is about me learning to be brave to create opportunities. It's aimed for people who are trying to figure out the next step of their life.

Norm Chan
Editor of Tested.com

Norm Chan is the co-founder and editor of Tested. com, a website and YouTube channel celebrating the interesting intersections of technology, science, art, and the maker community. Norm's been a technology journalist for 10 years and produces shows on Tested, including Adam Savage's costume builds and his weekly podcast Still Untitled. (Published 12/7/17)

Canon EOS 5D

The Canon EOS 5D is my go-to. That's the thing I probably use the most next to a smartphone or a computer. I definitely like shooting video with it. The 5D has a touch screen, lets you tap to focus, it tracks faces. It's a very good B-roll camera for me. I like the Canon user interface. I have a collection of Canon lenses. On Nikon cameras, the focus and the zooms are reversed. Whereas in Canon you rotate clockwise, on a Nikon it would be counter clockwise. So my muscle memory is actually tuned to the Canon lenses.

DxO One

There's a company called DxO, and they're a software company. They do software analysis for images. When you see smartphones come out, you may see a DxO score or rating for some of these cameras. But they also make hardware, and their first camera was a camera called the DxO One. The price has gone down a little bit, it's a $500 camera, which is still expensive in the pocket camera world. But it has a very large sensor, it's a 1-inch size sensor in this form factor that's no bigger than a lighter. A metallic lighter, like a Zippo. It's very pocketable, and it actually plugs in to an iOS device. So it has a lightning port, you plug it into your iPhone and basically you have a very nice camera. You can use the iPhone as the viewfinder and save the photos directly on to your phone.

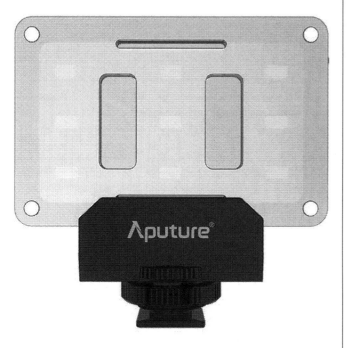

Aputure Amaran AL-M9

So working in a production pseudo-environment, we use a lot of traditional Kino lights, things you'd find in movie studios and big bulky lights with the switch-out bulbs. And the past couple years we've been moving over to LED lights. But more recently we've discovered there's a company called Aputure, and they sent us a sample of this very small, lightweight, credit card-sized LED light. The AL-M9 is the model and we have a couple handful of these in our studio and they're very backpack-able, even pocketable. Run off of built-in battery and they get incredibly bright, very bright with I think 9 or 10 degrees of brightness settings, so it can get pretty dim, and pretty bright. And

they're just so handy for, if you're shooting outdoors, using them for a fill light for example. Or when I do product shots or macro shots, as a backlight or even as key light. And then they have these magnetic swappable covers for color temperature. They're just very versatile.

Glowforge

This is like the new shiny toy. Having a laser cutter that I have in my home office is game changing. I have a 3D printer now and a laser cutter next to my computer desk at home. It just changes how fast I can prototype and come up with an idea and make it. It's a 40W laser or a 45W, if you go for the pro model. In the world of laser cutters, the way I understand, there are two fundamental laser technologies. There are tube lasers, glass tube lasers, and then there's metal lasers. And the big industrial lasers you see at maker spaces are metal lasers; they are pulse based. Tube lasers have a continuous laser but they don't last nearly as long — they're more hobby lasers. So this one is a tube laser. I expect it to last several years, but it's going to be replaceable. But it definitely cuts cardboard, foam core, 1/8 inch wood is probably the sweet spot for it. It's all cloud-based software they're rolling out. But one of the other features is a pass-through system. If I have a very long sheet of material I can cut a fifth of it and then slide it through, it'll re-align, resume a cut or resume an etch, and therefore I have a 20 inch by theoretically as large as I want.

Bob Clagett
Maker

Bob Clagett loves making stuff. He loves showing other people how he works to hopefully inspire them and empower them to make whatever it is that they're passionate about. (Published 04/19/18)

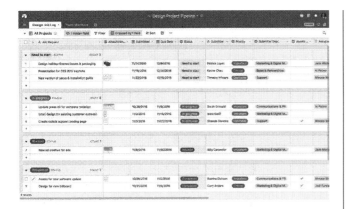

Airtable + IFTTT

Airtable is kind of an online spreadsheet. And that's one way that people use it. But the thing that makes it different for me and the way that I use it is more of a relational database. I come from a software background, so when you're programming you often have a database of tables, and those tables need to relate to each other. The way that I use that in my business is I have what looks like a spreadsheet that is my project schedule, and then I have a separate one that is project ideas that I come up with all the time and I just dump into this big list, and I use IFTTT for that. IFTTT is about taking multiple online services of all different types and connecting them together. So if something happens on one, it can cause something to happen on another. And I use that with Airtable. Through the IFTTT app, I've got a little thing set up where I can open an app on my phone that's just a text field and a button, and that's all it is. And if I type in a project idea, and I hit that button, it disappears. It's gone. But in the background it's sending that to Airtable.

It's putting it in my list of project ideas, and it just keeps it there, and then I don't have to remember it anymore, but I also don't lose it.

Nest Hello

The Hello is a doorbell, which for the price it sounds so unrealistic to actually get, because it's several hundred dollars. But it's an HD camera built into a tiny little doorbell, and it's the same technology that they have in their security cameras. It's small and kind of modern-looking and it hooks right up to the normal hookup

for a doorbell. So you don't have to really do anything special to get this in to place. And it's got some really cool features. It's very new, so I think some of the features that will be the coolest have yet to be added. But when you get it hooked up and someone walks up to your door, you get a notification on your phone or device that shows you video of the person who's walked up to the door. And you can press a button onscreen, and you can talk to them remotely through the doorbell. It's got some kind of canned responses that you can just press a button and this voice will say, "Just leave the package by the door." There's a few things like that. But one of the coolest things about it is that they've got some facial recognition stuff built in to it. So once it starts to take pictures, it gets this video of the people that come up to your door, and it keeps a log of all these pictures of the people.

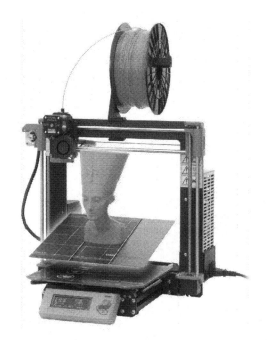

ISOtunes Bluetooth Earplug Headphones

They have basically the same features as far as listening that every other headphone in the world has. But they have an interesting phone insert on them that you roll up and you kind of heat it with your finger, between your thumb and your finger, and it squishes it down. And then when you put it in your ear it expands and completely fills the ear canal. So it cuts out basically all the noise that can come in. And the guy that works with me is maybe 10 feet from me right now, and I've yelled at the top of my voice his name to try to get his attention with these things in, and it completely blocks it out. But one of the things that I think is even cooler about them is that they have a consistent noise level suppression. So if there's a noise in the background, like if you had a saw running that was kind of the same noise the whole time or like a lawn mower or something, it can actively cut that sound out. So you can take a phone call while you're on a riding lawn mower, and the person on the other end doesn't really even know that there's a mower running. They just hear when your voice spikes and things like that. That's the part that they hear. And I have not heard of any other Bluetooth headphone that does that.

Prusa 3D Printer

I've had several different 3D printers. I use them a lot for my projects. And I'm in a position where a lot

of companies will send me things, and I get to try out really expensive things that I wouldn't ever justify buying myself. But I have a lot of people who ask me about a good first printer. And I think the problem with that question is a lot of people are looking for a good first cheap printer. And what you actually want is a good printer, not a cheap printer, because cheap printers that don't work very well are gonna make you hate 3D printing and think that it doesn't work. And so when I've looked at a bunch of different ones from the perspective of cost and functionality and tried to find something in the middle, I got the Prusa i3 MK2 a couple of years ago when it came out, and it was fantastic. It was like $699 for a printer that worked almost perfectly every single time right out of the box. You didn't have to do anything to it, and it was a great printer, I was really happy with it. And then they announced this Mark 3, which is an upgraded version of the same thing. But they added all these features that just make it awesome. It's now one of my favorite printers just because of its features. And then when you look at the price compared to a lot of other printers, it's very, very reasonably priced for what you're getting out of it. It's got a panic thing built in to it. So if it loses power, it has a little bit of a battery or capacitor in it somewhere that if it senses power dropping it will write the state of the print to some sort of a memory. And then when power is reapplied it'll ask you, "Do you want to continue to print?" And you hit yes, and then it re-homes the print head, just goes over to the corner, and then comes right back and starts printing. It's amazing. I'm sure there are other printers that do that, but I've never seen one, and it works great.

Laura Cochrane
Content Strategist

*Laura Cochrane is a content strategist living in
Berkeley, California. She currently works at NEO.LIFE,
a biotech publication. Before that, she was an editor at
two different DIY project publications: MAKE magazine
and Instructables. Her hobbies include rock climbing,
drawing, dancing, and yoga. (Published 10/12/18)*

Tom Bihn Daylight Backpack

A couple years ago, before a trip to Europe, I was on the hunt for a new day backpack. The JanSport
I had had since high school had holes in it. I wanted something with a clean, minimal design. It's
actually a challenge to find a backpack that doesn't have a bunch of random zip compartments,
pouches, folds, mesh details, and gratuitous textures added for seemingly no reason at all. So I was
excited when I found the Tom Bihn Daylight Backpack. It's got a simple rounded trapezoid shape
with a single diagonal zip that provides access to the front pocket. I got it in this really nice French blue color
that looks good with most everything I wear. It also shipped fast, and as I recall there was a handwritten note
thanking me for my order. It's made in Seattle, and the quality is solid. I've stuffed it until it's quite full and the
seams have held up for the past two years as I've used it as a work commuter backpack.

FoundPhotos.net

I've loved this website for a long time. It's an online photo gallery born out of the era of peer-to-peer filesharing. It was started in 2004 when a musician named Rich Vogel was using a filesharing program to find music and instead stumbled on a folder of photos. It's still getting updated periodically, though I'm not sure how often. The collection is thoughtfully curated, like an epic mix tape. Though I can't always put my finger on why one photo works so well next to another that seems unrelated in every way. When I want to be reminded of how beautiful the imperfection of real life is, I go here. These photos are often the mistakes, the ones the photographer never intended. Some are blurry, poorly framed, or double exposed. People have been captured with weird expressions or unflattering angles, but that's part of the appeal. They're stills from the cutting room floor of life. I find humor, horror, love, and glory in a way that feels rare.

Audio Dharma Talks

Audio Dharma is a regularly updated collection of all the talks and guided meditations given at the Insight Meditation Center in Redwood City, California. A massage therapist recommended it to me after a particularly emotional session a few years ago. I started out mostly listening to the guided meditations, but lately I've been more into listening to the talks. They work well for someone who is listening in short bursts, so I'll put it on for my 15-minute work commutes in the morning and evening. In moments where I'm feeling particularly stressed or sad, these talks can have the effect of helping me change what feels

like a less-than-ideal metaphorical posture: when I'm overly focused on the future or the past I have this sense of leaning forward, like my mind is two steps ahead of my body. Audio Dharma helps me realign to something closer to upright — a posture of gentle curiosity. My favorite talks are the ones where the teacher picks a simple human experience, like uncertainty, desire, grief, or generosity, and they explore it in a way that usually leaves me feeling like I have a new perspective on a very common human experience. Most of the podcasts or music I listen to feel like they fill my head with noise that requires additional processing or decompressing afterward, but this feels like the opposite. To use a computer analogy, Audio Dharma defragments my brain.

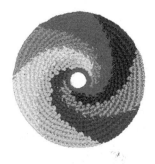

Pocket Disc

I like throwing around a frisbee, but I enjoy it even more with my crocheted frisbee. I don't remember how I came into possession of one of these, but I love it. The main things that make it awesome are that it never hurts if someone throws it at you hard, and it folds up and can fit easily in pockets, purses, and bags. Also it flies quite well, it can be given as a gift to people of all ages, and it's safer to use inside the house. When I'm feeling silly, I've been known to flip it inside out and wear it as a hat. The only places I wouldn't recommend it are around dogs, because I imagine they would quickly chew it to shreds, and on beaches. On the beach, the lip of the disc picks up sand when it lands on the ground, and then the next time someone catches it next, the sand gets released into the catcher's face. I'm sure I could brush up on my crocheting skills and make myself one from scratch, but I feel like these are a good deal for the money. They also make great gifts.

Collin Cunningham
Creative Engineer at Adafruit Industries

Collin Cunningham is an experimentalist at heart. His love for discovery has led him to explore the worlds of video, sound, art, and technology. He's created multiple web video series and apps, and is a creative engineer at Adafruit Industries. (Published 07/5/17)

Metcal MX-500S Soldering System

I jumped around to a lot of different irons. I tried your Hakkos and your Wellers and such, but the coolest thing about this iron is the stylus. It's like a big pen, and that's kind of rare, so you feel very nimble and elegant while soldering. You can get into all these hard to reach places. There is a little magic going on under the hood. I say magic because I'm not actually sure how it achieves proper temperature, because you don't actually set a temperature on it like a lot of other irons, and it heats up within seconds. Super fast. The coolest thing about it is, it has an auto shutoff. I never hear of that feature on any other iron, and it's so important. Like how often I say, "Oh, I left the soldering iron on," and it's just sitting there and killing the tip and being a fire hazard all night, forever, when I forget about it. That is the most

glorious, simple thing to add to this kind of a tool, and I use it always because I just leave it on, and it turns itself off like 10 minutes after I've stopped using it.

PLANCK EZ - FULLY ASSEMBLED WITH RGB

Preonic and Planck Keyboard Kit

Mechanical keyboards can be a rabbit hole — it's a Pandora's box. I caution anyone who has mild interest in it because you can get sucked in. You usually start because you like the feel of a different key switch, and I think mechanical keyboards appeal to people who have sort of tactility sensitivity or fetish or whatever you want to call it. This company, Ortholinear Keyboards, makes kits to build your own keyboard. The special thing about their design is that they are, as they call it, ortholinear. They're non-staggered. If you look at a normal keyboard, the keys are not lined up in actual rows, right? They're not in actual columns. And you might think, "Oh, well, the stagger is designed due to some ergonomics or there's some reason for it." No, it's legacy from typewriters. In actuality, if you have proper posture, you should be able to just slide your finger right up, and just hit another key right above it. And once you get adjusted, I would say, it is easier to touch-type on these ortholinear keyboards.

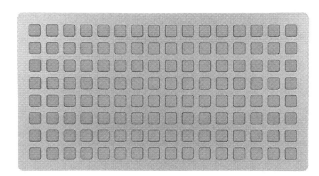

Monome Grid Reconfigurable Music Controller

This is something that's been around a while — the Monome grid, and it basically looks like, similar to the ortholinear keyboards, a grid of buttons. But they're sort of rubbery membrane buttons that each have a light underneath them, each have an LED, and it's controlled by software on the computer. Nothing running inside of the actual board determines its function beyond the serial data that's being sent over. And people can write their own functionality for it using MaxMSP. It runs on multiple platforms, and you can drag visual blocks around, of logic, like say an if-then statement. If blank happens, then, and then draw a line to another block that'll say, "Do this math," or "Make this noise," or whatever you choose. And it's designed, I believe, originally for artists, to make programming more accessible for artists, multimedia programming, for sound, and it has a large video control API or library for it. So people can write functionality for the Monome using MaxMSP and then make it do all sorts of cool things, generally to make music for them or allow them to make music more easily. My favorite application is Polygomé. It is basically an arpeggiator that shows you with the lights what other notes are being activated. Arpeggiator is basically when you press one key, other notes are then played in sequence after. So if you push one button that lights up, other lights appear around it that indicate the other notes that are playing from an arpeggiator. So it's like a visual arpeggiator, but also you can choose what mode, or basically scale, the whole board — the notes on the board — are in. So in effect it allows

you to just press a bunch of buttons and make music much more quickly and easily.

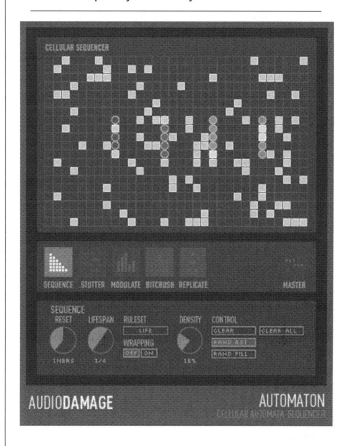

Automation plug-in by Audio Damage

This in a way kind of goes with the Monome. This plug-in is called the Automaton from a very cool company named Audio Damage, and it has a few different effects built in — I believe a modulator, a stutter effect, and a bitcrusher effect. A lot of sort of glitchy sound effectors in there. But the way it triggers, or activates, each effect is using this visual sequencer, and so if you can imagine a grid that has little points on it — let's say you put a blue point on there, and that'll activate a bitcrusher. And you put a red point on there, and it'll activate a stutter effect. Overlaid over that is Conway's Game of Life — cellular automata. So like a super simple simulation of life interacting, like a cellular level. So it allows this non-random, almost random, control to trigger the effects. It has this semi-repeating, but sort of random quality to it, which is really great, because I love to add a little random into electronic music. I just think it's a really fun, creative application of Conway's Game of Life, which is always a great recurring thing to use when, "Hey, I hooked up like an LED matrix. What can I do with it?"

Matt Cutts
Head of Web Spam Team at Google

Matt Cutts is a well-known blogger and the Head of the Web Spam team at Google. For more recommendations from Matt, be sure to check out his personal blog at mattcutts.com. (Published 02/3/15)

3 friends

Tweet
Share
Email

••• More

Hong Kong Takes a Symbolic Stand Against China Tech

The New York Times – Paul Mozur – Oct 3, 2:05 AM – HONG KONG — There's no sign to mark it. But when travelers from Hong Kong cross into Shenzhen in mainland China, they reach a digital cut-off point. On the Hong Kong side, the internet is open and unfettered. On the China side, connections…

zeynep tufekci RT @paulmozur: Smashing cameras: our look at how Hong Kong protesters are fighting not just police surveillance, but staging a stand against the tech-backed authoritarianism they see just over the border in mainland China and fear is coming to Hong Kong. t.co/yZbb0QbN4i
about 4 hours ago ← Reply ⇄ Retweet ♥ Like

Nellie Bowles RT @paulmozur: Smashing cameras: our look at how Hong Kong protesters are fighting not just police surveillance, but staging a stand against the tech-backed authoritarianism they see just over the border in mainland China and fear is coming to Hong Kong. t.co/yZbb0QbN4i
about 8 hours ago ← Reply ⇄ Retweet ♥ Like

Pui-Wing Tam RT @paulmozur: Smashing cameras: our look at how Hong Kong protesters are fighting not just police surveillance, but staging a stand against the tech-backed authoritarianism they see just over the border in mainland China and fear is coming to Hong Kong. t.co/yZbb0QbN4i
about 8 hours ago ← Reply ⇄ Retweet ♥ Like

Nuzzle

Imagine somebody posted a great link. Maybe three of your friends posted a great link on Twitter, but you happened to not be looking at Twitter at that moment. Nuzzle let's you see that and get a recap of what you might've missed, and it also bubbles things up based on how many people have been Tweeting about this. It's a really good way to just dip your hand into the stream and see what's going on without watching every single Tweet go by.

Uses This

The person who runs this website basically goes out and asks four simple questions to a bunch of different people. He gets an incredible amount of different people to participate. They'll talk about all kinds of different things that they do, or that they use. You can find out the hardware and the software that they use and also their dream set up. People

answer those questions in very different, very creative ways. It's almost like if you could be invited into somebody's house and look at their book shelf. You get a good feel for the things that they enjoy, and that can often help you find out and discover new things.

Logitech Wireless Presenter R400

This is a neat little device. Basically you pop in a couple batteries and it lets you wirelessly move through presentations. If you give a lot of talks or presentations, you're always tied to the computer, you're pressing the up down button or left right. This let's you walk around an auditorium. It's got a laser pointer built in. You can go forwards or backwards. I used it on my Chromebook recently to give a talk at North Carolina in Chapel Hill. It works with Mac, and Windows, and even Chromebooks. It works very well.

![The First 20 Minutes book cover]

THE FIRST 20 MINUTES

SURPRISING SCIENCE REVEALS HOW WE CAN:

EXERCISE BETTER
TRAIN SMARTER
LIVE LONGER

GRETCHEN REYNOLDS

The First 20 Minutes, by Gretchen Reynolds

Gretchen Reynolds writes for The NY Times, and she writes about health and fitness and sleep, and all kinds of different topics. This book, The First 20 Minutes, is sort of a summary of all the different things that she has learned over the years from reading through the research and talking to experts in the field. Some of them are almost like tricks or gimmicks. Like, stand on one foot while you're brushing your teeth and you can work on improving your balance for free. Or, pickle juice might help with cramps. A lot of it is just "Hey, here's what the current science says about the best ways to work out without having it be a totally bad experience."

It's very readable. It's a very fast read, but it's not simplified. It's just like her writing for the newspaper, she writes very well. It's very easy to get through.

DYI Project and GarageMate

I made my own bluetooth garage door opener. You can do it in a weekend. I suck at soldering and I was still able to make it, so anybody can really do it. The basic idea is you take a certain brand of Bluetooth receiver, you pop it open, you take a couple wires and you basically solder one extra little transistor. Then all garage door openers are actually built to allow people to insert wires very easily. This project is compatible with all the major garage door openers. Then you have a very simple phone app called GarageMate, let's say suppose you're going biking and you want to open the garage door and you don't want to take your keys with you. You can just open up this app on your phone, press one button, and the garage door opens up. It's just like magic. It turns out a lot of these garage door openers have a little simple way to insert a wire. They are actually much more interoperable than a lot of more recent gadgets. Unless you're buying a brand new house that has a really fantastic garage door opener, this is a simple way to do it where you can go biking and not take your keys with you. All you have to worry about is taking your phone, and it's much more convenient.

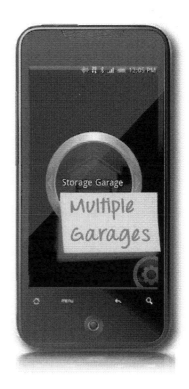

Barbara Dace
Pharmacist

Dr. Barbara Dace has been a compounding pharmacist for 32 years, creating custom medications, educating pharmacy students as well as the public, and improving health and quality of life for hundreds of patients. She loves to sing and play the autoharp, and has become an award-winning songwriter. (Published 12/29/17)

SECRETS TO A GREAT NIGHT'S SLEEP

74 MATTRESSES TESTED & RATED
plus **HELP FOR PEOPLE IN PAIN**, finding the **PERFECT PILLOW**, and warnings about over-the-counter **SLEEP AIDS**.

FEBRUARY 2017
$5.99US $7.99CAN

Consumer Reports

Consumer Reports is an independent, nonprofit organization that tests, rates, and compares all kinds of products, from cars to chocolates; they also advocate for improved consumer protections "to create a fairer, safer, and healthier world." They've been doing this for 80 years, have never accepted advertising, and have been instrumental in fighting for improved national policies in hundreds of areas, including seatbelts (which saved my life, for one), limits on predatory lending, fighting for net neutrality, prescription drug safety, etc. Your subscription isn't merely giving you access to a vast and reliable source of consumer information—it's making the world a better place, as well.

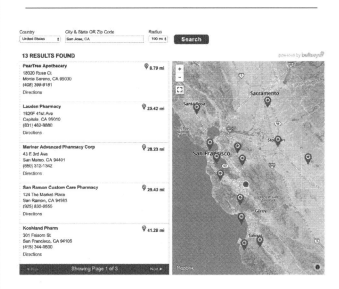

Compounding Pharmacies

Compounding pharmacies are a tool you may never need, but when a patient has unique requirements that aren't met by mass-manufactured medicines, compounding can quite literally be a lifesaver. Compounding pharmacists make custom medications "from scratch" to meet specific needs, such as: hypoallergenic meds for those with severe allergies; flavored liquids for children, the elderly, or pets; pain creams, which can include multiple ingredients and target specific painful areas with a minimum of systemic side effects; transdermal creams for people (or animals) that can't—or won't—take meds orally; customized bio-identical hormone therapy; medicated wound gels that can include antibiotics, anesthetics, and ingredients to promote healing; and medications that, while apparently safe and effective, are not mass-manufactured for economic reasons (i.e: the manufacturers won't make enough money from them). When I give talks to doctors about compounding, I give them this rule of thumb: when you run out of treatment ideas, call your compounding pharmacist. Chances are, they'll be able to help.

The Motley Fool

The Motley Fool Website

Most financial/investment websites are stultifyingly dull. Motley Fool manages to bring humor and enthusiasm to the subject without a corresponding increase in BS. I've found them a good source of information, and entertaining enough that I don't lose consciousness before I manage to absorb the nuggets of wisdom. There are plenty of free forums available to help with your questions. From debt reduction, to saving, to tax reduction and investing, they give solid advice, leavened with a bit of humor. To help with allocation, I'm also using "Future Advisor." You feed in all your investments and it gives you allocation suggestions which you can either execute yourself (free) or sign up to have them do it automatically (for a percentage). Unlike many other of these services, you can tag investments you want

not to be reallocated (I'll keep my Amazon stock, thank you very much!), so they won't advise you to sell those. It's a bit tedious to set up, but a breeze to use once you've got all the information in, and it'll help keep you from making potentially expensive mistakes over the years.

Autoharps

The autoharp is the only instrument I've ever been able to pick up and play almost immediately, from the very beginning, and still be able to sing at the same time. Despite the many benefits of playing an instrument — mental, social, and emotional as well as musical — many who didn't learn while young feel that it's now "too late" in their adulthood. One problem is the learning curve: it takes most people many months to sound halfway decent on a guitar, for instance — let alone sing at the same time. An autoharp makes this much simpler by damping every string that's not in the selected chord at the push of a button, so when you strum, you will get a D chord, or whatever other chord you selected. All you have to do is push buttons and strum; no odd hand contortions or painful fingers. There is, of course, a catch or two. First, you're tuning 36 strings instead of 6 or 12; but if you tune your autoharp every day or so for a while, you'll find it "settles in" and stays in tune much longer than it would if you only tuned sporadically.

Nelson Dellis
USA Memory Champion

Nelson Dellis is one of the leading memory experts in the world, traveling around the world as a Memory Consultant and Keynote Speaker. A four-time USA Memory Champion, mountaineer, and Alzheimer's disease activist, he preaches a lifestyle that combines fitness, both mental and physical, with proper diet and social involvement. (Published 02/15/18)

folds up super small, it's super light, and it just has so many different uses. I wear it kind of in between layers and on top of layers. It stops the wind and just keeps you toasty.

Mountain Hardwear Ghost Whisperer Jacket

I like to climb, I'm a big climber, and through my charity I do a bunch of big expeditions. So I've been up Everest a few times, where you're dealing with the elements, trying to stay warm and not get cold in different circumstances. You're trying to find the perfect gear that's not too heavy and gets the job done. So I've experimented with a bunch of stuff, and in 2016 I was on Everest, and I was introduced to this jacket and I haven't stopped using it since. It's just this really lightweight kind of down jacket that

Peak Design Anchor Links for Camera Straps

I love taking video of when I travel, when I climb, even for some of my memory videos, I'm shooting them on the go, interviewing people or trying to get a shot while I explain something and sometimes, I like to go really hand-held to get these angles or to just be run and gunning. Other times, it's strapped around my neck and I'm doing or holding something else. So, I kind of go in-between those things, and I've always hated Canon straps that have these double loops that take like, 10 minutes to sit down and fish them through the little loop and the Sony's DSLRs, which I've played with too, have these really annoying kind of clips that make noise if you keep them on, so people take them off . This little kind of contraption is basically getting rid of you ever having to do that again. They don't bother the camera at all, but you can just latch on when you need the strap or not and it's awesome for dealing with that kind of stuff.

The Memory Palace Technique

This technique supposedly was invented by the Greeks thousands of years ago and has been used to memorize massive poems and legions of armies' fighters names, and it's something people had to use back in the day to store information. The technique works around something that our brains are really good at, which is 1) thinking in pictures. The second step is to take advantage of what our brains are also good at, and that is spatial information. We're very spatially aware. Our brain is very good at scanning areas and keeping that information within our heads without really trying. And so, if you think about your house for example, close your eyes and picture yourself standing at your front door. I guarantee you, 99.9% of people listening could close their eyes and walk through their whole house without any trouble, right? So, if you can take those two things, thinking in pictures and using your house or some place familiar, the spatial information that's already memorized in your mind, you can actually memorize really large amounts of things, and this is the memory palace. Let's say you're memorizing all 45 presidents.

You would come up with a picture for each of the Presidents' names. So, like, Taft could be a raft, because you'd actually picture a raft. Wilson could be a tennis ball, because you think of Wilson tennis. Trump's face is actually memorable, or you could think of an orange. So, you have a picture for each of those things and then what you do is you place the pictures in order, because you want to know the presidents in order, around a path through the place that you're using as your palace. So, maybe your picture for Washington is a washing machine filled with a ton of clothes, and you picture that washing machine kind of pushed up against the front door and maybe it's rattling because there's a ton of stuff in there, it's really over-loaded and it's just shaking, making a lot of scary noises and kind of banging up against the door so much so that maybe even the wooden door is splintering and kind of shattering. So combine the images and have them interact with the space. The more use of your senses in that picture, the better it's going to be. And the idea is that, later on, when you're trying to recall this list, all you have to do is literally just think of your house and make that same walk through. And because your house is so ingrained, it's where you live, you've been through it a million times, there's nothing to memorize there. You can walk through it freely and easily like you did when you were memorizing.

Art of Memory

This is something I actually helped create with a few other memory friends, and it's basically a place to train your memory. I use it to practice, of course. And to teach others these techniques. You can play memory games online against other memory enthusiasts, and you can actually create your memory palaces through our software online. So, it's just a great kind of tool. All memory-training related. Great resource for learning techniques, practicing them and developing your systems.

Jimmy DiResta
Designer

Jimmy DiResta is a maker, toy designer, and TV show host. He's been the host of a number of DIY shows including Dirty Money, Trash to Cash, Against the Grain, and Hammered with John and Jimmy DiResta. He co-hosts the Making It Podcast, and has a fantastic YouTube channel called DiResta with videos on his latest builds and handy tool tips. (Published 08/17/15)

SOG Revolver

SOG makes a couple of really good utilitarian-type knives. This one is called the Revolver. It's basically one shank of steel. Half of it is buried in the handle, and there's a pivot point at the front forward part of the handle. Then you push a trigger and it unlocks. You rotate the blade 180 degrees. One half is a Bowie knife and the other half is a really sharp saw. It's perfect for a camping trip. I have two of them, and I just went on a camping trip in the Adirondacks and I had it with me the whole time. Of course, I didn't really need to use it as much as I did, but I'm like a little kid out in the woods. I have to use the saw, and I have to use the knife. It was fun. It has a lifetime guarantee, so if you ever happen to accidentally cut a nail with it, and ruin the blade, you can turn it in and they give you a new one.

Light-up Baseball Cap

It's one of those inventions that when it comes out, everyone's like why didn't we think of that. Everybody knocks it off. Power Cap is the one that I happen to see most often. The best quality ones have been available from Cabelas. I use them up to the point where I just go and buy a new one. You can change the batteries, but when you buy these four button-cell batteries, they cost as much as buying the whole new hat. All the knockoffs are out there now. You get what's available where you are. Home Depot sells a version and so does Lowe's.

Tactical Pen

If you walk out of the house and you have a pencil or a Bic pen, in 10 minutes you've given it to somebody, or you lost it, or you don't care. But if you carry

around a tactical pen, it just becomes like a semiprecious item that you're going to constantly remember, "Oh, I lent that person my pen. Give it back to me when you're done." That's really the main reason I like it. Because it looks good with my gear, and it's not something I would leave behind.

Ice Pick

It's incredibly useful. People always say, "What are you going to do with that? Are you going to kill somebody?" I'm like, "No, it's a tool, and if you carry one for a couple days in your shop, you're going to begin to realize how often you'll reach for it. That's what I tell everybody. Just to carry one, and you'll begin to realize how often you need it, and to keep it sexy and smooth, I put a thin little handle on it.

Dale Dougherty
CEO of MAKE

Dale Dougherty is the founder and CEO of MAKE, which produces MAKE: Magazine and Maker Faire, in addition to books and kits for makers young and old. He lives in Sebastopol, California. (Published 03/2/17)

O.M.R.A. Mini Home Electric Tomato Milling Machine

This is a way to process tomatoes. I grow a lot of tomatoes, particularly like Roma and San Marzano. This is just a mill. It's got a screw thing that drives the pulp and squeezes out the juice and other stuff goes out the other end. Then you boil that for a bit and just reduce it before canning it. I like to make both tomato soup and tomato sauce for canning. There's hand-cranked versions that I'd used. All of them usually have like a hopper where you put the tomatoes in and it goes down the chute, and so

you're cranking by hand. This is a motorized version of that. I know of this from our Maker Faire in Rome. Italians not only make a lot of food, but they make a lot of food machinery, and they are just pretty good quality.

Cider Press

There was a guy that makes these in Oregon, and I bought mine. It's made out of cedar wood from Oregon, and it's also motorized. Again, similar thing, you're taking apples and putting them into a hopper, and what the motor is doing is running as

a block that has blades on it, and it's just chopping them up into smaller bits that fall below, and that goes into a basket, and then you slide it over and you have a screw press that you use to extract most of the juice from the apples, and then what's left over becomes pomace. But that's how you make apple cider which is really fresh. Fresh juice usually oxidizes and turns brown, but then you can take that, if you want to make hard cider, and it's almost the same process as beer. You're adding yeast to it although you could naturally ferment it, and let it set. It will convert the sweet sugars in the juice into alcohol.

Cups not included

Rancilio Silvia Espresso Machine

One of the things that I liked about this was it just seems to be well built. Mine broke maybe a year ago or so, and I was able to go online and figure out what had gone wrong. I was able to open it up, get a new part from somewhere, and replace it. That made it an especially favorite tool, the fact that we didn't have to replace it.

Free to Make: How the Maker Movement is Changing Our Schools, Our Jobs, and Our Minds

In some ways "making" is not new, it's something we've always done. But to some degree I felt it had been marginalized a bit in consumer culture. We look to buy things, and we maybe have lost a little bit of the satisfaction of making something and creating something; not necessarily because it's cheaper or easier or better, it's a process that helps you understand things and that thing becomes your own. Again, I don't necessarily need to can tomatoes, but I find it satisfying to be engaged in that process, take the stuff from the garden, and save it for winter. And I feel like when I'm using that in the middle of winter, I'm kind of connecting to the garden I had in the summer. One of the points I tried to make in the book is that I think culturally we kind of celebrate the professional a lot more than the amateur, and I think the amateur can take risks and do experiments that sometimes a professional just will never do.

Michael Dubno
Co-founder of Gadgetoff

Michael Dubno is a former Wall Street CIO/CTO and a software developer. He's an inventor, artist, welder, machinist, polar explorer, photographer, roboticist, tech entrepreneur, mentor, co-founder of Gadgetoff, co-chair of FIRST in New York City, an exaggerator of accomplishments, and a collector and user of tools.
(Published 08/24/18)

Tormach 440 CNC Mill

I think that this would probably be one of the harder tools to lose, simply because just where my mindset is now is actually building fairly sophisticated structures and mechanisms and having a real CNC mill allows that to happen. You can actually cut steel, cut it accurately, cut aluminum, cut it accurately — brass as well. I did CNC conversions on an old Smithy three-in-one but it just didn't have the accuracy for building what I was building. It's not a cheap tool, and it's certainly not a hand tool, and it's not a tool for everyone, but when you make a lot of things, at a certain point, if you make the same part many times it's obviously incredibly useful for that. And I have it rigged out with tool changers and power draw bars and a fourth axis and things like that to make the weird things that I like to make.

DEWALT SWAG Portaband Table

I have a stand for the Dewalt Portaband. There's a company called Swag Tools that makes a very neat stand. In fact, almost everyone who's seen this has

gone out and bought the Swag stand and the Portaband saw. What it does is it takes a portable band saw and it turns it into a desktop-type of band saw. I happen to have a metal cutting band saw that is a horizontal one that's sitting here from Jet, I happen to have another vertical one for cutting wood also from Jet, and I tend to use the Portaband with it's little base as my go-to for cutting metal, and it is phenomenal at doing that. You can just rip through a sheet of steel or aluminum pretty quickly. And so with this table, you also have the versatility of it being portable, and so I love it.

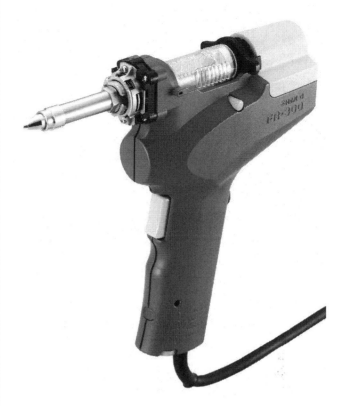

Hypertherm Powermax30 Hand Plasma System

This cuts through steel, truly as if it's butter, and if you're not careful you can cut through your welding table as if it didn't exist. So that's always impressive. And so it's a good way to demonstrate tools to people. It's not very dangerous — it is operating at extreme temperatures, but as long as you're not putting yourself below where it's cutting you tend to be fine — it's really wanting to cut metal, not you. So I've used it in the past to cut out metal bits for a number of sculptures, and I find it very handy. For fine work, I think you would need more of a plasma table that is more CNC, but I found that for ripping through a sheet of steel, it's as impressive as you can get.

Hakko Desoldering Tool

One of the things that I never had until recently is an easy way to desolder. I've used the little solder-sucking tubes and

stuff like that, and they're great, but suddenly when you can plug something into the wall that is basically a soldering iron with a pump built into it, and you just go to the work and you go slurping the solder off, it is something where you wonder why you didn't buy this whenever it first came out. Probably because I didn't have the money at the time, but it's still one of the most beautiful tools for doing electronics work I've ever played with.

ClickSpring

Amazing workmanship, tool building, and instructional videos.

George Dyson
Writer and Boat Builder

George Dyson divides his time between building boats and writing books. Some of the books he has written include "Project Orion: The True Story of the Atomic Spaceship," "Darwin among the Machines: The Evolution of Global Intelligence," and "Turing's Cathedral: The Origins of the Digital Universe." (Published 3/1/19)

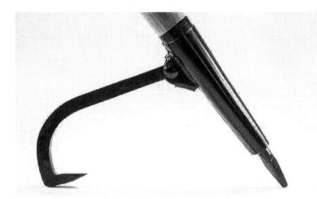

Standard Peavey

This is a tool that has literally not changed at all for 150 years, and it is still made by the company that it's named after: the Peavey Company in Maine. If you do any work in the woods, with logs, chainsaws, things like that, it allows you to basically put a big leaver on the end of a log and roll the log around. It's just a beautiful work of art tool and sort of a miracle that it's still made and survives. You spear the log, and then that hook catches and suddenly you have a really secure five- or six-foot lever arm on the log. I cut a lot of firewood on the beach, and before you cut a log you want to roll it over and clean the sand off. It's the only tool that'll allow you to do that without sort of killing yourself. It's a classic, absolutely essential and unequaled tool for any serious woodsperson.

Netting Needles

This the net needle, which isn't really a needle. Some people would call it similar to a weaver's shuttle, but it's a little, very cleverly-made design.

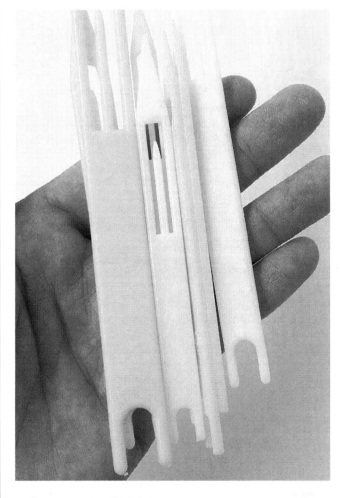

In fact, you can find them more or less unchanged in archaeological sites that are 5,000 or 6,000 years old. It's a small sort of cigar that you wind up with net-mending twine or string or anything like that, and then you have a pretty good length of string or twine on this thing that it gives you something to hold on to, and you can immediately mend nets, or of course I use them to lash kayaks together. So it's the kind of thing that I wouldn't go anywhere without in my toolkit somewhere. They're made in all sorts of sizes. There's flat ones, and there's three-dimensional ones, which are better. They're still made in Norway, and there's a company in the United States, the Loomis Company, that makes the Norwegian pattern. It just becomes almost automatic or second nature as you're weaving this thing in and out. It's a kind of tool that becomes part of your mind.

Lanolin in bulk

Lanolin, or wool grease, which is actually a wax, is a by-product of cleaning raw wool, but it's the best part — it's how sheep in wind-swept northern Scotland stay waterproof and warm. It is used in all kinds of products, from lip balm to anti-corrosion coatings, but you can buy it pure and unadulterated for about $50 per gallon, which is a lifetime supply for you and many friends. It is absolutely unexcelled for chapped skin and lips, and is favored by all serious mariners for lubricating through-hull sea-cocks and corrosion protection of metal parts and fasteners that may be exposed to years of saltwater before having to be taken apart. It's the greatest corrosion protection known to the maritime world. Even the most modern sailboats will still use lanolin. I gave a whole lot to everybody for Christmas. I bought little cosmetic jars. It's actually a wax, not a grease, so if you heat it up a certain temperature then it becomes liquid. You can fill the containers, and everybody loves it. It's like 100-proof lip balm with nothing else diluting it.

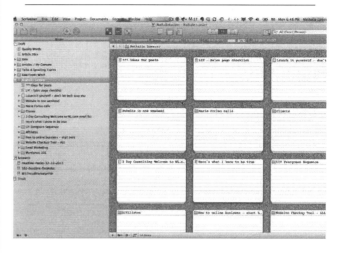

Scrivener

I make my living writing books, and so my tool for writing books is a software package called Scrivener. Neal Stephenson gave me sort of a beta version when it first came out. It changed my life overnight. I had been struggling writing. I wrote my first book with a typewriter, and the second in Word on floppies, and the third one with Word and a hard drive. And then I got Scrivener, and in 24 hours I was using the program and it became transparent, and I never used Word unless I had to again. It's just a miraculous piece of software written by one person. So I looked at my last book, Turing's Cathedral, and if you open up the Scrivener package it is 3,730 separate files of things that I collected and worked into the book, yet when you look at it from the outside, from the writer's side, you just are sort of looking at a typewriter, and you can pull out the ideas. You can just throw out all this stuff and then shuffle it. It's miraculous for a piece of software for organizing.

A photo of George's Four Favorite Tools.

Lenore Edman
Co-Founder of Evil Mad Scientist Laboratories

Lenore Edman is the Co-Founder of Evil Mad Scientist Laboratories, an open source hardware, hobby electronics, and robotics company. She likes projects at the intersections of cooking, electronics, papercraft and sewing. (Published 11/11/15)

Mini Diamond Pocket Sharpener

This is a diamond file and it is sold as a snowboard edger or a ski edger for finishing the surface on your skis. It's just a great file in general. The nice thing about it is that it's rectangular in shape with rounded edges and a plastic backing so it's not the least bit scary to TSA. I travel with this all the time.

Dritz Deluxe Seam Ripper

I love the seam ripper. I've had a seam ripper pretty much all my life. A seam ripper has a pointy bit and then a little bit of a hook which has a sharp edge inside.

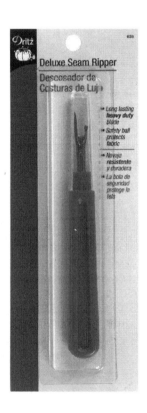

You can use the little pointy bit to go underneath a thread in a seam and then push it forward to that sharp cutting edge to cut the thread.

Patterns From Finished Clothes

This book is one of the ways that I really learned to be creative with my sewing and to not necessarily rely on patterns and things. I could look at a garment that I loved and figure out how it was put together and use it as a map for moving forward to

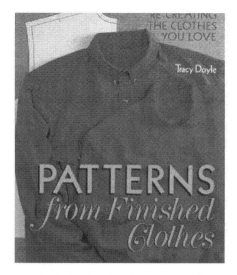

make something similar. That was a really great tool for me in learning to sew.

Quick Mill Silvano Evo Semi-Automatic Espresso Maker

When we got the Silvano, the other expresso machines that we had just felt like cheap plastic. It's just so nice to use. If you've ever used an espresso machine that doesn't have a plumbed-in drain tray, you'll know that they often have one huge flaw which is that the drip tray is always too small. It's really hard to empty, it's really shallow. This one has a two-inch drawer with a big handle on the front. It's really easy to clean up after and it's just a dream to use, never mind being beautiful.

budthrill

I ALWAYS FEEL LUCKY

Wordnik

Wordnik is a website that concatenates dictionaries and provides example usages for words. You just type in a word and it will show you all of the available definitions that it has for it, any etymologies. It will give you links to all the places that have available pronunciation, and then it will show examples of places it's being used like Twitter. It's a really neat site.

LED Throwies

A throwie is an LED and a coin cell, oftentimes with a magnet. The idea being you can make a piece of information or light or art very easily and have it available. I've done a lot of projects based on the LED throwie over the years, things like yard lanterns for parties and light up origami. I can't tell you the number of times the power's gone out and I'm able to grab the LED out of my wallet and just turn it on and find the candles or the matches or whatever I needed.

Jeri Ellsworth
CEO at Tilt Five

Jeri Ellsworth is an inventor, entrepreneur, and amateur scientist. Her career started when she dropped out of high school and formed a business building, selling and racing quarter-mile dirt-track cars. In the mid-90's she founded a small retail computer store chain, and in the 2000's she launched her engineering career where she designed a wide variety of electronic components and consumer products. She's passionate about educational outreach and maintains a YouTube channel devoted to demonstrating engineering and science techniques. (Published 11/9/18)

Amray Electron Microscope

I have an electron microscope. It's one of those things people don't think that an average human being can own in their garage, and it turns out it's not that difficult to get them and it's not that difficult to operate them. There's all different types of electron microscopes. There's types that are transmission, so they send electrons through the object that you're trying to image. Mine happens to be a scanning electron microscope, so it beams a very small spot of electrons down on to the subject that you're trying to image, and then it looks at what bounces off of it essentially. To use the device, you have to sometimes pre-treat your subject, coat it with metal. Then, you put it inside. You pump a vacuum down, and then you start out with very low magnification. You zoom in a little bit, and then there's astigmatism to this electron beam. So, it's

kind of off-shape. Then, there's just knobs that you turn to make the beam round again. Then you zoom in a little bit, and then you make the beam round again. You zoom in, and zoom in, and zoom in, and just keep that astigmatism adjustment going until you're imaging down into the low nanometers of feature size.

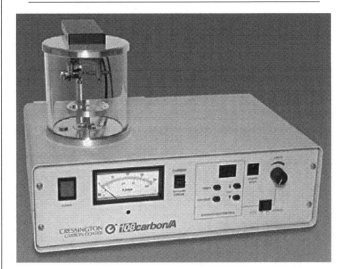

Sputter Coater

A sputter coater is a really interesting device where you can put a sample or your subject into it. You draw down a vacuum and it has what's called the target in it. The target is the source metal that you want to coat something with. You pump it down. You inject in some heavy gas, usually something like argon which is neutral. Then, you pump a bunch of RF energy into it and there's a magnet above this target which causes these ionized gas particles to strike the metal and it chips off the metal, and then it sputter coats the metal on to your object. So, you can sputter coat gold. You can do aluminum, copper, things like that. It's pretty interesting. You can make mirrors with it.

Plasma Etcher

I've just been getting into doing plasma etching. It's another exotic vacuum-based tool. So a plasma etcher is pretty interesting. You have a chamber in which you put something that you want to etch and that you can etch all kind of things in this. I have a tabletop version. So, the working volume on that is about the size of a milk container, just to give you like some real-world volumes. Basically the way it works is there's a couple of components. There's a chamber. There's a manifold that lets you inject gases into the chamber under a greatly reduced atmosphere, and then there's an RF generator. So, it generates a lot of RF. It's pumped into basically an antenna that's around the chamber. So, if you put, for instance, something that's got a glassy coating on it like what's used in semi-conductors, like there's an insulating layer, silicon dioxide, you grow that on silicon which is glass. You put it into the chamber, and you mask off different areas that you want to etch through with photoresist for instance or other masking techniques, and then you inject a Freon or something that has fluorine atoms in it. Then you excite those fluorine atoms, then you

have free-roaming fluorine that etches the glass, turns to silicon fluoride, and then it just floats away and goes into your vacuum pump. Then, you can cut holes in these glassy layers. You can do some very interesting etching where you can etch to a particular depth. For instance, if you have a layer of glass on top of silicon, the fluorine atoms don't really attack silicons. So, you can etch just right down to the silicon at the atomic level, and it will stop right there. You can etch very large areas like an entire wafer, like many centimeters across or down to almost as small as you want to go. It's as small as you can pattern an image on to the surface and expose the glassy layer.

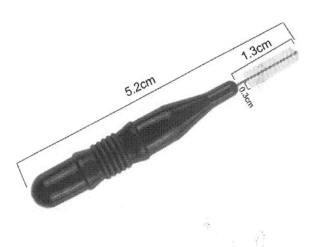

Interdental Brush for cleaning circuit boards

I've discovered something just in the last month or two. There's these little tiny tooth cleaners for cleaning between your teeth that have little brushes on them. They're little tiny brushes. It looks like an old school pipe cleaner. So, it's like a little wire with little bristles sticking out of it. They are fantastic. It's my favorite new tool for putting circuit boards together. You just go to the drugstore and get them. I mean in the past, I would be trying to use toothbrushes and other big brushes and you can't get in between the little components and get all the gunk out. These are just perfect. Maybe it's obvious to other people, but this is something completely new to me.

Rose Eveleth
Podcast Producer

Rose Eveleth is a writer and producer based in Berkeley who explores how humans tangle with science and technology. She's the creator and host of Flash Forward, a podcast about possible and not-so-possible futures, and it's covered everything from fake tumbleweed farms to million-dollar baccarat heists.
(Published 08/3/18, 04/27/16)

Text Expander

If you have something that you type a lot and you don't want to have to type it out every single time, you can put it into TextExpander, give it a little short code, and then whenever you want to send that chunk of text, you just type the short code and it pops it right in for you. I use it also for the shruggy emoji thing. I can't remember how to type that. So, I have it in TextExpander as a way to have it come up easily. I send a lot of interview requests where the format is often the same, where I'm explaining what the show is. Or when listeners email me, there are a couple of buckets that those emails fall into, and I will have templates for responding, that I then go back in and sort of customize for each response.

Trint

Trint is a system that transcribes audio, which obviously there are many of those. The difference

between most places and Trint is that it is algorithmic, so it's machine-learning. And so, you feed the audio in, and it gives you a transcript back out much faster than a human would. It is highly dependent on you having decent quality audio, and it can transcribe things really quickly, and then it has this interface that you can actually go in, and you can listen as it goes through the transcript, so you can correct things within the transcript really quickly. And the interface is pretty easy to use.

I Love Hue

This is my relaxation app. I know many people use things like Calm or Headspace. This app is my version of that. It is an app that is all about colors and color-matching. They show you a grid of colors. The grid is made up of 20 boxes, and then the boxes scramble up and you kind of have to put the gradient back together. And it's one of those things where

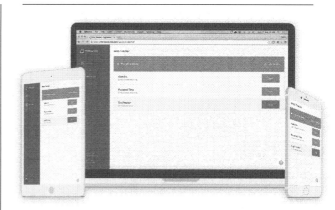

either you love it or it sounds like the most awful thing to ever use. I have friends who I've shown it to, and they're like, "This is a nightmare," because as you play, there are more and more boxes. And so, it gets be harder and harder to distinguish between the very slight changes in the color between the boxes and put them in the right order. But for me, it is incredibly soothing to take a disordered thing and put it into order and then have it be this beautiful gradient. I really enjoy the color-matching aspect of it. And so, it's just this game that I have on my phone that I play when I'm stressed out, and it works quite nicely for me. Again, I think that some people would look at this and think that it looks like the worst possible thing to do if you're stressed out, but I love it.

Top Tracker

This is a time tracking tool. Basically, you can tell it projects and you can start and stop tracking. It's also useful because it serves to delineate tasks that I'm doing where I have to be very conscious about, "Okay, now I'm going to do this." I have to type it in and I have to push the start button and then, I push the stop button when I'm done. It's a nice way to keep myself focused on a single task. I've been using Top Tracker now for about six months and I really like it.

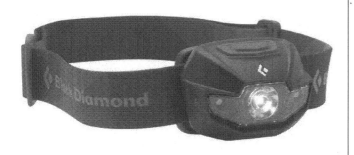

Headlamp

A headlamp is just basically a sweatband that has a light on the front of it. I think they're super useful. Of all the things that you might not want to forget, especially on a camping trip when you get up in the middle of the night and it's dark and you cannot find the bathroom, the headlamp is what you need.

Flash Forward

The show is about the future. Every episode is a different future. Every episode starts with an audio drama to kind of set the stage for what the future that we're looking at in that episode is like, and then I interview experts about that future. So, it's kind of a mashup of War of the Worlds and Radiolab, is kind of how I describe it.

Tom Fassbender
Writer

Tom Fassbender is a writer and former publisher of books and comics and a traveler who, along with his wife and two daughters, ventured on a yearlong trip around the world where they experienced 36 countries in 333 days. And he also posted about his adventures on Boing Boing, which was really fun to read.
(Published 07/6/18)

Think Tank Photo Cable Management

This is a cable cord organizer, and it's a good size. It's not too big. I always carry two of these. One sits at the bottom of my backpack and holds my large cords and adapters, like for my camera battery and the wall charger for my laptop. The second one sits at the top of my pack and keeps all my various device accessories, charging cords, dongles, and mobile Wi-Fi hotspot, neatly organized and readily accessible. If I'm out in the field or at a coffee shop and suddenly I realize I'm out of power or I need to sync my phone or whatever, I can just reach in my bag and I've pulled this out and all my cords are in there.

Outside Cover   Inside Page

Give N Go Boxer Briefs

This might be a little personal, but these boxer briefs are my favorite underwear. They're perfect for long-term travel. Not only are they lightweight and easily packable, but they dry quickly — an essential quality when you need to wash your clothes by hand during a trip. That also means they can double as swimwear in a pinch, like when your daughter who can't swim all that well wants to jump off the boat into Ha Long Bay.

Reporter Notebook

I have a collection of many different notebooks, but this is the one I use most often. It's perfect for when I'm on an assignment where I need to write quickly. I also use it for brainstorming, list-making, and scribbling down quick notes when I'm working on a project. And at 20 for $12, they're not precious, so I won't hesitate to start writing something that's not perfect.

BioLite Lantern and Power Bank

We use this a lot on family camping trips. This works great for cooking dinner in the dark or playing cards at the picnic table before bed. I own the 7800 mAh version, which is enough for our needs. It throws out 500 lumens with an edge-lit LED design, making it seem a lot brighter. It's also Bluetooth enabled so you can connect it to your phone with an app, allowing you to change the color of the light and turning your phone into a proximity sensor so it turns on when you stumble back into camp after sundown. On top of that, it can be used to charge your various electronic devices when in the wilderness.

Bran Ferren
Chief Creative Officer of Applied Minds

Bran Ferren is the former President of Research and Development of Walt Disney Imagineering, and is now the Chief Creative Officer of Applied Minds, which he co-founded in 2000 with Danny Hillis. (Published 09/14/18)

Kiravan

I got interested in expedition vehicles because I started in the film business where you're doing location production in places that are designed to look like another planet, and these are generally not nearby or easy to get to, and it's not just you enjoying a backpacking afternoon but it's bringing tons upon tons of equipment, crew, and support equipment. I also worked a bit on oil exploration and geo-technical work and it's the same thing, you're out in the middle of nowhere and it's not just you, it's equipment and mobility. It's not even 4×4 but it may be a 6×6 or and 8×8, meaning six or eight wheels, all driven. You are going to be traveling, potentially, several thousands miles away from any human contact. You need to have water. You need to have fuel. It's nice to know where you are and so you need navigation systems. So it's a combination of many things that all have to do with survivability of the vehicle and the person. If you get stuck, no one is going to rescue you. And this includes the technical equipment you need to support film production or whatever else you're there to do. The Kiravan has beds, it has kitchens, it has bathrooms. It has places to store food, galleys. The masts, the tall ones, will go up to 60 feet. They're designed to extend the range of your communications and also get cameras up to a high level, laser scanners, other elements like that. This is a tractor trailer configuration. It's a little unusual in that the trailer is powered at speeds up to 30 miles per hour. All rear axles are driven as well the main truck axles for off-road capability. And it's designed to be flexible so that you can, for instance, separate the tractor and the trailer, and do independent things with either of them at the same time.

ZEISS DSM-960A Scanning Electron Microscope

I use a digital scanning electron microscope, on one level in a utilitarian way, if I wanted to do elemental analysis of a metal or look at something that fractured. Look closely at things, the depth of field and the ability to look at objects smaller than wavelengths of light are where scanning electron microscopes are handy. But I actually use it for inspiration because looking at the miniature world, you can go get a fly and plate it with gold and put it in your scanning electron microscope and literally spend hours just exploring the surface features on a fly and pondering how evolution

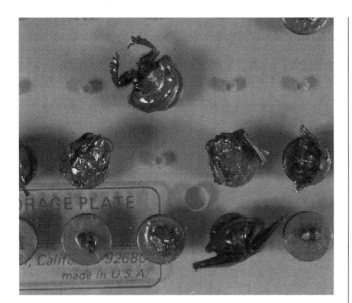

Insects at higher magnification

produced that design, the elegance of how joints are done. Why do the eyes have hairs sticking out of them? What's the sensory system, etc. So for me, on one level it's as much about exploration and creative exploration, and the ability to do it in the microscopic stage of things that are literally unseeable when you're looking at structures that are smaller than wavelengths of light — you can't see them with your eyes even if you had the magnification available.

VIZ-PRO Dry Erase Board and Dry Erase Paint

People would think it primitive but room-sized white boards are simply the best way to creatively think. I mean if you have a room with a 12-foot high by 30-foot

long white board, it gives you the ability to draw and visualize an entire project in front of you at one time, which you can't do with CAD where you're zooming and moving around. I've never found an electronic technique that works as well. And so, the ability to literally go into a room, emerge 15 hours later with a drawing that is literally the size of that wall — it's never quite big enough — to me is just a very different way of thinking. Just as when you're trying to then turn it into reality, how do you manage the project? How do you put it together? You have another wall, an opposite wall, filled with 3x5 file cards where you can sit back and you and your team can look at them all at the same time, discuss it, move them around; that ability to collaborate at large scale fundamentally changes, for me, both the creative and the engineering process.

Sony RX100 VI

I tend to wear bush jackets and I guess everyone needs a uniform, but being a slave to fashion that I am, lots of pockets turned out actually to be a pretty useful thing to have, and so for me a pocket camera is what fits in my pocket. And you need something durable so that you can bash it around a little as you're doing things. You need it with a good lens which has a good range in it because from a purely practical point of view, you don't have the luxury of getting too close or too far away from the thing that you want to work with. If you do what I do, you need good low-light-level sensitivity. I used to use the little pocket Canons, but I find the Sony, the RX100, the series six, is a really lovely little camera. It's razor sharp. The image quality is terrific, excellent size optics on it. The finder flips up and down so you can go into awkward positions with it and it will still be able to compose a frame and has great little pop-up finder. So it's really nice.

Tim Ferriss
NYT Bestselling Author

Tim Ferriss was listed as one of Fast Company's "Most Innovative Business People" and one of Fortune's "40 under 40." He's an early-stage technology investor and advisor and the author of four #1 New York Times and Wall Street Journal bestsellers, including The 4-Hour Workweek and Tools of Titans: The Tactics, Routines, and Habits of Billionaires, Icons, and World-Class Performers. He is the host of The Tim Ferriss Show podcast, which has exceeded 150 million downloads and has been selected for "Best of iTunes" three years running. (Published 06/21/17)

Logitech Keys-to-Go Portable Keyboard

In my bag of tricks, I have a Logitech Bluetooth keyboard and just to put this in perspective, it is slightly larger than say a paperback book, like a 5 x 8 inch trim paperback book. It is narrow enough that I will very often stick it into a journal to protect it, and it's probably the width of eight to ten paperback pages. And it holds a charge very, very well, so I use this often times if I have any issue with my laptop. I can pair it to my iPhone, which is a larger-sized iPhone, and balance the iPhone or lean it against a glass of iced tea and I can get any writing done that I need to get done. Also, if I feel like taking a day trip, but not taking my backpack — which is one of my main pieces of luggage and stuffed full of stuff, it's kind of heavy — I can take the keyboard and my iPhone and head off to some coffee shop, say 10 to 15 minutes away, without carrying all of my gear with me.

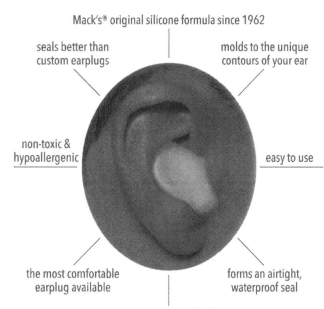

Mack's® original silicone formula since 1962

seals better than custom earplugs

molds to the unique contours of your ear

non-toxic & hypoallergenic

easy to use

the most comfortable earplug available

forms an airtight, waterproof seal

no pressure, cover-only design

Mack's Pillow Soft Silicone Earplugs

Mack's silicone earplugs, unlike foam earplugs, are not inserted into the ear canal and then left to expand. These are effectively smeared over the ear opening and you have in all caps – DO NOT INSERT, JUST COVER EAR OPENING. These I found through swimmers and they are very waxy and almost look like candies, some type of caramel, but they're white colored and I find them to block sound much more effectively than any type of foam earplug. I definitely reuse these. I would say if I had to guesstimate, I would say four to five nights and then they start to lose their adherence, because they get less tacky over time. The most important feature or benefit that I don't want to overlook is that as someone who tends to rotate from back to side, foam earplugs will very often hurt. They'll get pushed into your ear when you roll onto your side. That is not the case with these.

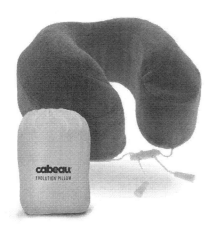

Cabeau Evolution Memory Foam Travel Pillow

Most of travel pillows are very uninspiring and even less effective for helping me sleep. What I found is not only does this pillow help me sleep if I'm sitting upright, but it's also very, very helpful for getting to sleep when I'm laying prone, whether it's on an airplane or even a hotel room if the pillows are of dubious quality. It's self-expanding, so you can think of it almost like a sponge-like material that you can compress down and then when you release it, it inflates, or, I should say rather, expands automatically. It is horseshoe-shaped; if you imagine a horseshoe being hung around the back of your neck, that is the shape. It can clip in the front and the design is such that there's a ridge that supports basically the occipital area at the base of the skull. It's the most comfortable neck pillow that I have found.

Apnea Trainer

An app that I use a lot when I'm traveling, and I use it at home as well, is called Apnea Trainer, and I don't use it for it's intended use. I have an off-label use. Apnea Trainer is used by people who are training for free diving and want to improve their breath-hold times. There are different types

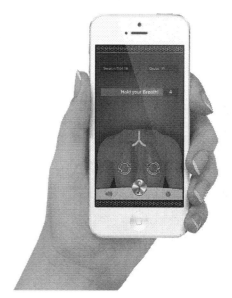

of tempos that you can use for different types of training, so there is Pranayama breathing. There is the apnea breathing, which would be a ratio of inhale, hold, exhale or inhale, hold, exhale, hold. What I found is that if I only have, say five to ten minutes and I don't have time for my usual morning meditation, which I like to do, that five to ten minutes of breathing training with a voice that will countdown for you is very much grounding for the rest of the day.

Yellowtec iXm Microphone

This is a microphone that can capture just tremendous quality of audio. It automatically equalizes and it has playback buttons on the side. It all records to an SD card that's inserted in the bottom, and it's battery powered so that you can take it on the road. Everything is contained and housed in this one unit, that then goes in a tiny zip-up bag, so this just lives really inside my backpack, so if I don't have a chance to bring more gear or don't want to bring more gear, I can use this anytime, anywhere and shizam.

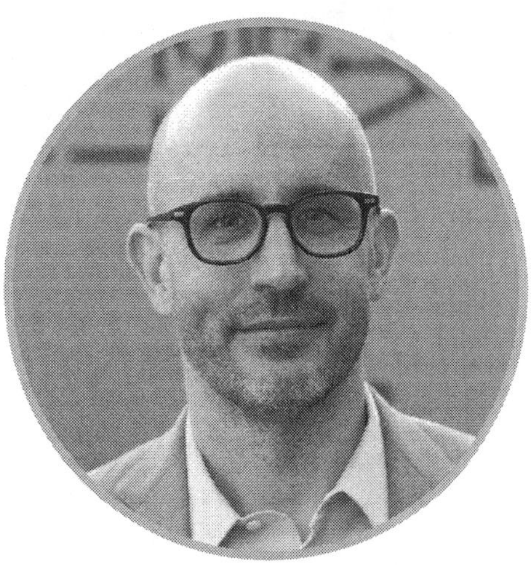

Adam Fisher
Author of Valley of Genius

Adam Fisher grew up in Silicon Valley, playing Atari, programming computers, and reading science fiction. He still lives in the Bay area, but now spends his time thinking about the future, tracing its origins, and writing about it for Wired, MIT Technology Review, The Economist, and The New York Times Sunday Magazine.
(Published 09/7/18)

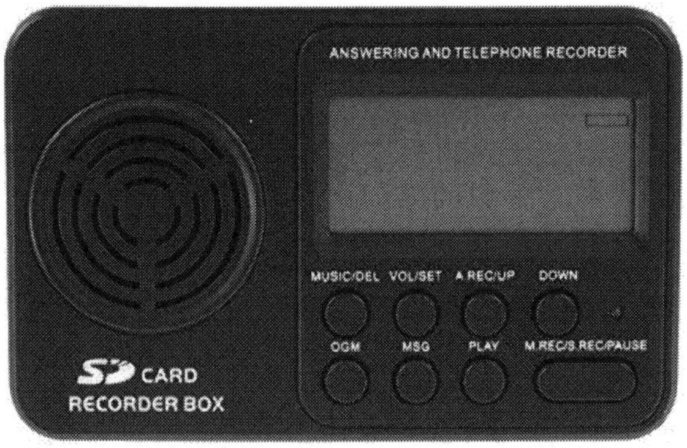

RecorderGear Landline Phone Call Recorder

It's super simple. If you have a landline you just plug the phone in and you can record at any time, which for a journalist, is super key. One button, and it writes to an SD card. I used to use Skype recording and try to do voiceover IP to record directly to the landline, but I was always getting problems where I'd have issues with Skype or one of the other IP services. You can set this up so every time you answer that phone, it records. I use Google Voice and it'll ring my cell phone and ring the landline at the same time.

Plantronics Handset Landline Telephone

This is a landline telephone that is only a headset. There's a dial pad and to answer it, you have to

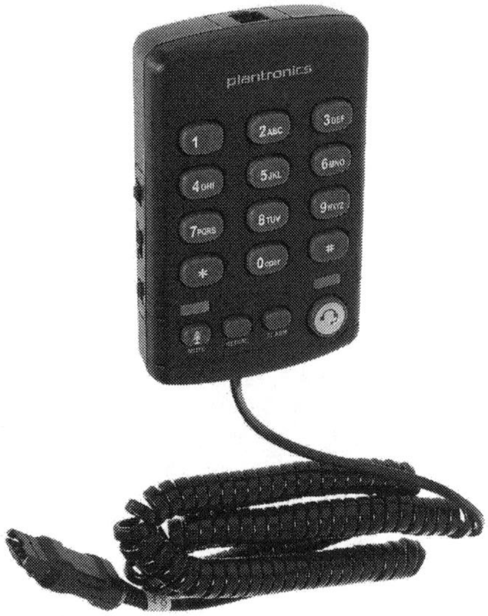

press the little button that looks like a headset. This is what professional sales people use who are on the phone all day or what people in call centers use. The reason I love it is because I can be interviewing someone while I'm on the computer, while I'm taking notes with my fingers, while I'm looking something up on Wikipedia. I have this set up to the RecorderGear.

Alice Audio Transcription

I get this LinkedIn message, and it was like, "Hey, I'm an app developer and you're a journalist and I really like your story. If I were to develop a transcribing app, what would it look like? What would you need?" Long story short: turns out it's a real dude. He's a software developer, works for a big company in San Francisco, and this is his side hustle. Three months later, he shows me something, says it's called Alice and oh my god, it's not just to my spec, but he took it and made it much better. It just went into public beta, so anyone who's listening to this will literally have the first crack at this. It's a one-button thing. If you press it, it's on and it's recording and it'll just pick up the first couple words and that will be the title. You don't have to name the file and it will record where you are, because it has it on a map when you did it and it's recording in such a way that it's both pushing it to the cloud and writing it to the solid state memory in the phone at the same time. Even if iOS crashes, you have it. Even if someone takes your phone at the border or says, "Give me your phone," or puts a bullet through it, you still have the recording. That's not all. Five minutes after the recording stops, whether there's a bullet through the phone or you just press stop, not five minutes, five seconds if it's a shorter thing, it'll come back transcribed. It uses the Google API to do the transcription, so it's basically the best AI transcription you can get.

Piezo — record audio from any application

Piezo is from this little Mac-only software company called Rogue Amoeba. They make this tool which is just a little piece of software. I have it in my little toolbox at the bottom. Often, when I'm in person, I have a USB mic and I have the computer on and I launch Piezo and it has this skeuomorphic-like GUI. It looks like a piece of recording equipment with levels, and there's only one button. Then you press

the button and that's just red and so you know you're recording and you can see the levels. What's important is that the levels do not go on if you're not recording. It just records right to your hard drive or solid state and you have it. There's no fussing with getting the SD card out and getting the reader and getting it in. It's my favorite way to record when I'm in person and it's the one piece of software that I've never messed up, but there's nothing to it. That's what I like.

Valley of Genius: The Uncensored History of Silicon Valley (As Told by the Hackers, Founders, and Freaks Who Made It Boom)

The first thing to understand about the book is it's this niche, non-fiction genre called oral history, and what it really is is more like a documentary film than a normal book. I interviewed about 200 people, a lot of billionaires, but also a lot of their interns and proteges and secretaries and helpers and asked them how they did it, how they created their contribution to Silicon Valley. Then I would cut those interviews together, like you'd cut together a documentary film. I get those transcripts and I cut it together as if they were all in the same bar, drinking and swapping stories and arguing and giving you a really 360 kind of view of what happened. In a sense, it's not me telling you, the reader, what the story of Silicon Valley is, but the people who actually made Silicon Valley telling you the story of what Silicon Valley is.

Jane Frauenfelder
Techie teenager

Jane Frauenfelder was born and raised in Southern California, she co-hosted a podcast called Apps For Kids for two-and-a-half years, and now attends a robotics academy at her high school. In her off time, she designs video games, and she aspires to be a video game designer when she's older. (Published 01/11/18)

Quizlet

Quizlet is very, very popular among most middle school and high school students. It's a way of studying. It's a website online, and you just simply type in a bunch of terms as if they're flashcards and then they have many different ways that you can learn them through writing them down and they can generate quizzes themselves. They even have games you can play to memorize them. It's just a wonderful way to memorize facts or terms or memorize anything for school. I used to use it for Spanish class all the time and history and English, and just everything.

Prusa 3D Printer

Compared to other 3D printers that I've seen, this one's by far the best personal 3D printer. It's really easy to swap out the plastic, and it prints really

well. It has an SD chip, which you can plug into your computer and then upload your files, and then you plug it straight into the Prusa and you just select the file you want. It has a little screen on the bottom, which is great. You select it and it will start printing, and it has different types of plastic that it can use, and it has a heated bed, which is great.

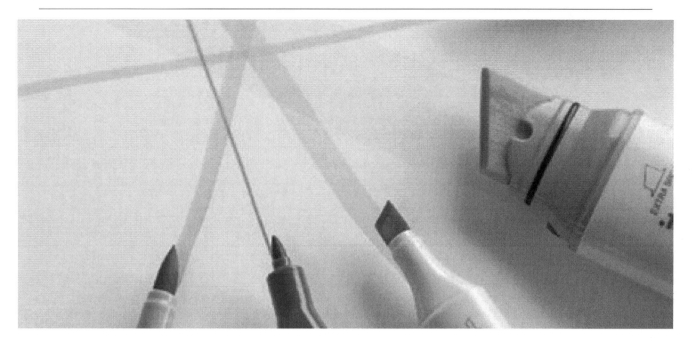

Copic Markers

I'm going to assume that the majority of artists that do fine art and drawing know about Copics, because they are very widely known since they're just very incredible. They're alcohol-based markers and they blend so wonderfully because they have hundreds of colors, and if you take similar colors you can blend them so nicely that it looks almost like paint. If you're coloring something with these markers you can make it so that there's no strokes. If you're using a lot of water-based markers you're going to get stroke lines and it's kind of messy-looking, but Copics just glide so smoothly and they're really great.

Piskel

I like doing game design, but sometimes I just want to do small projects. I recently did a school project and it was a video game that I designed. Piskel is an online website where you can design GIFs of a pixel animation. It gives you a board and you can draw on it however you want and it's all pixelized. That's a great way to make pixel art and pixel sprites — a sprite is like the object in the game, the main character that you play, the images of the characters — which is kind of popular nowadays. I feel like

8-bit games and things like that are coming back. I just find it really great when I'm designing games because I'm not like a huge artist — I can't do like these elaborate character designs — and pixel art is able to be so simple.

Wendy Frauenfelder
Crafter and amateur chef

Wendy Frauenfelder likes to cook, fix things, pretend to be a bartender, and do therapy dog work. She also is fascinated with wild yeast and slow food.
(Published 09/21/17)

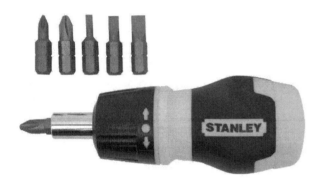

Stanley 66-358 Stubby Ratcheting MultiBit Screwdriver

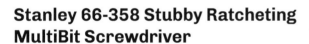

I always keep a screwdriver in the kitchen, just so that I don't have to go to the garage if there is something inside the house that I need to work on. So this is my new screwdriver inside the house, and there's a couple things I like. First, it's small. It's like four-and-a-half inches long, and so it fits in a junk drawer really easily. The second thing I really like about it is it's a ratcheting screwdriver. So, if you're fixing a knob on a cabinet, you don't have to spin it around in your hand, you can just kind of ratchet it in, which I love. But you can also make it just a steady, regular kind of screwdriver. Then the third thing that I love about it is you unscrew the cap on the top of the screwdriver and inside are five other tips. So you've got three Phillips head and three regular screwdriver tips, and they vary from pretty tiny to large and fat, and they're right there in the cap, so you can grab your screwdriver without knowing what kind of screw you've gotta work on, and you'll have the right tip.

Buy me a pie!

I am kind of like a connoisseur of grocery shopping list apps. This app is actually organized by store, so I have a Whole Foods list, a Target list, and a Costco list. Basically, I can open whichever one I want, and then I can add items to whichever one I want. You can have the same item in different lists. You can have as many lists as you want if you buy the paid version. I think with the free version you're limited to maybe two or three lists. What I really like about it is that you can color-code these items by grocery store area or by aisle. So everything that's veggie is green and fruit's green, and meat is under the red category, and cold foods are blue and frozen foods are gray. So that way, as you're going through your list, you go to produce and you just see all the color-coded produce that you need to get is all in one section.

24oz Mason Drinking Jar & Stainless Steel Straw

It's actually a Ball jar, not a mason jar, and then it's got the regular kind of screw-on lid, but whoever made this took the little flat part of the lid on top and put a rivet in it and made a hole so you can stick a straw in there. It is actually pretty waterproof. I wouldn't say you should leave it upside down in your car, but I'll usually put a smoothie in here, and every once in a while I'll shake it to just kind of mix up the liquid again, and it doesn't come out at all. So, it's that waterproof. A lot of times these will come with a metal straw, and I don't like that because, since I drink a smoothie out of it, I'm afraid I'm never really getting that clean, so I found some straws on Amazon that fit to the bottom. It had to be an extra-long straw. It fits to the bottom of the jar, and it's got a little bend in it, and then I just toss it when I'm done. I just feel like glass gets really clean. And you don't have to worry about BPAs.

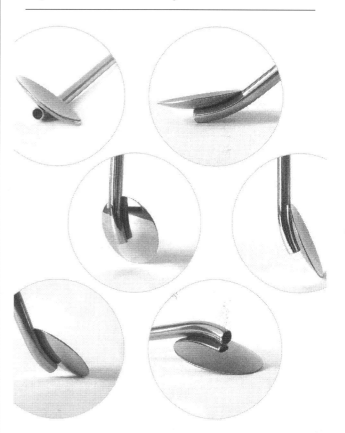

GFDesign Drinking Spoon Straws

I was looking at cocktail items, and this drinking spoon straw caught my eye. We started using it when I was making mojitos. You gotta stir up a mojito, because you've got some granulated sugar in the bottom of it when you muddle the mint leaves. So you stir it up with this thing, and then I'm thinking, "This is great, because then you just leave it in there, and you sip through it." And if your sugar didn't all dissolve, you can still start drinking your mojito and kind of stir it as you go along.

Greg Gage
CEO of Backyard Brains

Greg Gage is the co-founder and CEO of Backyard Brains, a company started with Tim Marzullo as neuroscience graduate students at the University of Michigan. Greg is a published neuroscientist and engineer, and has helped develop tools, curriculum and experiments that allowed the general public to participate in neural discovery. Greg is a senior fellow at TED and the recipient of the White House Champion of Change award from President Barack Obama for his commitment to citizen science. (Published 09/13/17)

Neuron SpikerBox Bundle

This is something that you use to investigate things or to do things. For example, you may wanna use the SpikerBox to control things like turn the light switches off in your room. We've done things, where in one of our TED Talks, we did a human-to-human interface. We have one person recording the EMG that sends a command to another stimulator, which makes the other person's arm move at the same rate — so you can take over the free will of another person. This is all just limited to your creativity of what you can do when you have access to these signals. What we provide are the raw materials that give you access to that.

Google Scholar

We use our literature archives, like scholar.google.com, because there's so much that has been forgotten in the literature. We move on so quickly and we forget there's this entire era about anywhere between 50 and 150 years ago where a lot of cool experiments were going, and those have been quietly forgotten. We've been successful in rediscovering these things and bringing them back into fruition. There's a lot of cool things that are out there.

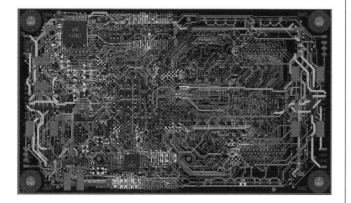

EAGLE PCB Design Software

As far as technology tools, we use the EAGLE CAD. It's a free software. It's a way to design circuits. It's a PCB layout tool, but basically if you have a number of

resistors and capacitors and chips, and you wanna wire them together, it's a way that you can slide them onto the screen and then wire them where you want them to go. Then on flip side, you can see the board and what the chips actually look like. You lay them out and then you draw where you want the traces to go. Then when you're done, you can either print that out or make your own. It's really changed the way we do our electronics.

Arduino

An Arduino and an amplifier is really what you need as a minimal tool set to do what we do. What you need is a way to access the signal. Arduino is a very beautiful way to do that. Then once you have that, it's all about the creativity. What we've been playing around on the last few years is wrapping wires around plants and putting them into the Arduino and then recording what happens within there. We've been doing some fun stuff with Mimosas. They are shy, bashful plants. These are ones that if you touch the leaves, they curl up. It turns out that you can also trigger these cells inside the plant by sending them a little bit of electricity yourself. We're using Arduino to record the action potential from, for example, a Venus Flytrap. We would send it into the Mimosa, so that the Mimosa thinks that somebody touched it. So you can have an entire other plant move in response to another plant that's communicating through their action potential, and it's kind of neat.

Eri Gentry
Co-founder of BioCurious

Eri Gentry is the founding president of BioCurious. It's the first hackerspace for biology, and she's also a research manager at the Institute for the Future. Some interesting facts: she shares a birthday with President Donald Trump and Sheriff Joe Arpaio. (Published 05/4/17)

Niice.com

For my work at Institute for the Future, we're often trying to distill these nebulous concepts about the future into images and into words that people can understand. It's really important that we get the visual part down right, but most sites aren't really great for visual inspiration. Niice is this incredible website that shows you really creative imagery and often a lot of original art from artists, which is great because sometimes it can be hard to access the people doing really interesting creative work. Niice is meant, I believe, for designers and for design firms to do premium mood boards. The great thing about this site is it can make me associate new concepts that I hadn't before. It's a really neat way to think about the future visually.

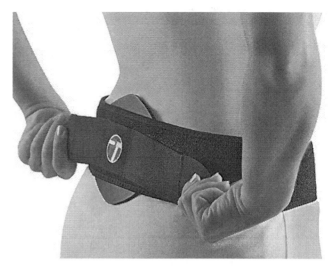

joints can dislocate pretty easily, and this belt is the difference between me being able to walk fairly comfortably and hobbling, grabbing the wall for support.

Double Eyelid Tape

Double eyelid tape is literally a small strip of adhesive that you place on your eyelid to create or change your crease. There are women who are getting surgery actually to create that fold in the eye. It is a mark of beauty, but there is, I think, a really practical reason for using the tape and for having that fold, if you consider being able to wear makeup without it smudging, really practical as I do. You may not have had this experience where you look in the mirror and think "If only I could have a larger, more pronounced fold in my eyelids," but it's actually a really common issue. It's not just for Asians and not just for Asian women. There are many different people who might have uneven eyelids, for example, whether it's genetic or they may have an illness which causes puffiness in one eyelid and not the other. For those of us not blessed with pronounced eyelid creases, this product is amazing. Life-changing.

Fancyhands.com

The story behind this is that for years I've been reading that you should outsource your life. Fancy Hands is a website and platform that has a bunch of people who will do small tasks for you on the back end. As a user you pay some monthly fee and you buy a package of tasks. These are things that can be done in 20 minutes by somebody who may not be an expert in the field, and it's things like making reservations, doing a little bit of online research, finding doctors that work with your insurance, etc.

Sacroiliac Belt

This device helps me walk when my back and hips go out of whack. It's a simple tool that straps tightly around your hips/pelvis to stabilize the SI joints. My

Simone Giertz
Robot Maker and YouTuber

Simone Giertz is a Swedish native who now resides in San Francisco. Millions of people come to watch her build shitty robots on YouTube, and she recently launched her own astronaut training program to get herself into space. Simone's videos have been featured on The Ellen Show, The Late Show, Mashable, Business Insider, Wired, Conan O'Brien, and more. She most recently joined master builder Adam Savage's Tested team.
(Published 04/17/17)

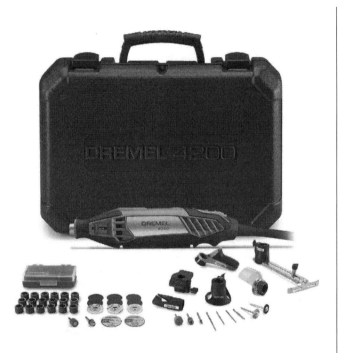

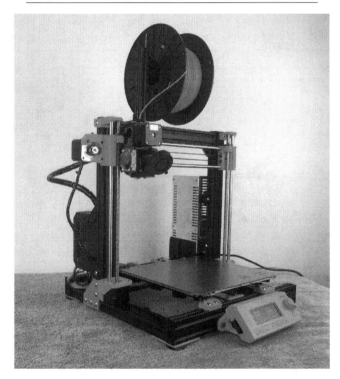

Dremel 4200

I started building stuff about three years ago and I'm rediscovering everything that people have known for a long time. Dremel tools kind of go in the line of that. It blew my mind because I do a lot of aluminum fabrications. I make parts out of aluminum frames or customized parts that I already have, and for that it's freaking great because it's like having your own arm do it but at a much higher RPM. It's like a little pen. It's just such an accessible tool. You're just sitting there and you're cutting. It has the tiniest little cutter blades and it's just nice. It's a super versatile tool and it takes up no space.

Prusa 3D Printer

I am definitely not an authority in 3D printing. I am a total 3D printing novice. I think in some way that gives me a bit of authority to speak on this because I've used a fair amount of 3D printers and I'm always like, "I have no freaking idea what's going on." The Prusa has, from the start, worked brilliantly. It's a really open design. It looks like a very maker printer because you can definitely tinker with it without having to take some big casing off. This is the first 3D printer that has worked well enough for me to actually use it on a regular basis.

Glowforge

One of many unique features that this has is that you have a view. It's all in the browser. You just go on your printer's domain or you log into your account and there you have the bed view of your printer. You can see the material and that's where you upload and place the designs. You can also scan stuff on it. You can draw something on the material and it scans it and then it can etch it or rasterize it. It's really an improvement of the work flow.

Shaper Origin

This is a great tool. I'm not sponsored. They did let me take home their beta version and try it out. It's a handheld milling machine. Basically you load an

SVG on it — a file or your design. Just like a CNC machine but it's handheld. Then it auto corrects your path. It shows you where to move out. You could be making the map of the United States on your wall in your bedroom and just hold it up on the wall. I think it's just super cool and it works. I've just tried their beta version. I haven't tried the final version, but I'm really impressed with the capabilities of the beta version. It's just worked really really great. You can do a cut halfway through and then take a break for a couple of weeks, and then get back to it and keep on doing it and it knows where it laid out all the parts.

Hitachi KNT50AB Air Compressor

The virtues of an air compressor. Where do I start? Building robots and tinkering with electronics used to be my hobby, and then it became my job. I had to find a new hobby, so I've been doing a lot of wood working in my free time. I do it at home. I have a little workbench in the garden. I've always covered in sawdust. Just being able to blow off my tools with this before I bring them into my bedroom is amazing.

Alex Glow
Hackster.io

Alex Glow creates electronics videos and tutorials at Hackster.io in San Francisco; she loves building wearable tech, EEG, music, bikes, holograms, and more. Alex grew into hardware as a FIRST Robotics team member, then as a director of the AHA and Noisebridge hackerspaces and Artist in Residence at Autodesk's Pier 9. (Published 07/13/18)

Pikazo App

This app is for is using a neural network to impose Picasso's visual style on other images. You could take a selfie and make it look like Picasso, it could be a portrait or whatever. In this case it's basically Polaroids for neural style transfer, which means that you can make one image look like another or like someone else's style using convolutional neural networks. It takes the structure of your original image, your content, like your selfie or whatever, and

it takes your face and the visual style of Picasso or Monet or any other image that you can feed it. I've been playing around with using the Arduino circuit diagram to turn things into, basically sort of circuitified versions of what they are, and especially in the context of using traditional ritual symbols like for alchemy, for Nordic runes, for crop circles. Taking those and turning them into something that a machine might produce. It's really fun.

USB Capture HDMI

This is kind of a frustrating tool for me honestly, because it's what people always ask about when

I'm trying to present about something else. I'll be setting up a video with Raspberry Pi or with a guest in the video studio, and I will pipe the HDMI output from their computer or from the Raspberry Pi or whatever into my computer as a USB webcam using this device. It sounds so simple, but it's so magical, like the fact that you don't have to point a camera at a grainy monitor in order to try and capture something from the Pi. It's a little silver box that has an HDMI port on one side where you plug in an HDMI cable, and then you plug in the other end of that cable to your source such as a Raspberry Pi or your guest's computer or whatever. On the other end of it, it has a USB port and you basically stick a USB cable into that connected to your computer, and now it's a webcam. You can also use it just to use your Mac computer or Windows computer as a monitor for something else, which is something where I haven't been able to find another tool that does this. It basically means that you don't have to lug around a huge monitor.

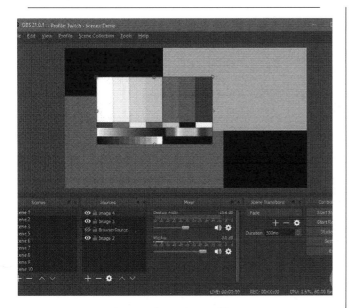

Open Broadcasting Studio

OBS is used for compositing video, which is another really awesome tool in its own right. Basically it's a free open source tool. It's a lifesaver. I can put in all kinds of different audio inputs and turn them on and off. I can have a persistent setup that basically includes text and logos, and my little face in the corner, and then a number of video sources that I can configure as different websites. There are other ones that other people use. I've tried them and to be honest, they kind of sucked. Whenever I try another one, it always either required some kind of weird plug-in that would eat all the video that I tried to send to other places on my computer, so I couldn't use Google Hangouts anymore or something. It was just a nightmare or it was super expensive or it just didn't have as much power as I wanted. This one is so configurable, you can setup multiple scenes.

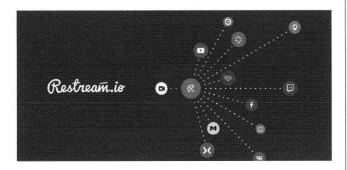

Restream

Restream helps with simultaneous streaming on multiple sites. The cool thing is I stream from OBS to restream.io, which basically splits it into going to Facebook and YouTube at the same time. It can go to Twitch at the same time as well. I think that's mostly free. There is a charge for adding extra links.

3D Hubs

This is a super cool service, where basically there's people all over the map who have their own 3D printers at home, and they've decided to make a profession out of it. You will send in your file, you upload it to the site, and that's an STL file or anything that you created from a 3D modeling program, for example Tinkercad or Fusion 360. I use onshape.com a lot, which is a browser-based one, and from that modeling program you'll export your 3D model, and then you basically had to figure out how to print it. If you don't have your own 3D printer or if you're not very good with it yet and you need a really pro-level model, then you can upload it to this website, and choose from a list of people to print it for you. Since these are individuals working wherever, there are often a lot of people in your own city who will do it, and you can go and pick it up instead of waiting for delivery.

Theodore Gray
Co-founder of Wolfram Research

Theodore Gray is the co-founder of Wolfram Research, makers of Mathematica and Wolfram|Alpha. He's also the founder of app publisher Touch Press, and the author of many books, including The Elements, Molecules, Reactions, and Mad Science. He's also the proprietor of periodictable.com. (Published 07/27/18)

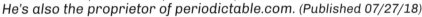

GU Eagle BF-1309 Laser Cutter

I used to have a lot of different tools that I really liked. I like tools. I'm kind of a tool guy. But once I got this laser cutter, it's like everything else has fallen by the wayside, because this thing is just so much more fun and more enabling of things that any other tool I've ever had. Their smallest and cheapest model is a 130-watt CO_2 tube with a 51-by-35-inch working area. I mean, this thing is the size of a grand piano. And it's huge. It's way, way bigger than I had any intention of getting, and frankly more than I had planned to spend on a laser cutter. It's just huge, and it's very powerful, and it's very fast, and it can cut half-inch acrylic like butter. You can actually cut inch-thick acrylic if you're willing to go a little slow.

Milwaukee M18 Fuel Deep Cut Band Saw

More than 20 years ago when I was building a house — I had just bought a farm, like a farmstead —and I was building stuff, big things out of wood. We built a greenhouse and docks, floating docks on a lake and a whole house. So I had every kind of tool there was. And then I saw this bandsaw. It's like, "Oh my god. It's a bandsaw you can hold in your hand." The bandsaw is like a precision surgical instrument compared to the demolition saw. You can just go up to the side of a building and just gently and calmly saw through whatever you want to saw through. And I just love the concept of this saw. And it worked great. And what I love about it now is that over 20 years later, it just runs. It's never given me the slightest trouble. I abuse it, and the blades pop off, and they just go right back on again. It seems to be indestructible, and I still use it regularly whenever there's something that needs hack sawing but on a larger scale.

LED Photo Lights

When I started photographing things, incandescent photo lights, you know, 500 watt quartz halogen bulbs and even 1,500-watt halogen bulbs, that was what you used. And now there's LED lights. It's just a complete night and day because you get really, really, really bright lights with almost imperceptible heat. I did an experiment once where I set up every single one of the LED lights we have. And we've got some extra Fresnel lenses to go on past the end of the regular focusing lenses — just blindingly bright concentrated light. And you stick your hand in there, and it feels very slightly like there's a bit of warmth coming on your hand. But basically no heat. And that's been revolutionary in our ability to do filming of particularly sort of delicate substances, like wax. Because in the case of Elements, it was all elements. But now that we've moved on to Molecules, a lot of these things, they're sort-of-delicate objects. They might catch fire. They might melt. There's all kinds of things that might happen. It's just nice not having to worry about that anymore.

Wolfram Language

Every day I'm using it for something. One example is quilting patterns. So this was actually a project I did a few years ago

with a current ex of mine making stitching patterns for elaborate art quilts. The problem with quilting is that you can't cut the thread. Like it's bad to, you want to make a continuous line to stitch your pattern without stopping. And if you have to stop you can, but it slows everything down and it's a pain. So you end up with a problem of, here is some line art. Here's a vector file and it's in Illustrator with a very complicated pattern of lines that cross each other and that hit each other and T connections and things like that. And you want to find a single line path that traces out all the lines that are in the original design in the optimal way. Like you have a city with streets in it and it snowed and you want to plow out all the streets, but you don't want to run over the same street twice anymore than necessary. So this is a mathematical optimization problem, and it turns out that the commercially available software for doing embroidery design and quilting designs is mathematically unsophisticated, shall we say. So now I do it in Mathematica. I can take the graphics, paste them into the notebooks, and it comes back with an optimized path, which we can then output and load on to this giant quilting robot.

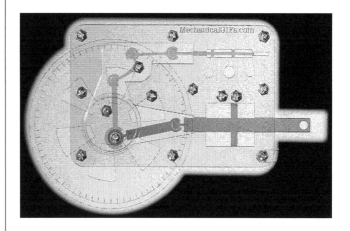

MechanicalGifs.com

Mechanical gifs are physical models you can hold in your hand. There are things like differentials, transmissions, rack and pinion steering, steam engines, and you get these beautiful laser cut acrylic parts and then assemble them, and then you have — exactly what it says —they're mechanical gifs that show how these things work in action.

Saul Griffith
Inventor

Saul Griffith is a compulsive user of tools, and he works across disciplines with a focus of making tools and technologies that help us solve climate change. Consequently, he ends up doing thermodynamics, precision machine design, and robotics on a daily basis. (Published 10/19/18)

Monarch Toolroom Lathe

We joke around at our office that humans used to have spirit animals, but now we should have spirit tools. As we were assigning spirit tools, I spoke out quickly to get the lathe. It's about 4,000lbs of precision tool. It's extremely accurate, and honestly I just find excuses to use the lathe. I love this tool that much. I find my own zen moment; the perfectly turned set of chips excites me to be honest. The lathe is where I find my most inner peace. This model is probably the F150 of tool room lathes. It's strong and versatile, and it lasts forever. As long as you lubricate it and treat it nice, it's absolutely a workhorse, but still very precise. There's definitely an organized market in professional tools for this

type of tool. I think we paid about $20,000 for this lathe including all the tooling. It's a 3,000lb block of cast iron that has some sort of streamliner, industrial design aesthetic, so it invokes the best of and the sexiness of the Vespa scooter, and the speed of a 1930's cross-country train.

FabLight Laser Cutter

I happen to think that a laser cutter is the most versatile and useful of any CNC machine you can have. 3D printers are fun, but laser cutters just have this enormous variety of materials that you can use, and they can be very fast. We've owned a lot, but the reason I like the 3D FabLight is it has a 4th axis, so not only can you cut two-dimensional sheets of material, you can also cut tubes. Honestly I just think all laser cutters are on my list of favorite tools. I just happened to choose this one because we're currently making them and they're great. Currently I'm on a kick. I use the 3D FabLight for my hobby, which is making all manner of strange bicycles. So we do all the coping, and all the tubes, and it's just incredibly satisfying because lasers are so precise to cut a full tube set and a couple pieces of flat metal for a bicycle, and it's cool to have them all going to the jig with perfect tolerances the first time. I'm really loving that process.

Cyclus Tools Spoke Cutter

At the circus when I was a child, there was a clown riding a bicycle with two eccentrically spoked wheels, meaning the hub of the wheel was not in the center of the wheel, so that when you rode it, the clown would sort of go up and down, and bounce up and down on this thing. So to do that you need to cut every single spoke on the wheel to a different length, and it was the excuse of really, really wanting to do that, that I found the most obscure and bespoke of the bicycle tools, which is this amazing little machine. You feed it fresh, long spokes, you set the length of the spoke that you want, and then you turn a crank, and it not only magically cuts it to the right length, but puts the perfect thread on the end of every spoke. Then we wrote some software, I think it was in Partner and MET lab, to say, "How much centricity do you want on the wheel? What type of hub do you have? What type of wheel do you have?" And it would give you the lengths of all the 36 different spokes to your eccentric wheel. I have a complete list of bike tools. I just think, some people collect vintage cars, and I kind of treat bicycles the same way. That's really my passion and my hobby, so I have a really nice set of one of every bicycle tool. This one is the most obscure, and the most fun, because you just turn the crank and it has this satisfying mechanical feel, and you can feel it carving the tiny, little, precise thread into the spoke as you turn the crank and it just magically produces these spokes. I love that tool.

Sailrite Edge Hotknife

I do a lot of work on soft goods, meaning things made out of fabrics. We make soft robots, and we've made a lot of kites in my life. When you're working with synthetic fabrics, specifically, you'll want to cut the fabric with a hotknife, not just a sharp knife, because it then seals all the little plastic fibers where they get cut so that they don't fray. A hotknife literally is just a hot knife, so it's a resistively heated knife, it has nice ergonomics, and if you're cutting nylon, like backpack materials, or if you're cutting synthetic rope, or if you're cutting spinnaker fabrics, or kite fabrics, this is just the way to do it. It cuts, it seals, and it does absolutely nothing else. But it's great.

Kuretake 36-Color Set

I really love drawing, and I think drawing and writing are really integral to the creative process. I also have children who always need occupying and I'd like to have them not occupied with iPads always, so I've taken to carrying a complete drawing and watercolor set with me everywhere. The particular watercolors that I found are a sort of obscure Japanese brand, called Kuretake, and they just have a great set of colors. You can use a little bit of water and they go on like a tempura paint, which is really nice if you want a really thick, opaque paint, but you can also water them down a lot and get a really lovely, light-flowing watercolor feel to them.

Danny Haeg
Director of Creative Collisions at the San Jose Tech Museum

Danny Haeg is currently the Director of Creative Collisions at the Tech Museum in San Jose, California. He moved here from Minnesota to jump into the simmering maker-melting-pot that is Silicon Valley.
(Published 12/29/16)

Allbirds

I feel slightly irresponsible for advising people to buy $95 shoes. I didn't think I would do that either, until I put these on. Now I get it. I'm converted. Allbirds are very new and they're fantastic. They're not like technical running shoes or anything like that, they're sort of lounging shoes. They're all merino wool from New Zealand. They're so comfortable. You don't wear socks and your feet don't get sweaty. It feels fantastic. It's been the shoe I've been wearing every day since I got them, because I've just been going to work and doing my business. I just suggest people give it a shot. They send you the shoes. If they don't fit, you send them back. It's free returns. They're like the Warby Parker for shoes. They're also

a certified B corporation. It's in their mission to do good. It feels good, they're a good company. It's one of those things that I keep getting questions about, so it must look good, too. They're very minimal, without any sort of crazy lines and swoops. I'm really in love with them.

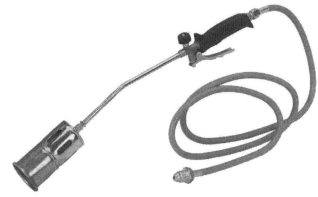

Propane Torch

I was a small part of a Battle Bots team behind the robot Complete Control that was on Battle Bots recently on ABC. This $20 propane torch was on a robot. It was heralded as — I'm gonna sort of humble brag here — it was heralded as the most effective flame thrower in Battle Bots history because it recorded the first robot kill ever, which was really exciting for us. There's a YouTube video of it. A minute-and-a-half into the match, we get the robot in the gripper. We grab under the robot, lift them up, and then turn on the flame thrower. It's a 3,000 degree torch, it's coming from just a regular propane tank. The brilliance of this Harbor Freight tool is someone engineered it and figured out how to have it properly aspirated. A lot of the flame throwers you see on Battle Bots are giant, orange flames. Those aren't very hot, they don't do anything. This flame is blue and it's also extraordinary loud, it's like a jet engine. It's crazy hot. It turns out just with a few little tweaks, including this spark gap generator, it became a robot killer. That was pretty awesome to see.

Cold Saw

I think this is my favorite tool of all time. I didn't even know about it until a few years ago. Everyone knows about abrasive cutoff saws. I'm talking about saws that cut metals, specifically. Abrasive cutoff saws, those are the really loud ones that throw sparks and make awful cuts with lots of burrs and junk on them. It's building up tons of heat, and that can affect your metal in ways you may not want it to. It's also just a mess. The cold saw is different in a lot of ways. It's slow, which is very perplexing. The cold saw is moving so slowly that it's not really generating heat, but then they typically have a pump on there that's just dousing coolant on it. It's so slow that you can just see the individual teeth rolling around. It's like 100 RPM. It makes these perfectly smooth cuts. There's like a little burr that you can knock off with a file. It makes smooth cuts, it makes them square, it makes them fast, it's really safe. I love it. I'm not advising anyone purchase it. That's sort of the tough part with it, it's a big, expensive tool. I use it at the TechShop.

Computer Keyboard Shortcuts

That's one of my favorite tools. I'm not talking about beautiful, awesome keyboards, necessarily, or the technique of typing really quickly. I don't have that. I'm just speaking to, in general, proper usage of the keyboard. I've seen a lot of very computer-illiterate people who aren't knowledgeable about shortcuts. I sound like a huge dork saying this, but it's a big deal. I can't say enough how important that is. Alt tab, switch programs, or command tab on Mac, it's such a big deal. I taught for a little while, and I'd show my students how to change programs without their eyes pulling away from the screen so that they could have Facebook open or something while they're at school without people knowing it. There's sort of like digital laziness that can come over you if you're just using your mouse, but the computer just lets you fly. I'm feeling like I'm already an old grandpa telling people they should learn to have better penmanship or something. This is 21st century penmanship. I do think it's a big deal that once you can move quickly with a keyboard, you do different things, you do it better. Maybe that won't be as learned because people are on their phones and iPads so much, but it's sort of a wonderful, profound skill to have.

Ron Hale-Evans
Author of Mind Performance Hacks

The open source software blog, Planeta Diego: Linux Y Software Libre, once described Ron Hale-Evans as "writer by profession, game designer by vocation and psychologist by training." He's the primary author of the 2006 book Mind Performance Hacks and co-author of its 2011 spiritual successor Mindhacker. (Published 10/13/16)

WhiteCoat Clipboard

The WhiteCoat Clipboard are folding clipboards and they're all medical editions of one sort of another and, one morning a few years ago for some reason, I woke up with the idea that I just had to have a folding clipboard to fit in my bag. I searched for "folding clipboard" on Amazon and The WhiteCoat Clipboard was pretty much it. It folds up so it will fit into a doctor's or nurse's coat pocket. You can put stickers on it or decorate it in some other way, but I keep mine plain, because it's kind of fun to look at. It's also good for when you just throw it in your bag, if you have notes in it, they don't get all creased and crumpled, because the folder protects it.

Alphasmart Neo

This is kind of like a calculator screen, but bigger. It's just great, you just type in it all day and then at the end of the day, you plug it into your laptop or whatever via USB and it pretends it's a keyboard, and it essentially simulates typing into whatever document you've got open and it dumps it that way. It's very good for getting away from different things, go sit out in the sun, and not only are you not connected to the internet, but you've got a screen that's visible in bright sunlight. It's great for just throwing in your bag and going anywhere and the battery life is like forever.

```
* Working with source code

#+BEGIN_SRC emacs-lisp :results html
   (defun bye-bye-world ()
     (interactive)
     (message "\"Hello world!\" examples are boring"))
   (bye-bye-world)
#+END_SRC

#+RESULTS:
#+BEGIN_HTML
"Hello world!" examples are boring
#+END_HTML
```
```
-:--  website.org    All L17   [0]  [(Org 45 Fill Narrow)] sam. sept.  8 08:13 0.34
wrote /home/guerry/website.org
```

Emacs Orgmode

This is a package for Emacs that makes it much more useful in daily life. Emacs is GNU Emacs — it's a text editor that has got all kinds of Swiss army knife bells and whistles on it. It's very great, a lot of people prefer more minimalist editors like VI, but there is still a bunch of people who like Emacs like me. I've been using Emacs for a long time. I think since college, but Orgmode is an add on package that lets you do things like freeform notes, calendar, to-do lists, embedded spreadsheets, literate programming. I use it for journaling with embedded quantified self data. You can write a book manuscript in it and then render it as LaTex PDF, EPUB. If your publishers want Word, you can convert it to Word with no problem. It's just very, very, powerful and useful. It's all keyboard driven, there's really no mousing necessary.

Oblique Strategies

Oblique Strategies comes in many forms, from decks of cards to phone apps or web apps, and you press a button or pick a card and it gives you advice about something you're stuck on creatively. The advice is very good, it comes from Brian Eno and Peter Schmidt. Brian Eno is a musician, Peter Schmidt is a painter. It's just wonderful, it doesn't hold your hand too much and it doesn't give you airy-fairy kind of advice that you can't do anything with. There is a good balance between general and specific, they only give you a specific task, like a prompt, you know, that you might get from a writer's book. They give you a general idea that can be applied to a lot of creative problems, but that seems specific.

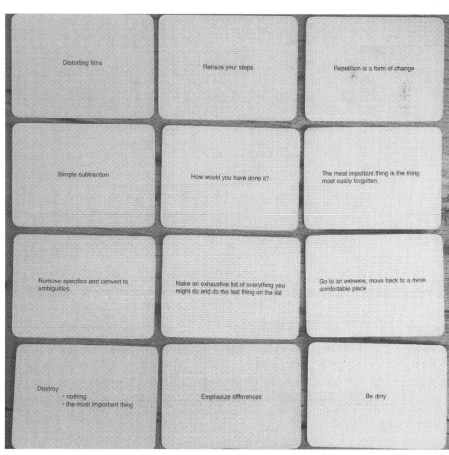

Kishore Hari
Scientist

Kishore Hari is a scientist/science educator who's been building science events for the last decade, but he really sees himself as a community organizer for science. He's currently the science correspondent at Adam Savage's Tested.com and the host of the weekly science podcast Inquiring Minds. (Published 05/25/18)

26-Piece Steel Dapping Doming Punch Block Set

The reason I'm so obsessed with this tool as of late is I grew up reading comics, and the comics I read all featured this character Thanos, which has now entered the cultural mainstream with the Infinity War movie. Ever since I was about 10 or 11 years old, I wanted to build an Infinity Gauntlet so I could have control of all of the space and time, I guess. And with the emergence of all of these Marvel movies, people started creating all of these different versions of Infinity Gauntlets, like 3D-printed ones, and I wanted to make it in my own way. And there are lots of way to do it, but I found somebody who was posting all these videos about hand-shaping metal. It's not something I've ever thought of in my life or something that I've done since metal shop when I was a kid, but I have to say it's one of the more satisfying things I've ever done — just pounding metal on mini anvils and shaping it slowly over time. Nothing comes out perfect. It has a lot of little nicks and scratches because I'm hand-shaping everything, but I love that. Dapping is sort of what the set is referred to as. And there are all these different punches and anvils and other kinds of components, and you use a hammer along with this dapping block. It's most commonly used in jewelry-making, so a lot of jewelry makers have used this. You can make different sorts of textures using that tool and different hammer sets that come along with it, so you're able to shape and create depth in the metal you're creating. You can create different sorts of structural elements with this.

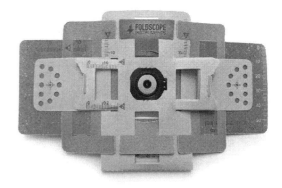

Foldscope paper microscope

Foldscope is one of the most exciting tools I've seen in a long time. Stanford professor Manu Prakash is sort of like the poet laureate of the science world. I find him lyrical. And what he's obsessed with is creating low-cost, high-quality scientific instruments as a hobby, and so one of the things he did was create a paper-based microscope. It's kind of a die cut piece of paper along with these very cheaply constructed lenses that you can actually get up to 40x to 100x magnification with, so that you can build your own microscope in the middle of a field and examine stuff in real time. It's an incredible piece of technology because what that means is we could be out in the Saharan Desert or we could be in our backyard in your woods, and you could take out a microscope and all of a sudden actually be looking at the microscopic world in a different way.

Zoom H4N PRO Digital Multitrack Recorder

My H4N travels with me everywhere — recording has become a way of life for me. And it isn't the newest, or best, etc. — but this recorder has been incredibly reliable for me. This is basically the size of a soda can, and it's been out for, I don't know, probably eight, nine, 10 years, something like that since this recorder first came out, so it's not fancy, but it gets really high-quality audio. It allows you to plug in microphone inputs. But moreover, it's a story about the stories I've collected with this thing that just sound great because it's simple to use and it's so portable. It has allowed me to capture stories in the oddest of places. I use it every week for my science podcast, so my H4N has the voices of Nobel laureates on there to my mom. This is a podcaster's dream tool, I think, because it's easy. It doesn't go wrong unless you do something wrong, like forget to put batteries in it. I think it's the gold standard for anyone recording audio, especially on the go.

Boa System Shoes

I don't like tying shoes. I've never liked tying shoes, and if you were to really pin me down I would tell you that I am bad at tying knots, and I have been since I was like six. And so this is a silly thing, but I've always thought shoelaces are antiquated technology. I don't understand why we all our tie our shoes, because there's better things out there. A couple years ago I got turned onto this shoelace system called the Boa System, which is a ratcheting lace system. So your shoe is basically a slip-on, and you slip it on, and then there's a gear on one of the sides of the shoe, and you just turn the dial, and it ratchets it down to the tightness you want. It takes a half-second for you to get the right tightness, and then you're on your way. And to release, you just need to snap out there. You pull it — it has a quick-release — and your shoe just comes right off. I've never gone through TSA quicker than with this shoe system.

Nicole Harkin
Writer and Photographer

Nicole Harkin lives in Washington, DC with her family. She recently published her first book, Tilting: A Memoir, and she's currently working on a mystery set in Berlin. She also runs a small photography business focused on family portraiture. She is from Montana and before becoming a writer worked in government oversight.
(Published 10/13/17)

Yuba Mundo LUX

My bike is the mini-van version of the cargo bike. The most amazing thing about my bike is how much more interaction I have not only with my environment, but also with my kids. I have my bike outfitted with one giant pannier and the "Monkey Bars." I have had up to four kids on the bike at once but generally ride with my two boys. However, the bike can carry, in addition to the rider, 440 lbs. Mine is the 2nd version I believe. They are now on the V5. My bike has Bionx system. My battery is a bit older and I unfortunately have to charge it anytime I stop riding.

I have the Rack Bag for the front "bread basket." It's waterproof and holds my phone safely for me.

Yama Glass 8-Cup Stovetop Coffee Siphon

My husband and I have two small children. Before kids, we made pour overs every morning. When the kids came along we switched to the Technovorm Moccamaster, which is a lovely machine. I had the siphon on my Amazon wish list and my mother-in-law purchased it for us. To our utter surprise, we have started using the siphon for our daily coffee. It takes less time than the pour over and makes substantially better coffee than the

Moccamaster. For two cups of coffee it is perfect. We use four scoops of beans and eight ounces of water per cup of coffee. First, you fill the coffee pot with water, put the siphon on top, and bring to a boil. There is a filter with a metal chain already in the top of the siphon. Once the water is boiling, you put the coffee grounds into the top and the water will climb up the chain into the upper glass siphon. Once it has boiled for two minutes, you turn it off and the cooling water in the pot reverses the vacuum, pulling the hot water back down through the coffee. One weird thing though is you have to keep the filter in the refrigerator in water.

SodaStream

After years of lugging cases of sparkling water into our third-floor apartment, my husband asked for the Penguin for his birthday. We've never regretted it. I also once dropped the entire machine onto the floor. It naturally broke. I called SodaStream, explained the situation, and they sent us a new one. So I recommend springing for the more expensive Williams Sonoma version rather than the cheaper

versions. Additionally, I like that the carafes are glass rather than plastic.

Windi the Gaspasser and NoseFrida Nasal Aspirator

Our kids are too big for these now, but when they were babies, these things were super helpful. Babies cry for four reasons: hunger, tired, diaper, gas. The Windi helps with the fourth. When a kid is sick and can't breath well, the NoseFrida snot sucker comes to the rescue. I think that people used to use a blue bulb thing to try to suck snot out, but those blue bulbs don't really work well. This thing does. The company is Swedish. If you give this as a gift, the parents-to-be will look at you like you are crazy. But in a few months they will thank you.

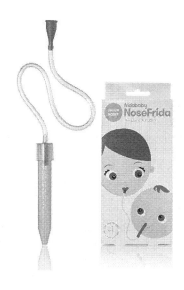

Matt Haughey
Creator of MetaFilter

Matt Haughey is the creator of MetaFilter and the co-creator of Fuelly, among many other sites. He spends his free time shooting photos and also rides and races bikes. These days, he works on the editorial team at Slack. (Published 01/26/16)

Belle-V Ice Cream Scoop

This is one of the few Kickstarters that showed up with big promise and totally delivered. It is easily the best thing for just rock hard ice cream that you just pull right out of the freezer. The handle is just so beefy. It has a massive handle that feels great in my hand, just really over-built compared to the size of the scoop. It distributes all the force, and the angle of the scoop is right. The best thing to do is take ice cream out of the freezer, wait 5 minutes, and then scoop, but if you want to eat ice cream immediately, you just drag and skip across the ice cream. This ice cream scoop just dives into the hardest ice cream I have in our deep freeze and works. It's just awesome. Bulletproof-like. It's built like it'll be here for a hundred years. I've spent 5 years trying to find a perfect ice cream scoop, and this is the one for me.

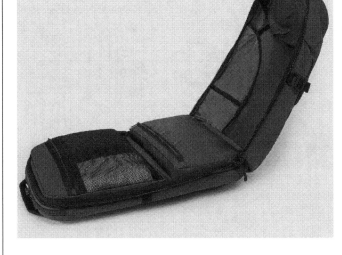

Minaal Carry-on 2.0 Bag

For the last 2 years I've been travelling with this backpack. I can take 4- or 5-day trips now with the computer and nice clothes. I've gone to conferences where I have to dress in a suit. There's a pocket for everything. Anytime I would think, "Oh, I wish it did this," I'd stick my hand there, and there is a special clip just for that thing. You could store the straps instantly and pull them out. It acts like a carry on when the straps are put away. The zippers go all the way around, so you can pack your stuff flat on the table. It's got a laptop sleeve, a tablet sleeve, and then all these pockets for phones. There's a clip for you to hold your keys. In the very bottom of it, there's a rain cover that zips into its own special pocket. There's a side pocket for a water bottle, and it has a cinch strap. That's the forethought that goes into it, that whatever you are carrying on the side, it make sure it fits perfect. This is the most thoughtful bag I've ever had.

The Athletic Community Socks

There was the guy who said in a bar a couple of years ago to his friends, "Hey, we should make clothes that match the Portland Airport carpet as a joke." He thought, "Maybe I'll sell 20 pairs." I think they sold out in an hour, and he just kept taking more orders. I think by 2 days later, he had sold hundreds of pairs, and now to this day, sold thousands, to the point where he and his wife quit their jobs. They opened a socks store, and now they custom design socks. They just have these amazing colorful socks. They're mostly for cycling, that's what they're designed for. It's just a thin sock, like a dress sock. I just really just love them. They're mostly nylon, partly wool, some are all wool. There's no other place I found with just a ton of wacky colored socks that you will get complements on constantly when you wear them.

EO1 Digital Art Display

The original idea for this was, it was just a 24-inch monitor turned on its side, portrait style, with a Raspberry Pi connected to it. Then he thought what

if you could control it from a website, any image you find online, you could right click and say, "Send it to my wall?" Now basically, they're building up an art gallery. It's less about just grab any image off the internet and send it to my wall. It's more like we have these curated art collections from actual artists that we pay, and that is included with this. So you just scan through your iPhone app. Then you can pick from artwork rotating every month. They've got 5 or 10 new pictures. You can also upload your own as yourself, and send it. You can also see anybody else on the system, and what they're putting on their wall. You can copy what they're uploading and can display it on your wall too if you see something cool.

Alan Henry
Editor in Chief of Lifehacker

Alan Henry is the Editor in Chief of LifeHacker, a site that offers tips, tricks, and downloads to help people live their best, most productive, and most fulfilling lives. He's also a recovering physicist, music lover, and self-proclaimed lover of dorky and niche hobbies.
(Published 12/13/16)

AKG Q701 Quincy Jones Signature Premium Headphones

I'm kind of a headphone nerd. I have a lot of headphones. I'm a big believer in spending just a little bit of good money on a superior listening experience, because I love music. I use these every day. These are open back headphones. Open back headphones are headphones that look kind of like they have a little speaker on the outside, but that really is just a way of opening up what we call a sound stage. That feeling that when you're listening to music you can hear where the instruments are around you and each individual instrument that's playing. They're great for a very immersive listening experience. You'll notice that there's these 2 little bands that go over and a little leather strap in the center. Those kind of self-adjust when you put them on your head, which is another reason I love these so much. You don't have to do that kind of clack, clack, clack thing that you do with a lot of headphones to try and get them on your head. They're perfectly designed for long, long listening sessions. I use them to listen to my turn tables or my MP3s on my computer or even when I play video games. I just keep them on. They're much superior than a lot of "gaming headphones" that will get uncomfortable over long periods.

Takeya Cold Brew Iced Coffee Maker

This is probably the simplest cold brew maker I've ever used. You just dump the coffee into the filter in the center, and you fill it up with cold water and put it in the fridge. Just wait overnight. When you're ready for coffee, you just take the filter. You dump out the grounds. You rinse it out and let it dry. Meanwhile, you have this pitcher of cold brew coffee that's still in your fridge. It just tastes delicious for no fuss at all. It was a no-brainer. Even when I picked it up, I realized that this is probably the cleanest cold brew I've ever made in my life, and I've tried many cold-brew-making techniques. My only thing that I don't like about it is that it's only a quart. I get like maybe 2 cups out of it, and then I have to make it again and wait another night.

Das Keyboard 4 Professional Mechanical Keyboard

I spend all day in front of a computer, so the keyboard I use is intimately important to me. A Das keyboard is a long-standing manufacturer of mechanical keyboards specifically, for writers, coders, and just general all around geeks. I've gotten waist deep into mechanical keyboards recently. This keyboard uses Cherry MX Brown Switches, has media controls, has a nice volume knob. It looks nice on your desk. The beautiful thing about MX Brown Switches, specifically, is that they're quiet, so you get the tactile feeling of using a mechanical keyboard, that very kind of clicky sensation while you're writing, but it's also not so loud that it would annoy everyone else in an office with you. I work in an office with other people, so it's nice to not make enemies while I'm trying to write articles. It's really about the switch inside each key. Most commercial keyboards are membrane keyboards. There's a circuit board on the bottom and a little rubber membrane that's laid underneath all of the keys. When you press the key, the rubber membrane makes contact with the board, and then it sends a signal to the computer that says "Oh, you pressed 's'". They're inexpensive to make

and that's part of the reason they're so popular. They get the job done. Mechanical keyboards, on the other hand, have individual switches for each letter. You can usually tell you have a mechanical keyboard if typing on it kind of sounds like a typewriter. That's really the big tell. They're very, very loud. They're often heavier, and they're often more expensive. The reason they've had a bit of a resurgence is really among gamers and people who miss those old IBM Model M keyboard days, where every key sounds like ka-chunk, ka-chunk, ka-chunk. That nostalgia has propelled them forward. They're also just a lot of fun, and they're really satisfying to type on. I have the soft tactile version. The soft tactile versions give you that feel but not the sound. I have used these keyboards in MAC OS and Windows with great success.

Todoist

No LifeHacker editor would be complete without their favorite to-do app. Todoist is my favorite. It's not the prettiest. It's not the flashiest. The reason I particularly love it is because it's the smartest I've used. It will recognize things like "pick up the laundry every 2nd Thursday at 10 p.m.," which is something that back in the early days of the web lots of to-do apps used to know. As we've progressed forward toward more design and free apps, they've dropped that. The nice thing about Todoist also is that they have plug-ins and apps for every platform: iOS, Android. They have plug-ins for Chrome and Firefox. They have plug-ins for Outlook and Thunderbird and any tool that you've already used most likely; Todoist will have some kind of integration with it. So you can say "Hey, this website was really interesting. I want to write about it. Let me add it to Todoist," and I will click one button and there it is as a reminder to myself.

Michelle Hlubinka
Former Education Director at Maker Media

Michelle Hlubinka has made a career of promoting playful learning through people-centered uses of technology in schools, museums, and neighborhoods. She spent most of the past 12 years at the forefront of Maker Media's efforts in education, establishing key kid-focused programs—Young Makers, School Makerspaces and School Maker Faires—and running Maker Camp.
(Published 08/2/19)

Snake Top

We all love magnets in my family. They're just these invisible powers that enchant any kid, and my kids will just stay wrapped with this stuff for hours. This was something that I didn't even know what it was until I walked into the store Joie de Vivre in Cambridge, Mass., and they said, "Have you seen this?" I love this sweet spinning top and pair of metal snakes. It uses magnetism mechanically, translating the rotational motion of the bottom tip of the top into the wiggly, linear motion of the snakes. You spin the top and feed the little snakes in and zip, the wavy edge of the snakes tuck into the tip and the rotating top tip pulls the snakes forward. There are two snakes. You have to try to get both of them to kind of slide around it at the same time. It's one of those classic metal toys, and it was a great little souvenir to bring home to my kids.

Toysmith Euler's Disk

This is a toy based on a physical phenomenon that you can also see in a spinning coin. The specifics of the Euler's Disk were worked out by an aeronautical

engineer named Joseph Bendik working with some colleagues, not by Euler, but I gather it's named after Euler because he studied similar physics a couple of centuries ago. You spin it and it spins and spins and then at the end it does something truly unexpected — it levitates for a split second before it zaps down. It's best experienced in person. They tried to make it into a party toy by adding all these holographic magnets that you could stick to the top. So you can dim the lights and shine a light and have things reflect on the ceiling.

Micro:bit

Micro:bit comes from a tradition that we call "programmable bits" where you've got a a programming environment where you can communicate with this microprocessor to tell it what you want it to do. And they really souped up this particular programming board. The micro:bit has a 5x5 LED display and it's got a couple of buttons and several output ports and you can connect to it with USB and

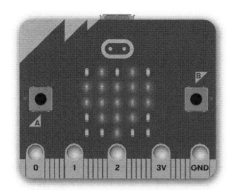

radio and Bluetooth and you can connect servos and lights and speakers, just about anything that you pump power through, and it'll produce an effect. So it's really versatile and the barriers to entry are low. It has what my mentor Mitchel Resnick describes as important aspects for any "lifelong kindergarten" tool: low floors, high ceilings, and wide walls. It's also super cheap, like $15, and a little more if you buy a kit with things to plug into it. Best of all, it's a quick onramp to get something done with it. The BBC did a bang-up job of putting together materials to support its use.

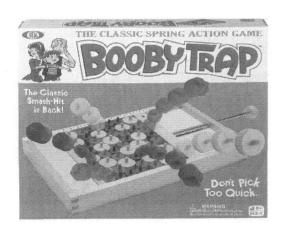

Booby Trap Classic Wood Game

This is a game that I found at Community Thrift, which is this great resource in the Mission in San Francisco. I would routinely go in there and find all these beautiful vintage games, and this was one of them. It was made by Parker Brothers. It's just gorgeous. I would put this around 1950, 1960. The rules of the Booby Trap are truly mechanical in that they are all physical and it's as much a competition against your opponent as it is against the laws of nature itself. In this way it's not unlike Jenga, but in Booby Trap, you use your skills in observation and prediction to decide which piece to remove next

without letting a spring jostle the whole setup. There are three colors of playing pieces, shaped like disks with little knobs on top you can grab. The three colors are different sizes and point values, and your goal on each move is to remove just one of these disks without the entire thing collapsing on itself, rearranging into a new structure with a different set of force vectors pushing this way and that way against the spring. It's such a simple game that you can learn how to play it in well under a minute, and yet I find it very satisfying, with a little bit of that tension of the notorious game Perfection, and as I mentioned Jenga, but not as cataclysmic and chaotic nor as anxiety-producing.

Diffraction Grating Sheet

The diffraction grating sheet is this thin piece of plastic that's been etched to create prism behavior. So usually people use this inside of a spectrograph to analyze light. I was trying to create something like my Rainbow Center. I have this Kikkerland Rainbow Spinner on my window with a crystal at the bottom and a solar panel at the top where it would activate the gears, and I was trying to make a cheap toy version of this for a science kit that I was designing. So we got this sample and I just happened to put it onto my window because I wanted to see if I can see something interesting through it. Then, on one of my work-from-home days, all of a sudden I noticed this brilliant, gorgeous rainbow across the top of my ceiling, and anyone who knows me well knows that I love rainbows and it drives me crazy that we live in drought-stricken California where the rain does not happen enough for my rainbow needs, and ever since we discovered that, we've left it on our window and we'll move it around a little for different seasons to make sure we get enough light on it. This casts a rainbow or a spectrum about 10 feet long and a foot wide on our ceiling every afternoon that's sunny enough.

Tommy Honton
Experience Designer

Tommy Honton is a Los Angeles-based experience designer who specializes in weaving interactivity and game mechanics into narrative storytelling. Across the United States, he's produced interactive and immersive work for audience sizes ranging from 1 to 80,000. He's also the co-creator and designer of the critically-acclaimed escape room Stash House, and co-founder of the interactive exhibition Museum of Selfies. You can follow him on Twitter @angelalansburyd. (Published 02/15/19)

Scheduling system: Using Trello with Google Calendar

I live and die by my calendar. I struggled to find a way to organize tasks by project and deadlines along with my daily agenda and personal schedule that could fit in one space on my phone and computer.

I finally found my rhythm with Google Calendar integrated with Trello. All my projects are on Trello, and every deadline or milestone now appears automatically on my calendar which makes it easy to manage and schedule my entire life in one spot.

Note-taking system: Ultra-fine Sharpie and Field Notes End Papers Edition

I take notes constantly. I prefer to keep everything digitally in the Google Drive ecosystem, but there's something satisfying about using a good notebook and pen. Plus, in meetings, typing on a computer or phone can give off the appearance of being distracted or not paying attention. I prefer using ultra-fine-tip Sharpies as my typical writing

tool in a durable notebook. I used to use pocket-sized Moleskines (they're actually vegan which is important to me), but lately I've used Field Notes-brand notebooks. My favorite is their End Papers version which is thinner and slimmer and fits in pockets very easily. Once I finish with a meeting, I always photograph the pages and mark them through so I know I have a digital copy. Then I'll transcribe them or add notes in Google Keep which I'll transfer over into a Google Doc sorted in Google Drive based on the project.

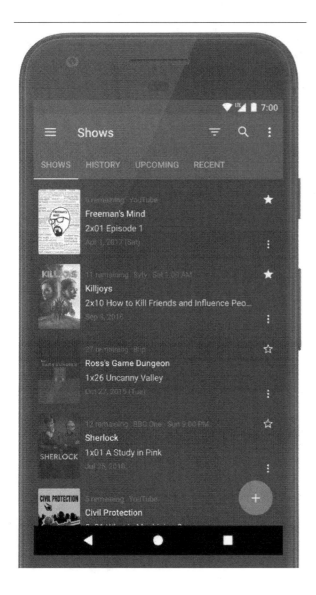

Consumed media list: Trakt.tv integrated with Series Guide

I like keeping track of all forms of entertainment I consume, not only because I like data for some reason, but it's been practical when I'm trying to remember a show or something I've listened to or want to make notes on it. For media, the service Trakt is fantastic, and I have it integrated with the app Series Guide on my phone since Trakt doesn't have a first-party app. I wish they kept track of books, podcasts, etc., but they don't, so I just have a Google Sheets page where I keep track of that stuff manually. And, me being me, I have a sheet for escape rooms, immersive productions, LARPs, and other stuff that I have to do manually as well.

Toolbox: Sugru, E6000 and Rustoleum Multi-Purpose Clear Paint

Creating tactile experiences means stuff is going to break, crack, tear, smear, etc. I've really learned to appreciate the magic of three things. Sugru, which is a putty-like glue that cures into a hard rubber. E6000, a craft adhesive that bonds pretty much any material to any other material. And a good clear coat to protect or finish any surface to make it smooth and safe from UV damage, scratches, or peeling. I prefer Rust-Oleum-brand's Painter's Touch Ultra Cover Latex Paint in Clear Gloss.

Hugh Howey
NYT Bestselling Author

Hugh Howey is the New York Times bestselling author of WOOL, SAND, BEACON 23, and over a dozen other novels. He lives on a catamaran he custom built in South Africa and is now sailing around the world.
(Published 07/30/16)

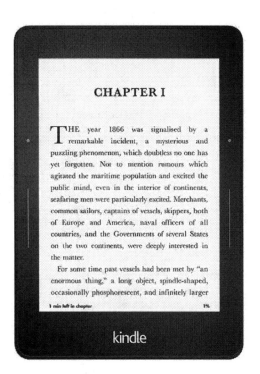

Kindle Voyage E-reader

This is the perfect reading device. It weighs almost nothing, it's comfortable in your hand, and I can fit an entire library. The only ding that people have said about the device is its price. I read a lot of classics. When I look at all the free books on gutenberg.org, the device has paid for itself already several times over. The Voyage uses the same screen as the Paperwhite. The body is just slimmer and there's physical page turn buttons now, and my favorite thing about the interface is that there's a very wide side so that you can hold it with the kind of fat part of your thumb, the way you would hold

a book without covering the screen or accidentally turning pages. I have the same sort of emotional attachment to my e-readers as we've always had toward books because what I've found is that I imprinted on books by reading and enjoying them, and now I'm doing that with my e-reader device. The people who say, "Well I'll never feel the same way about it," well that's because you haven't read enough books yet to have that imprinting take place, but once you do you'll love the smell of plastic in your hand.

Oceanic OCi Wrist Dive Computer

My Oceanic OCi is a magical piece of technology. The original dive watches used to be enormous. They're about as big as the dive computers you carried on your scuba gear, but this is a very normal-size watch. You can wear it every day for telling time, but when you go out for a swim — I'm doing a lot of free diving now — it keeps track of how deep you go and how long each dive is. You basically get a log of your entire swim, like every single time you surface it resets and logs that as a separate dive, so I know if I'm staying down for a minute, if I went down to 60 feet, all these nice metrics which motivate me to work on my freediving even more. The great thing about this watch is it's wireless, and when I put on my scuba gear it communicates with my tank and it'll tell me how much air I have left.

Hario Ceramic Coffee Mill

Something I love is my coffee mill. I could easily have a little plugin electric coffee mill, but on my first sailboat I had very little power and I got as many hand-powered things as I possibly could, including my drill was a hand-powered drill, which was a lot of fun. And this Hario ceramic coffee mill gives you a perfect grind. It's less than $30 for this thing, and one of the things I really like about it is it's quite a bit of work. It might not seem like a selling point but I get more of a boost to my morning to making my coffee than I get from the coffee itself, and there's also a meditative quality about it. You really feel — between that and the French press

and the whole coffee making process — that it just fits with the boat lifestyle more than getting up to a coffee machine and pressing a button or getting in line at Starbucks.

Magic Bullet Blender

This is something else that I use every single day and I see these everywhere now. They've become very popular. If you have all the right ingredients it makes for a wonderful replacement meal, very healthy. I started using it on land and it became indispensable. I actually traveled with my Magic Bullet Blender and I do a smoothie every day for lunch now. It's one and a half bananas, some peanut butter, yogurt, blueberry, strawberry, and protein mix, and then some camu camu and chia seeds. This all sounds like a lot of stuff, but I have one little cabinet that has all my smoothie accoutrement in it. I pull it all out, and it's so quick and easy and you're not hungry until dinner time. This blender, it's wonderful, it's very small and compact but it's powerful enough to crush ice. You drink right out of the thing that you blend in so you don't have a lot of extra cleanup, and the blade has held up to 6 months of abuse so far. It comes with all kinds of blades and containers. You don't need a lot of it so you can really kind of figure out what you need and recycle the rest, but it's a beautiful blender. I love it.

Oliver Hulland
Emergency Medicine Doctor

Oliver Hulland is a former editor of Cool Tools, after which he ended up pursuing a career in medicine. He's currently a third-year resident in emergency medicine at Yale University. When not working in the emergency department, he enjoys spending his time foraging for mushrooms and wild plants. (Published 07/12/19)

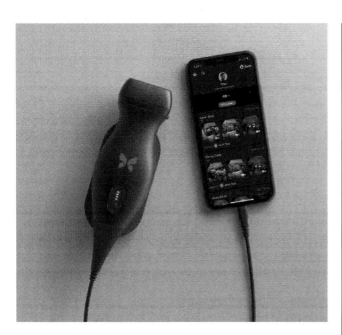

Butterfly iQ Personal Ultrasound

This is a very new piece of tech. It just was released in the past two years and it's a personal ultrasound that you can buy and that plugs into iOS devices now, and then in the future it should have support for Android. On my day-to-day job I use ultrasounds to quickly evaluate potentially life-threatening illnesses. I can use it to check to see if there's fluid in someone's lungs, to see if they have a gallstone in their gall bladder, to see if they have free fluid or blood in their belly. It's a really incredible tool with which we can very quickly intervene and figure out what's going on. The big difference now is that historically ultrasounds have been $30,000-$50,000 just for a set-up. The Butterfly iQ is really different because they have brought the price down all the way to about $2,000. Instead of using crystals they use a silicon chip, which can be much, much more easily produced and also is a lot easier to adapt for different circumstances. I would say in five or 10 years, people with certain conditions will end up taking these home. It's something that can be quickly taught to people. They can use it as a means of checking to make sure their heart function is where it's supposed to be, checking to make sure that there isn't a ton of fluid in their lungs. If there is, they can quickly call their cardiologist or primary care doctor and schedule a visit. The technology is definitely evolving. Right now it's predominantly for health care providers, but I think the future will see a democratization of the technology.

Leatherman Raptor Shears

This is a foldable pair of what are called trauma shears, which are heavy duty scissors. I carry them in my pocket on a daily basis. They're really great because it really makes it a form factor that's just easy to pop in your pocket or pop in your bag. They're a really, really useful set of scissors. I've found that I use them just as much outside of the emergency department as I do in the emergency department. Leatherman has also built in a couple of other additional tools, as they're famous for. One of them is a seatbelt cutter. Then in addition to that, they have a ring cutter, which is actually really great in my line of work, but also, it's amazing how often people get rings stuck and have to go to jewelers. I think for me, I probably use the ring cutter as much in terms of intervening on a patient as I do the shears themselves. It can get through most metals except for hardened steel. They come with a Molle nylon strap thing that you can slide them in. I personally don't like that tactical look. I like to have a more streamlined look, so I just have them in my pocket when I'm working. Then I just keep them in my bag when I'm not. I have a little pocket in my bag. I can actually attach the Molle holster and I just keep it there for safekeeping so it doesn't slide around or get lost. They are super strong. You can cut coins. You can cut almost any type of metal that you can think of. I'm on my second pair because one of them got pilfered, but my first pair I had for about three years and I never had a problem. I didn't run into anything that I couldn't cut within reason.

The Batclip

It's a stethoscope holder. It's a piece of leather with a clip on the back that closes with Velcro. It attaches to either a belt loop or I keep mine on the outside of my pocket. It allows you to keep your stethoscope folded up and on your belt without having to keep it around your neck. The alternative would be keeping it on your neck or keeping it in a bag or in your white coat or whatever pocket that you have. It's something that I probably use 20 to 40 times a day. It really makes a difference in terms of having my stethoscope easily handy. It keeps it from sliding off my neck. It's just a really simple, useful tool. I like it also because it was designed by another emergency medicine physician. He's a great guy. When I had problems with my first-generation one, he immediately replaced it with an upgraded model with better Velcro. I can definitely attest to the fact that it's a very well made and useful tool, especially if you work in the medical field and you find yourself using a stethoscope.

Pedi STAT

In the world of emergency medicine, there is a need to quickly draw up dosing for anything that comes in. Specifically, there's a range of neonates to babies to children, and the drug dosing and interventions that we do vary based on how old they are. What it allows you to do is you put in the age or size of the kid that you're taking care of. It will tell you everything about what kind of dosing for, let's say pain medications or fever medications, and/or what the normal vital signs are. From the perspective of being useful for patients outside of the world of medicine, it can be really useful for specific dosing of things like Tylenol and Ibuprofen, which oftentimes parents get wrong, because they aren't doing a weight-based dosing. They'll just give what they think is the right amount, or it's too confusing on the bottle. This is just really nice because you just plug in the weight or the year or the age, and it will pop out the appropriate dose and/or tell you what the appropriate vital signs are for your kiddo. This is just reassuring because it will tell you quickly. Even for me, it's still hard to remember all the different variations in terms of what the expected heart rate is or respiratory rate is for somebody who is young, because they can often be the primary indicators for when something is wrong or when somebody is sick.

A.J. Jacobs
NYT Bestselling Author

A.J. Jacobs is the author of four New York Times best sellers including The Year Of Living Biblically, and The Know-It-All. A sitcom based on The Year Of Living Biblically aired on CBS. He is a contributor to Esquire and NPR. (Published 11/24/17, 08/27/14)

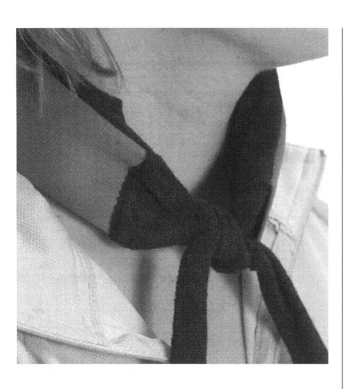

Ice Bandana

Basically, you wrap this around your neck, and it's a little scarf that has ice in it. Re-freezable ice. I wear it all summer long because we all know lots of people wear scarfs in the winter and no one thinks twice. But very few seem to wear these cooling scarfs in the summer. They are just as comfortable and just as helpful. What I do is just put it in the freezer overnight, and then it's just this little black band. I tie it around my neck during the day, and it lasts a good four or five hours. You can switch them out. It's like a little air conditioner for my neck. It cools my whole body down.

Walker's Game Ear Low Profile Folding Muff

These are in the same area of those great earplugs that are like sonic defenders that are designed for the military. They came about because when I was doing my book, "I'm Trying To Be The Healthiest Person Alive," I read all of these studies about how noise is actually a health hazard. It's an under-reported, under-valued health hazard and it can raise your stress level. So I've become more aware trying to cut down noise in my life. They look like Beats By Dre. Not quite as cool, and they don't have any music capabilities. They're just like the earmuffs that they wear on the tarmacs of airports, but they're smaller and slicker looking, and I love them. I wear them all the time. I'm wearing them right now. I wear them while I work. I wear them around the house, and they turn the volume down from 10 to five. It's 31 decibels of noise reduction. My kids sometimes are embarrassed, but they are much better than those huge massive tarmac deals, and also, I used to wear the Bose noise-canceling headphones, which are great, but they cost $300 and I kept losing them.

Easy Adjustable Reading Portable Desk

I do like working with my laptop on my bed. Even though I'm not sure it's the most efficient because you tend to fall asleep. But it is enjoyable, except when I suffer from overheated crotch syndrome. So, there are several of these brands of portable desks. I have one, but I'm sure the others are good too. These adjustable laptop trays that have these legs. They look like the AT-AP from Star Wars attached to a tray, so you can adjust the legs and they even have

fans, which I don't bother with. But they've got little built in fans to keep it cooler. I found out that does increase my productivity when I'm working on my bed because I'm not quite as distracted.

Lock Laces

I am not a good shoe tie-er. For years I wanted to get the Velcro shoes, but my wife won't let me because she says they're for five-year-olds or for eighty-five-year-olds and I am not one of those. So, about a year ago a friend of mine told me about these elastic shoe laces. Lock Laces they're called, and they're like bungee cords, and you lace them up but you don't have to tie them. They have a little lock and you lock them in and they are as tight as your regular shoe laces and they cost about ten bucks. I haven't tied my shoelaces in about a year, and my wife doesn't yell at me or walk ten feet ahead of me because they kind of look like normal shoes laces. And I've talked to runners who use it, so it's not just for walking around. You can actually use it for sports, and the other thing that's interesting about it is even if your shoelaces are too long, you cannot trip over your shoelaces because they stretch, so if you step on the shoelace it just stretches out. So, when people say, "Tie your shoe. You're gonna trip!" I say, "No I'm not! I'm fine. I can step on my shoelaces all I want!" It's so liberating.

Andrea James
Film Director and Activist

Andrea James is a writer, director, producer, and activist. Her last film, Alec Mapa: Baby Daddy, aired on SHOWTIME. She's -currently developing a talk show called Conversations with Coco and will direct the film Becoming a Man in 127 EASY Steps.
(Published 10/27/17)

Braun Silk-épil 9

I own one of the oldest websites on hair removal, and that came out of some work I've done helping transgender women with consumer issues. And when I started on the Internet it was the Wild West and there were a lot of scams, and so I just started answering questions and putting them online, and now it's 1,300 pages of information. This is a kind of rotary tweezer. So it's a rotating head like an electric shaver, but it has tweezers on it, and as they spin they open and close and can tweeze much more quickly than a standard one-at-a-time or two-at-a-time tweezer. And the reason that this Braun Silk-épil 9 is really great is that they've added a little LED light on it so you can see the hairs, which

is really helpful for someone like me who has very fine blonde hairs on my legs, and I can see them much easier as I use this.

Streamlight ProTac Tactical Flashlight

I had a detached retina a few years ago, so my night vision is not great in one eye, and so I've become quite the connoisseur of flashlights. And I keep one on my desk at all times, and I keep one in the car. The Streamlight ProTac from my desk is a super, super bright police-style flashlight, but it's only about six inches long. Last night there was a skunk out in my yard. It was trying to get in under the house, and I went out there to see what was going on and turned on that light, and I could see everything very easily and quickly. And it has a strobe feature as well, so it's designed for if you're in distress on the highway and you have that with you, you can click it twice and it'll strobe, and people can see that from a very long distance. The other one is a hand-cranked rechargeable light by Energizer. It's called the Weatheready 3-LED Carabineer Rechargeable Crank Light, and I love this light. The other day I was at a grocery store and this woman came running up to me and said, "Oh, I dropped my wallet. I think it was underneath this car. This is where I was parked." I just pulled that out and cranked it up, and we looked around. And it was wasn't there, but it was so handy. And you don't have to worry about the batteries running out. It's really great to put in your emergency kit, whether it's for hurricanes or earthquakes or whatever. It's just a very handy little thing to have that you always know is going to work.

causes the pinchers to pinch together. And if it's too high up, it also has a string that hangs down so that it goes all the way to the base and you can pull on that string if you're up past the pump-action part, and so you can get like 9, 10 feet away from your body with this thing, and it's just really great for cutting things that are high up. The second-most popular thing I use is also by Fiskars. It's this Pro Pruner, and what I like about it is it has a curved blade. So a lot of times with pruning shears they kind of have a square blade, and you can't get as much torque on that and sometimes the branch will squirt out, but with this curved hook it really keeps the branch in there and uses that curve to get some torque on the branch.

Fiskars Extendable Tree Pruning Stik Pruner

Nature's Dog MACE

I have this huge bougainvillea in the front of my house, which is very pretty. It's very red and vibrant, but they have really hardcore thorns on them, and so you have to be very careful as you prune it. And one of the things that I've found is super helpful is the Fiskars brand pruning stick, because I'm pretty tall, but this thing is probably 25 feet tall. And I can get pretty much anything with just a standard step ladder and this pruning stick, because it extends way out and it has sort of like a pump-action shotgun. It's like you pull down on it, and that is what

I love dogs, but there are some ne'er-do-wells afoot in my neighborhood who don't like to clean up after their dogs, and without this stuff I was probably getting about three new batches a day between my sidewalk and the street, and so I was looking for something that, 1) wasn't harmful, and 2) would be very effective, and I found that this worked gangbusters. It comes in two different forms, and it's the brand Nature's MACE. It comes in a sort of granular shaker form, and it also comes in a liquid form, and I find them both helpful for different uses. I have some gravel, and that's where most of this problem was happening, and then owners would either scrape up the gravel or they'd kick it out in the street and I'd have to replace the gravel all the time, so I put the granular stuff in the gravel. It's organic, and it smells kind of minty and lemony to us, but I think there's a rotten egg smell to dogs, because I've actually seen dogs cross the street to avoid going in front of my house now, which is fine by me.

Xeni Jardin
Co-editor of Boing Boing

Xeni Jardin is the Co-editor of Boing Boing. She is an American weblogger, digital media commentator, and tech culture journalist. She has also worked as a guest technology news commentator for television networks such as PBS NewsHour, CNN, Fox News, MSNBC, and ABC. (Published 08/29/17)

AmazonBasics High-Density Foam Roller

I work with a physical therapist, I had lots of surgeries and stuff, and when I travel, I get sore. I didn't realize how cheap foam rollers on Amazon are if you're just doing like the cheapo, basic — no kind of weird serrations, no crazy space-age material — just basically a 36-inch foam roller with about six-inches diameter. I overnighted one of those things to myself here in Utah the day that I arrived. I can stretch out everything that gets stiff, either from exerting myself on hiking trails or just getting out there. It's just amazing what some really basic physical therapy tools like this do.

RIVA Turbo X Wireless Speaker

This is a high-end wireless Bluetooth speaker. You get about 26 hours of playing time on it. I don't know how to exactly describe how the sound is great. Compared to, say, some of the other $50-and-under speakers, there's just no comparison. I hear a lot of crispness and a lot of definition if I'm listening to more complex orchestral cinematic compositions. I can even do calls on it, too. If I'm listening into a conference call, or an audio book, or something while I'm cooking, they're just really great. So I wanted to put a shout-out to this fantastic little speaker brand. You can also charge your phone or tablet off of it.

Oral-B Black Pro 1000 Electric Toothbrush

When I was looking on Amazon for a toothbrush, I wanted to spare no expense and get the absolute top of the line. It turns out most electric toothbrushes now are like $100 and they include a lot of crap that you don't need. The one that I like is called the Oral B Pro 1000, and it's $39. Basically it gets your teeth super, super clean if you use it correctly. You don't have to move it back and forth like you do with manual toothbrush. You don't have to press down into your teeth and your gums, as many people often do when they're transitioning. There's a little buzzer on it that buzzes in your hand every

30 seconds to let you know it is time to move on the next quadrant of your mouth. Minimal price and no feature creep.

30% Pure Vinegar

There's lots of different ways to use simple household ingredients like baking soda or Epsom salt or vinegar to clean up around the house. People who are into not supporting big chemical companies might be interested in this. I'm a cancer survivor and I just don't like having lots of extra chemical ingredients around that I don't actually need. 30% Vinegar is a cool tool that you can use in some of those household cleaning practices. You can use 30% Pure Vinegar also as a weed killer. I think some people mix it with orange oil for certain things like that. There's lots of crazy uses for it. I like to dilute it and use it in laundry.

Richard Kadrey
NYT Bestselling Author of the Sandman Slim series

Richard Kadrey is The New York Times bestselling author of the Sandman Slim supernatural noir series. Sandman Slim was included in Amazon's "100 Science Fiction & Fantasy Books to Read in a Lifetime." Some of Richard's other books include The Everything Box, Hollywood Dead, and Butcher Bird. He's also written comics and is a photographer. (Published 07/5/19)

Evoluent VerticalMouse

I've been in some car accidents, and have been in some motorcycle accidents, and I have some nerve damage from those, so a regular mouse didn't work for me. Track balls didn't work for me. I used a track pad for a long time. That didn't work for me after a while, and the vertical mouse has been a real, real lifesaver for me. It's a weird device. There's a big learning curve when you first get it, but I think it's a wonderful bit of technology. There are two buttons on one side and three buttons on the other, and in the end they're all really useful, but you really make a lot of mistakes at first, and you're moving the device around incorrectly. It's a very frustrating process. It's like if you've ever used Photoshop. It's the same thing where you have this long line of tools on the side. You don't know their names, they're very mysterious. Even the icons don't necessarily match what they do. The vertical mouse is kind of the same thing. It's just a complete mystery at first. And like Photoshop, the best way to learn it is just to play with it.

Holga Digital Camera

This is a wonderful, wonderful device if you're a photographer. If you like photography that is imperfect, and I'm a big fan of that, the Holga is a great camera. I used to use a film Holga, but because you have no idea what you're going to get from a Holga from shot to shot, using film was incredibly expensive. Your traditional Holga is plastic. The viewfinder is virtually useless. The lenses tend to be cheap plastic. So the fun of the Holga was the mystery of it, taking a chance and never knowing what you were going to get. But it became incredibly expensive, shooting whole rolls of film in which you got virtually nothing out of them. But with the Digital Holga, you can shoot away and it doesn't matter if you get things wrong. You can always go back and try it again. And if you shoot 50 shots and 50 of them are bad, all you've used is a little bit of memory on a card. It's chunkier than a little point-and-shoot and smaller horizontally. It's like if you took a regular point-and-shoot and just kind of squeezed it in a bit and it kind of squeezed out the other way. It looks and functions like a toy camera, and in a lot of ways it is, because you have no real control over what you're going to get. You can set it for black and white or color. I prefer black and white for me, especially if you're going to get weird, off-center, grainy shots, I think black and white is perfect and mysterious enough.

My Passport Wireless Pro

I'm very big on controlling my media, and I tour for my books, and I travel a lot, and I like to bring my media with me because I don't trust hotels. They have garbage channels on television. It's hard to stream things. So, I'll just bring my own media. Now with the My Passport Wireless Pro, you can get several terabytes on there, and you can load on photos and music and movies. I tend to put on movies and television shows. And what it is is just a little streaming box, and you don't have to rely on hotel wifi, because it uses Bluetooth, and it goes straight to your iPad. There's a little battery inside so you can just recharge it. It's about the size of the old Sony portable Discman. It's very energy efficient. It's also very rugged, too.

Region-free Blu-ray DVD Players

It's very easy to find region-free DVD players, or you can hack them. I used to have a very old cheap Chinese player, and it was well known that essentially it was built to hack. There were a few codes you would put in. The codes are almost like what you'd use on a game controller. It's like up, up, left, three, two, and you hit it a few times. And the wonderful part was when you got to the screen where you could turn off the region codes there would be a big message saying

you're not supposed to be here. And you knew it was one click away from being able to turn off all the region controls. Region-free Blu-ray is a whole other matter, because with DVDs it's just changing the software. The region-free Blu-ray is a hardware hack, so you have to find them on the gray market. They'll pop up on eBay and even Amazon now if you search on "region-free Blu-ray." You can get them through there, and I was very surprised to see them. I do weird searches like that every now and then just to see where the technology is landing, and you had to go kind of underground a few years ago, but now I don't suppose law enforcement looks or cares, but they're much easier to find. And they don't cost that much more than a regular player. They used to be around $600-$800 because people were doing hardware hacks. Now you can get them for in the range of $250 to $300.

The Grand Dark

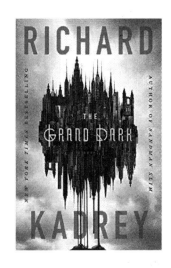

It's a big book for me. It's actually, literally, my longest novel. It's my most complex. It's a big step for me. I didn't want to be known as a pulp writer forever. The Grand Dark is a much more serious book than I've ever written before. I've been obsessed with the Weimar Period in Germany for many years, and so this is a dark fantasy riffing off the Weimar Period, but being a fantasy, there are also robots and genetic engineering. And it's a very different kind of protagonist than I've written. I usually write very powerful,

driven people, but this is about a 21-year-old bike messenger. He likes to take drugs. He likes to hang out with his girlfriend, who is a pretty actress, and he's really a very ordinary guy who gets sucked into a government conspiracy simply because of his own desire to be oblivious. This is a book with robots, genetic engineering, secret submarine bases, action, adventure, but it's all couched in this story that's of a city between two wars and they know the second war is coming, and there's nothing they can do about it. So they are extraordinarily decadent, trying to get in as much sensory joy as possible before the next war destroys them.

Lloyd Kahn
Editor-in-Chief of Shelter Publications

Lloyd Kahn is Editor-in-Chief of Shelter Publications, and is the former Shelter editor of the Whole Earth Catalog. He is also an author, photographer, and pioneer of the green building and green architecture movements. He has spent much of his life researching the best possible tools and products for any purpose. (Published 07/30/14)

Olympus OMD E-M1 Mirrorless Camera

This camera got me to put away my Canon cameras which weighed five pounds. This one is just so much smaller and it's one of the mirror-less cameras. It's a magnesium body. The mirrorless part is what, I think, saves on the weight. When you look at it, if you're a Canon or a Nikon guy, it's going to look just like a miniature of one of those cameras. The most immediate thing about it for me is that it's small enough so that when I, say, walk around the streets of Manhattan, where previously I would have my little pocket camera in a fanny pack, but now I carry this camera and a telephoto lens and a 50mm lens with me at all times, and it just gives me the ability to have a real camera. Not that my pocket camera isn't a good one, but this is a revolutionary camera.

Fourth Gear Flyer Surf Mat

This is inflatable. So instead of lugging this surfboard around and worrying about getting it smashed up on the airplane or paying a hundred bucks to have it shipped, you just fold up this surf mat in your backpack, and when you get there blow it up and go surfing. They are faster than anything else out there. Faster than surf boards, faster than boogie boards or kneeboards. I'm not sure what it is, but if you look on YouTube for pictures of people riding these things, they're just going across the wave really rapidly.

DaFINS

I have fins called DaFINS that are made in Hawaii. They're smaller than the normal fins you see and more flexible and they're touted as being preferred by world-class body surfers.

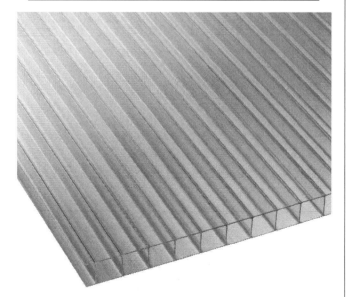

10mm Clear TwinWall Polycarbonate

This is expensive, but it's double-walled so you get some insulation and it's clear like glass. It has a

ten-year guarantee and I bought 4x12 sheets. We tore off the fiberglass on the greenhouse and put that on so everything in the greenhouse is much happier now. The plants that were leggy under the failing fiberglass now are almost as happy as they would be in full sun. Plus, we have the added feature of that it's insulated at night, so we close up the greenhouse at night and the plants that like warmth like it. I've washed it once since we installed it. I just take a soft brush and a hose and wash the dust off the roof.

Makita 18-Volt Lithium-Ion Cordless Variable Speed Impact Wrench

I didn't really know what the impact driver was before this. This weighs less than the typical drill that you see. There are really no controls on it other than a trigger. You can't set it for different speeds or different torque. What it does is it backs up a little bit. Each time it goes forward it goes back a little bit, so it kind of chatters. It's just really great for grabbers and screws. It just kind of goes "tuk-tuk-tuk-tuk-tuk" like that, and it's just a big improvement over the type of drill drivers that I was using for years.

Lillian Karabaic
Host of Oh My Dollar!

Lillian Karabaic is the host of Oh My Dollar!, a weekly syndicated financial advice radio show and podcast for covering the kinds of modern money issues that aren't represented in the mainstream media. Her book, A Cat's Guide to Money, just went into its second printing. She eats three tacos for breakfast every morning.
(Published 08/16/19)

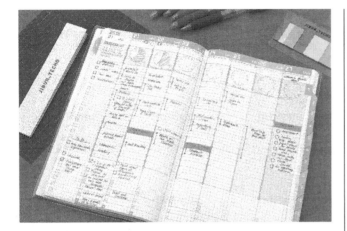

Kokuyo Jibun Techo 3-in-1 Planner

I'm one of those people that, even though I use a lot of digital tools, I still really need a paper planner. And the reason I need a paper planner is that there's infinite space on my digital to-do lists and I will overextend myself. So I have to have a paper planner so that I can actually see if I'm over-committing myself to a number of tasks in a day or a week. I absolutely love this planner. It's a paper planner, I picked it up in Japan. I get really excited every time I pull it out. I track a ton of data about myself and I use a lot of apps to do that. But if you want to do all of that in a planner, you can do it with this. It's extremely Japanese in how both efficient it is at like cramming a bunch of stuff into one space, but also how extra it is in what it thinks is a necessary thing to have in a planner. Like it has little icons everyday where you color in what the weather is and write down what you ate for each meal and who you ate with and how your mood was and a little tiny bit of journaling. But what I also love about it is the

24-hour timeline. My ritual with my planner is that I don't put my appointments out months in advance on my planner. I use it as my Sunday ritual where I take everything from my massive to-do lists and my Google calendar, and then I transfer it all to my week view. And that is kind of my way of assessing, "Oh, you said that you were going to do these seven things this week." But realistically once you start putting it down on paper you realize you can't.

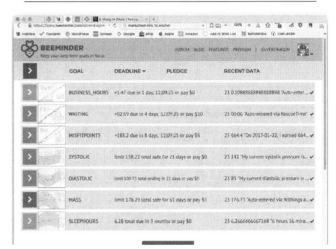

Beeminder

Beeminder is kind of amazing. I charge myself money for things that I am supposed to do. The tagline is it's "reminders with a sting," but essentially you can set it up to track anything you want and they have literally hundreds of integrations, but you can also use it for manual things. Say you want to average seven hours of sleep a night. If you have something like a Fitbit, you can just hook up that data source and as long as you're averaging seven hours of sleep a night, you will never pay anything. But if you start to go off track, you will pay them money. A lot of people use it for writing. A lot of people have used it to finish their PhDs or for working out. I have to run a certain amount of miles per week. And It's great because I'll wake up and I'll check Beeminder, and Beeminder says, "You're going to get charged $5 if you don't run half a mile today." Well, half a mile is not that much, but I know that if I run two miles, that means I don't have to run it all for four days. Obviously I'm trained as an economist, so I love the behavioral economics behind it because I hate paying anyone money.

YNAB

So You Need a Budget or YNAB, as most of the super fans call it, is the budgeting software I've used for six years now and I cannot recommend it highly enough. I think it's probably one of the most hands-on budgeting apps, but I think it's one of the best ones for actually making you engage with your money. YNAB completely changed my life and I was already pretty good with money. What I love about it is that I am able to enter transactions on the go. It automatically remembers where I'm at with geolocation and assigns the categories. It even remembers the payment method. It is the only thing I have found that makes me track cash. It was instrumental in me saving half of my income on a nonprofit salary, and being able to save up and start my own business.

Spot Trace GPS

Spot Trace GPS is a GPS beacon, so it isn't a thing that you use to navigate. It's just a thing that shows your location. And it's about the size of a small iPhone. If it can

see the sky, it reports every four minutes where your location is. It's really, really helpful because you can just broadcast that. You can give people access to a link where they can see you. I have used this as a beacon to update my website with my location while on a 13-country train/ferry trip from Ireland to Shanghai, China. It's phenomenal. The reason I use this one is it's one of the smallest and it has the longest battery life, and it runs on regular batteries. No matter where I'm in the world, I want to be able to buy the batteries. I don't want it to have a proprietary battery. And so this one is great because it runs on four AAA batteries, and I just get the long-lasting ones. It lasts for two or three weeks. And it is continuously broadcasting.

A Cat's Guide to Money: Everything You Need to Know to Get Control of your Purrsonal Finances

This book is just cats explaining personal finance. So there's lots of puns and there are illustrated cats to explain everything from investing to budgeting. My cat uses her toys to explain investing allocations in her basket. So it's meant to be something that makes the terrifying part of personal finance really approachable

with adorable fuzzy kittens. But it doesn't dumb it down. It just makes it something that is less terrifying. All the cats in the book were illustrated by Fiona Wu, who only illustrates cats. And all the cats in the book belong to people who backed the book's first Kickstarter. There's even an index of the cats in the back. So if you want to go look up the cats and their favorite activities, you can find out what page they're on.

Guy Kawasaki
Chief Evangelist of Canva

Guy Kawasaki is the chief evangelist of Canva, an online graphic design tool. He is also a brand ambassador for Mercedes-Benz, and an executive fellow of the Haas School of Business. He was the chief evangelist of Apple and a trustee of the Wikimedia Foundation. (Published 05/3/19)

MEATER

Meater is just a slick little tool if you're into barbecue. It is a bluetooth thermometer that you stick into your chicken, turkey, beef, whatever it is, and it pairs with your phone, and then it tells you the outside temperature, the ambient temperature, i.e. in the grill. It tells you the inside temperature of whatever meat you've stuck it into. You tell it what kind of meat it is. For example, for chicken, you want 160 degrees, and steak, you want 145 for rare, et cetera, et cetera. Then it starts giving you real-time feedback about what the temperature is of the meat, and then about three minutes before it's going to hit the desired temperature, it tells you to start getting ready to take it out. It can even ping you on your phone to say, go back to your barbecue and take the meat out, and it's flawless. You charge it in this little bamboo container that has a AAA battery, so there's no cables.

MacBook Pro (Retina, 13-inch, Early Technical Specifications

Configure your own old MacBook

I own a 2018 MacBook Air, a 2018 MacBook Pro, and between those two computers, there's a total of six ports. Four USB-C in the Pro, two in the MacBook Air. So that just drives me crazy. One day, on a total whim, I take a picture of my 2012 MacBook Pro, and I say, "Remember the good old days when you had two USB ports, your SD card reader, HDMI, headphone out, all that?" And lots of people commented that, yeah, I'm still using a 2012, '13, '14, '15 MacBook Pro, and I wouldn't switch. And I said, how can this be, that people are using four-, five-, six-year-old computers? Then I'm on an airplane, and I read an article about this company that takes old Datsun 240Zs, and guts them, changes the engine, just soups them up, and how happy people are with this. And I thought, why don't I do that? I have a friend at Mac Sales/OWC named Larry O'Connor, and I say, "Larry, am I crazy? Can you actually do this?" And he said, "Yeah, no problem!"

So I said, "Get me the latest MacBook Pro that has all the ports, and put in 16 gigabytes of RAM, and whatever SSD you can." So now I am so happy with a MacBook Pro that's four years old. I can see when it's charging or not, and I don't have to carry any dongles or docks or anything, and I never would've thought I'd be happy. I call this Mac to the Future. I would recommend people go to Mac Sales and go configure one.

Anker PowerWave Fast Wireless Charger Stand

There are a lot of wireless chargers that lay flat. But in my experience, you're never quite sure if you hit the right spot, so you have to wait for the phone to wake up to confirm, and you can't really use the phone while it's charging, because it's laying flat. The beauty of this Anker product is that it's at a 60-degree angle or whatever it is, and also, it doesn't matter if you put it on this charger portrait or landscape. So you have a portrait or landscape phone charging wirelessly, and let's just say that if you keep this by your bedside, it's much easier to just reach over and put it in a stand than plugging in the cable. And it's even easier than putting it on a flat charger and hoping you hit the right spot.

Peak Design Everyday Backpack

I love to buy bags, all right? I have everything. But Peak Design has built this beautiful bag that has a great sleeve for your MacBook Pro and an iPad. The sides open up so that you can take your DSLR in and

out very easy. Not from the top, but from the side. Then the inside has that kind of material that you can put shelves and padding with Velcro, because it's really for photographers to put DSLRs and their extra lenses. It's just a beautiful backpack/camera bag. There's two sizes. One more like a backpack, like a student backpack. One more like a day pack. Then there's also the messenger style, over-the-shoulder style.

Wise Guy: Lessons from a Life

The book is called Wise Guy, and it is not an autobiography or a memoir in the sense of, look at me, I'm so great. This is a collection of stories that shaped my life that I believe each contain a nugget or nuggets of wisdom that I'd like to pass along. So if you are familiar with Chicken Soup for the Soul, it's kind of like Chicken Soup for the Soul, except they're all my stories. Basically, think of it as miso soup for the soul.

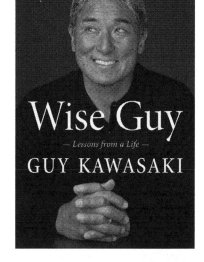

145

Jeremy Kirshbaum
Research Affiliate at IFTF

Jeremy Kirshbaum is a researcher, strategist, and entrepreneur. He splits his time between West Africa, China, and California, where he is from, partnering with people to build new things, innovate, and explore. He does this through action research, design, and a variety of creative media. He is a proud research affiliate at Institute for the Future, a research affiliate of the Shenzhen Open Innovation Lab, and a research fellow at the Johns Hopkins Immersive Storytelling and Immersive Media Lab, and works with large organizations of all kinds to innovate more effectively and imaginatively. (Published 08/9/19)

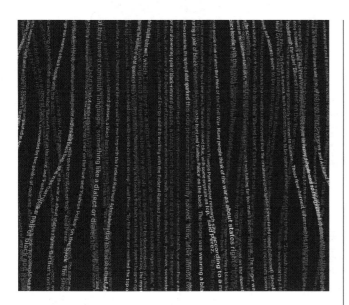

GPT-2

GPT-2, which is sometimes called transformer, is a AI algorithm that was released by OpenAI. It very realistically mimics human language in a very natural way based on a prompt. I've been trying to use it as a front end to research projects because it basically is predicting the next most likely word in a sentence. It's a little bit like what you and me do when we're listening to each other, actually. If I'm talking to you, your brain is trying to guess the next thing that I'm going to say and make meaning out of it. You can download it on GitHub, and the link is on the OpenAI website. I downloaded it. The install instructions are really simple to use. It's pre-trained. You don't have to do that work. There's a file in there called developer.md. You open that up, and you follow the instructions. And you're off and

running. You don't really have to do much in terms of designing or anything like that. And you then put in whatever kind of prompt you want. I've found that longer prompts produce higher-quality stuff than shorter prompts, and the things it produces are very uneven in the sense that you might have to try two or three or five times before you get something really interesting. I have been using it at the front end of research projects to help with a kind of hybrid brainstorming and researching. What it will actually be used for is clogging the internet with maliciously intended fake information and gibberish until we choke on it, but I am trying to find something useful for it besides that.

Universal Copy (Google Play App)

I travel to a lot of out-of-the-way places for my work that don't have English-langauge services even on the internet, and this is a completely indispensable part of my life. It is an app/widget thing that you install on your phone, and it allows you to select and copy any text on the screen, even clickable buttons within apps. So when I am in China and desperately need to order a pizza and 20 fidget spinners to my

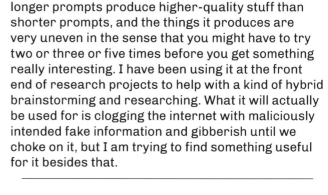

apartment at 3am, I can navigate Eleme and Taobao using this thing combined with Google or Microsoft translate. I copy the Chinese characters into Google Translate and then look at what the English says. And then type in the English answer and translate it back into Chinese and then put it back into the section.

Token Factory (Jeremy's how-to article)

This is a great little tool for instantly creating your own cryptocurrency. It takes about 15 minutes and zero computer coding. It's all UI based, and it does cost about 10 or 15 bucks to deploy the contract onto Ethereum, but it's cheaper than all of your other automated cryptocurrency creators. And what I mean by deploy a contract is basically publicly listing this line set of code that says, "This is a token. There's these many tokens in this token set, and there can never be more or less, and they move around according to these rules." The rules on Token Factory make it automatically compatible with certain Ethereum wallets. You then use Ethereum token to help you move it around. The token is permanent and immutable and relatively indestructible once you create it, but it's useless until you invent something to do with it. I, for instance, created Jeremy Coin, which is my personal currency. It is pegged to 50,000 Jeremy Coin to four hours of my time, so whatever that's worth to you. And you can only mine Jeremy Coin by knowing me personally. So the more that I trust you, the more Jeremy Coin you get. And then you could either spend it hiring me to do things, or if you know other people in my network who also value my time, you could just trade with them directly. I would call Jeremy Coin somewhere between a real project and a performance art piece about creating trusted networks or networks that enhance trust instead of trustless networks which I think are a terrible idea.

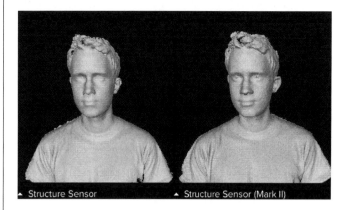

▲ Structure Sensor   ▲ Structure Sensor (Mark II)

Occipital Structure Sensor

I make a lot of virtual reality stories and art for fun, love and profit, and the Occipital Structure Sensor is really core to that. It is a 3D scanner that attaches to an iPad. It takes pretty high-quality scans if you do it right, but what I love is the artistic way it is imprecise. This interaction of fictional and reality-derived assets is my favorite tension in virtual art right now. You can also put it in robots if you're into that, but for me its an artistic tool. For instance, I made an experience about an area of Shenzhen, the city that I'm now in, called Dafen Oil Painting Village, which is this kind of beautiful section of this city where they make about 50% of the commercial art in the world. But it's outside. It's beautiful. There's kids running around. There's cafes, and they're mass producing incredible amounts of art, so there's just piles of art everywhere. And so in China they don't mind if you awkwardly stand behind them and scan them for eight years while they're painting. And there's a trade off with the scanner. Things that move it doesn't do well with at all. So if something is still, the longer you do it, the better, the clearer it gets. If something is moving, the longer you do it the less clear it gets. And they come out looking really painterly and ghostly. And I think it's really evocative. I actually think that the imprecision of the tool to me is as important as the precision. Because in art as opposed to science, no one's sitting around like, "Oh, I'll get into clay when it's more efficient and easier to use." The point of art is much different than the point of science. And the fact that things are hard or are imprecise is as much an asset as a challenge. And so I think that you can hook it up to robots or put it in your self-driving whatever. And I think it is actually meant more for those kind of applications. But I think it's also perfect for my use as making terrible immersive art that no one looks at.

Erik Knutzen
Author and Podcaster

Erik Knutzen is co-author of Urban Homestead:Your Guide to Self-Sufficient Living in the Heart of the City and Making It: Radical Home Ec for a Post-Consumer World. Check out Erik's Root Simple website and podcast RootSimple for more on how to build yourself a sustainable DIY lifestyle. (Published 02/11/15)

KoMo FlicFloc

For a long time I was a Grapenuts addict. It's like crack to me. And it's terrible! It's just like a low-quality carb with a vitamin pill thrown in to it. I had thought about this grain flaker by this amazing German company for a long time, and I finally threw down the money and got it about a month ago. What this allows you to do is you throw basically raw oat seeds into it, you turn a handle — it's manual — and you get flaked oats which then I've been using mostly for muesli, and it's totally changed my breakfast life. It's easy to use and delicious and very, very nutritious.

KoMo Fidibus Classic

This mill is dove-tailed solid wood on the outside. It has two stone mills inside of it and a very powerful electric motor. I'm a real avid whole-grain baker. Just like rolling your own oats, you can keep the grains on hand and mill them as you need them to make bread. What this does is it opens up a whole world of grain. When you have your own mill, you can choose the grain, the variety of wheat that you want to mill, and what I think a lot of people don't realize is that there's a huge biodiversity in wheat and rye and other grains, and when you have your own mill you can select different grains to work with. I've been working a lot lately with one called Joaquin Oro which, in addition to having this delicious, nutty flavor, has this kind of beautiful golden texture when baked with it. This mill has allowed me to work with that and other things, like Sonora wheat is another one that I had no idea about. It was a grain that the Spanish brought hundreds of years ago and Native Americans kept alive for hundreds of years. It has another whole different flavor profile. Texture, color, all kinds of things. It's really interesting what having your own mill allows you to do.

want to use has just totally changed my life actually. It made breakfast exciting every morning.

Xtracycle Electric Cargo Bike

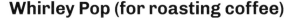

This is sometimes called a long-tail bike. It's like having pannier sacks on steroids or kind of like having a bike for two that instead of the second person it's all cargo. Unlike a lot of cargo bikes, the European-style that are kind of big and broad, this one is narrow so you can squeeze through traffic in L.A. on it, gracefully. I can easily put four bags of groceries on that thing.

Whirley Pop (for roasting coffee)

With the Whirley Pop all you do is put it on the stove top and one of the tricks is getting the heat right. There's some amount of trial and error in that. Throw a half pound of green coffee beans in there, turn it, and in about nine, 10 minutes, you've got roasted coffee beans. It's just that simple.

Sweet Maria's Coffee Beans

Even with the mail order charges from Sweet Maria's, I'm basically getting $20-a-pound coffee for $10 a pound. Again, being able to select the green beans that I

Ben Krasnow
Maker and YouTube Star

Ben Krasnow works at Google[x], Google's semi-secret technology development facility, where he creates advanced prototypes. Ben previously developed virtual reality hardware at Valve. After work, he spends time on various projects that usually involve circuit design, machining, and chemistry. You can follow Ben's projects on his YouTube channel, Applied Science. (Published 06/29/15)

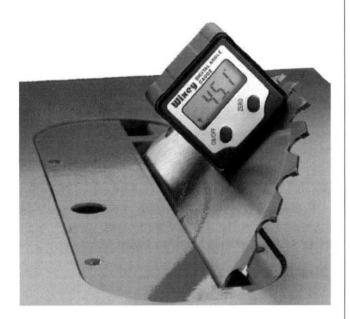

Digital Inclinometer

This is a small box about the size of a pack of gum, maybe, or a little bit bigger. It has a magnetic base on the bottom of it and a digital readout. What you do is you stick it down with the magnets to something, like a table saw, and zero it. Then, you pick it up and stick it onto the side of the saw blade and it will tell you the angle between those two surfaces.

Fiberglass Scratch Brush

This is the size of a large ballpoint pen. Instead of a pen coming out the end, it has about a quarter-inch

diameter cluster-like bundle of fiberglass fibers. The glass fibers are very abrasive. What you do is you push the brush down onto something that you want to clean and swirl it around. The tips of the glass fibers actually scratch away at the surface of the thing that you want to clean. The glass is really hard, so it will clean metal parts. It will erode away plastic parts if you brush them long enough. Then, as you use it, the glass bristles break off and expose fresh, sharp fibers.

AmScope Stereo Microscope

This microscope is used a lot by electronics folks. If you have one sitting on your desk that you use for surface-mount electronics part assembly, you will start using it for, basically, everything

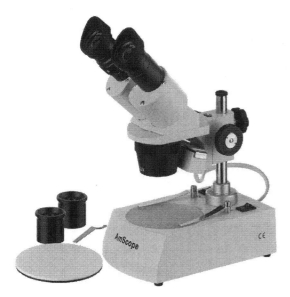

else. Then you realize that it's just completely indispensable and you really can't set up a desk without one.

Nitto Tape

This is a craft paper tape with an acrylic adhesive on both sides and it's extremely strong.

Devcon Plastic Welder

There are other brands that sell plastic welder, but it's actually not the same stuff as Devcon. You've got to get the actual Devcon stuff. It's basically a two-part adhesive. It looks like epoxy. It comes in one of those twin syringe packs, but it's actually not an epoxy. I believe it's an acrylic glue. It smells really strong, so you know it's going to be really good.

Kapton Tape

Kapton is a really good electrical insulator. If you want to stick something down to your circuit board, Kapton Tape is really good because it keeps your circuit isolated, and if it's double stick, then you can put a little bit of Kapton down on the board and then stick something to that and still have pretty good electrical isolation.

Liz Kruger and Craig Shapiro
Executive Producers of Salvation

Liz Kruger and Craig Shapiro have been married for 26 years, writing together for 20. Most recently, they were the executive producers and showrunners of the CBS sci-fi thriller Salvation. Together they've written and/or produced dozens of projects, including the sci-fi thriller Extant starring Halle Berry, Necessary Roughness on USA network, and Girlfriends Guide to Divorce on Bravo. (Published 03/29/19)

Artemis Pro

For the first time, I just directed an episode of television. I was terrified, and someone turned me on to this app — it's a director's view finder for smart phones. You've probably seen this, where cinematographers will hold one of those little view finders to their eye, or directors will wear those around their necks, and they walk around looking through it, and adjusting the lenses to line up a shot. What this app allows you to do is you can input into your phone whatever camera your DP's gonna use — all the lenses that he has in his camera that are available to him when he lines up shots — you can have those lenses input through this Artemis app. And when you go to your scouting location, you've got all the lenses on your phone, and you can line up shots, you can see different lenses, and you can be prepared much better on the day that you show up, as opposed to having to use other peoples' view finders, you can actually take photos of a location, you can make videos of the location. This really gives you so much information about what you're looking at. It gives you so many different ideas, and it really educated me on what different lenses look like.

Dry Erase Magnetic Strips

The charm of these is, because it's dry erase, it can be written and rewritten over many, many times. But also because they're magnetic, they can be put up on this special magnetic board, and quickly moved, rearranged, erased, and rewritten. Because when we're breaking stories for shows, the whole idea is to keep it as loose and as in the flow as possible, and you don't want to have to stop every single time an idea is changed or an idea is moved, and rewrite the whole card, or unpin it and move it. And this gives you a flexibility that within the writers' room, everything flows so much easier and faster.

A Guided Sleep Meditation by The Honest Guys

So how many people out there have trouble falling asleep at night? I know I do, and I searched far and wide for something that would knock me out, other than just a club to the head or sleeping pills. I'm not into that kind of stuff, so I found I was just listening to various things on the internet, and I found these guys, they call themselves The Honest Guys, which of course makes me very suspect. However, they had these guided sleep meditations. And the first time I listened to one, I fell asleep before I even got through minute three. And I thought, this is crazy miracle. But the voice on it is very quiet, I think it's a little British; it's really hard to define the accent, but what I am most concerned about, and I can't be sure, is it might be turning me into the Manchurian candidate, because I never get to the end of this. So I don't know what they're actually telling me while I'm asleep. But it's 30 minutes, and I am definitely asleep by minute three or four. It's pretty amazing. But I did one time try to stay up to the end just to hear what they were saying at the end, and if any political assassinations occur, and I'm somewhere in the vicinity, I am going to be a little concerned, but for now it seems to just be knocking me out cold.

DreamStation CPAP with Humidifier

This changed my life. This is the coolest tool out there, even though it is about as unsexy as a tool can get. I actually couldn't breathe. And also, several times, I also realized that I was so tired all the time. So I went to the sleep clinic, they show me my EEG and all my work, and they go, well look at this, the first four hours you are sleeping, you have zero REM sleep. Zero. That's bad. The doctor said to me, after I did the testing, he said, "You wear the CPAP machine, you will feel different tomorrow morning." And I said, "How can that be?" He said, "One day, it's gonna make all the difference." And he was so right. I obviously was waking up dozens of times in the night. I wasn't getting enough oxygen, and not only

do you feel tired, but it really negatively impacts your cognitive abilities, and so anyway, one day later, not only does it stop the snoring completely, it has a kind of a quiet little hum about it that I actually kind of like, it helps me sleep. But most importantly, I don't wake up anymore in the night, and I'm never tired anymore. It really, really did change my life.

Derri-Air Bicycle Seats

I had an exercise bike at home, which when I bought it, had this big, cushiony seat, and I thought, "Oh, isn't that amazing, it's so comfortable." Only to realize, it's enormous, it's meant for someone who's probably 7 foot 6 and weighs 800 pounds. And so when I would ride on it, not only was it uncomfortable, but my butt would go numb. And so, I got on this website for comfortable seats and they delivered exactly what they said they were going to deliver. Craig figured out how to put it on to the bike, and it really has been a life changer. I couldn't ride the bike before, and now, no more butt numbness.

Tod E. Kurt
Co-founder of ThingM

Tod E. Kurt runs ThingM, an IoT device studio in Pasadena. He is creator of the blink(1) USB notification light and BlinkM Smart LED. He co-founded CRASH Space, a Los Angeles hackerspace. He is the author of "Hacking Roomba" and long ago worked on cameras for Mars probes. (Published 05/31/18)

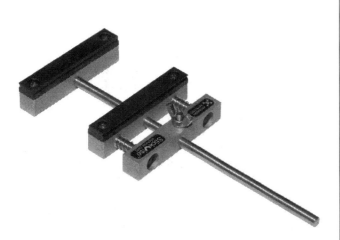

Stickvise PCB Vise with Standard Nylon Jaws

The main difference between this vise and other vises you might use to hold your work is that it maintains your work parallel to your desktop. And that's the other thing: it isn't attached to a surface. It just kind of sits on your desk. It's very small, and it's made for doing electronics work. But I've seen people use it for things like jewelry and other sort of small work where you're kind of on a desk and you need to have something that's held flat. And the reason why you need it to be held flat for electronics is because you don't want the parts to slide off as you're soldering them down. If you're doing surface mount work, this is for things that are just kind of sitting on top and then you have to solder them down.

Viltrox Super Slim LED Light Pane

Anyone who has a work bench has had to try to solve the problem of how do you light up the space you're working in. And for me I've tried fluorescent light tubes. I've tried an LED strip that I then stuck to a base. But they've all been a little fiddly, and it becomes hard to either adjust the brightness or adjust the color temperature. A lot of lights now you can change if you want them to be a noon, like a bluish-white that you'd see during noonday, or a more orangey-yellow white, like one you'd see during the evening. And now there's all these lights, all these LED-based lights out there, where you can have a knob to tune the color temperature. And this LED light panel is about maybe six inches on a side, and it's normally meant to be mounted on top of a camera for photography people to take pictures and to light their subject, but I found you can just mount it above your bench and it becomes a great task light.

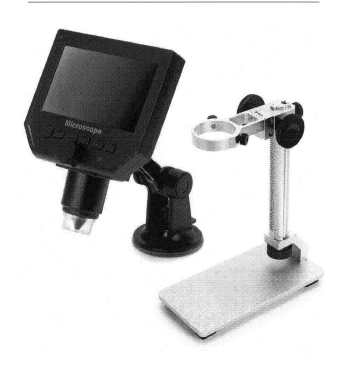

Koolertron LCD Digital USB Microscope Magnifier

I stumbled across this little microscope, and it's perfect because it's super portable. I can just kind of drag it around wherever I need it, and I'll stick circuit boards that I'm looking at to see how the manufacturing of them went. When I'm soldering stuff, sometimes I'll stick the circuit board I'm working on underneath it to see it. And because it is fully self-contained — it's a digital device, digital microscope, but it's got a screen built in— I don't need a computer or have to look up at a computer all the time. I can just look at the microscope. And so it's just brilliant.

Asus Chromebox2

Everyone's probably heard of Chromebooks. They're the little notebooks that run only the Chrome browser. This is exactly that, but it looks kind of like a Mac mini. So you have to bring your own keyboard and mouse and screen to the game, but it's a lot cheaper. And so you plug in your mouse, keyboard — or what I do, I've got a little combo

mouse-keyboard thingy — and an old display, and suddenly you've got a working computer that's on the net. You can just log in with your Google account, and you've got a Chrome browser that just is on the net. You can watch YouTube. You can look at documentation. That's what I use it for. I have the schematics that I'm working against or maybe some educational videos that I'm following along with. I have that next to me. And because it's this little, tiny, cheap computer, I don't care if it gets a little dirty from being in the workshop.

blink(1)

It's a non-obtrusive notification light. You can hook it up to events on the Net you care about like "new mail", "server down", or "it's going to rain," and it will notify you by blinking.

David Lang
Co-founder of OpenROV

David Lang is an entrepreneur, writer, and National Geographic Fellow. In 2012, along with Eric Stackpole, he co-founded OpenROV to create a low-cost robot to explore an underwater cave. Since then, OpenROV has raised over $900,000 on Kickstarter and become one of the largest underwater drone manufacturers. The team also created OpenExplorer as a digital field journal to empower and connect citizen scientists and explorers. Lang is the author of Zero to Maker — part memoir and part guidebook for participating in the growing maker movement. (Published 11/3/17)

Garmin Inreach Explorer+

This is a satellite hand-held GPS navigator. So what it does is you can be anywhere in the world, totally off the grid, and it's going to bring up a map and show you exactly where you are. It communicates using the Iridium satellite network, but it also serves as a two-way communicator. So you can text anybody from anywhere in the world no matter where you're at. It's pretty amazing and it comes in handy in surprising scenarios, and my experience over the past five years as we've kind of gone on these expeditions with these underwater drones is that connection is just absolutely necessary. And I think there's been a lot of press and stories around trying to shut off your phones and get outside, but I think the reality of the world we live in is connection is absolutely vital and this device is fairly cheap. It's a couple hundred bucks and then you have a monthly payment plan. But it keeps you connected, whether that's through an emergency or you're going off the grid or whatever comes up.

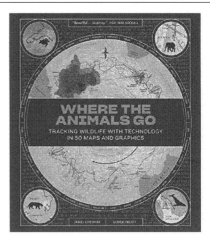

Where the Animals Go

This is one of those things that you want to hold and look at. It is a collection of 50 stories and it's put together by a cartographic designer and an ex-National Geographic writer and they go around the world and tell the stories of scientists who are tracking animals using all sorts of different technologies that have kind of just become popular. And the book, aside from being beautiful, is actually pretty interesting. It uses all the latest technologies, and each story kind of follows a different animal. It's like where a pack of baboons are going. How the mountain lions are traversing through California.

How the humpbacks are going around seamounts, and it starts to talk about birding and just the different things that have happened in ornithology over the past half-century. It's no longer just people with telescopes. These birders are out there, wired up, and they're measuring the flora and fauna on this planet in an incredible way. It's also really inspiring and I think there's a lot of things, especially towards the end, that will inspire you to kind of go out and want to start kind of tracking and following individual creatures wherever you are.

Who you are
You'll need to make an **iNaturalist account** and please only post your own personal observations

Where you saw it
Record both the coordinates of the encounter as well as their accuracy. You can obscure the location from the public

What you saw
Choose a group of organisms like **butterflies** or better yet a specific organism like the **Monarch butterfly**. If you provide evidence you can leave this blank and the **community can help**

When you saw it
Record the date of your encounter, not the date you post it to iNaturalist

Evidence of what you saw
By including evidence like a **photo or sound**, the community can help add, improve, or confirm the identification of the organism you encountered. Help the community by taking clear well framed photos, by including multiple photos from different angles

iNaturalist

Pretty simply, this is just a camera app and you go out and you can snap photos of birds or bugs or plants or whatever, and you can upload it to iNaturalist. And it's been around for probably almost a decade at this point. It's now at The Cal Academy of Sciences and there's an incredible team there. And for the past 10 years what it has been is you go out, and you make an observation. You snap a photo and you say, "This is a butterfly." Or, "This is a fiery skipper." Or, "This is a cabbage white." You could identify the actual species and if you didn't know what it was you could say, "I don't know." And the iNaturalist community would come in and there's these naturalists all over the world who kind of sit and monitor and go in and say, "Oh, actually that is a nodding trillium." Or, "That's just a common land snail." So there are these people who will go in and kind of either correct you or help you with your identification. And for the past few years that's what this tool has been, but just in the past six months what's been really amazing is this tool has evolved. So they have so much data. They have so many photos and identifying metadata information about these animals that they started applying some of these machine learning techniques to these photos. So what iNaturalist is now, is you can go outside and you can snap a photo of some creature that's in your backyard, or some plant, and the iNaturalist app will

actually generate a suggestion based on all of this A.I. and it's remarkably good.

Trident Underwater Drone

This is the newest kind of product from our company, OpenROV. We're starting to ship the first beta units right now, and we'll have those shipped hopefully by the end of January. We gotta get through the entire backlog. But we've spent the past two-and-a-half years working on not just a DIY kit of an underwater robot, but an actual product. And the reason I brought it up is because it is actually a really cool and fun tool, and I can't wait for the world to try it out and to start to send back videos and stories. But also for me personally, it's been an incredible learning experience. To go from the Zero to Maker thing not knowing anything and now to building and shipping products, actual hardware products, all over the world. It's like a thick laptop. It's a swimming camera that you can control from the surface, and you have to use your phone to see what it sees, and you can drive it around and control it from there. It can dive to pretty deep depths, a 100 meters, so 328 feet. And most divers aren't going more than 60 feet, 100 feet, so you're actually getting into territory that most divers don't go to. I live in Sausalito, and one of the things that is happening in and around the San Francisco Bay right now is all of these leopard sharks are starting to die off. And there have been, I think, over a thousand deaths of these leopard sharks in the Bay in just the past few months, and they think this is a brain parasite, but they don't really know. They also don't know how many sharks have died because they're negatively buoyant. So when they die, they sink to the bottom. So what I've started doing is going out on my little kayak and sending the robot down and trying to get video of the seafloor, trying to collect data. I'm gonna submit that to iNaturalist. It's kind of the full circle of all these different tools I've shared.

Rick Lax
Magician

Rick Lax created the TV show "Wizard Wars" and has written several books on deception. He's a non-practicing lawyer, a former MENSA member, and now spends his time creating tricks for other magicians and for Penguin Magic, the biggest magic retailer in the world. (Published 04/18/16)

Facebook (as a marketing tool)

I became a mayor of Facebook overnight and I'm still trying to process exactly how it happened. I've treated Facebook marketing like an experiment. If you Google, "How to make a good Facebook video? How to make a viral video?" 12 different people are going to tell you 12 different things, so I just put enough videos up where I can experiment and I can see for myself what's working and what's not working. I see what days are they posted, what time are they posted, and that has not been a factor in the video's success. Which in itself was a surprise because everyone ask, "When is the right time to post on social media?" This is a big thing that everyone talks about, and what I have found personally is it doesn't matter at all. Here's my

guess. Whatever the Facebook algorithms are, "EdgeRank" I think it's called, is figuring out if you have a good post or a bad post. If Facebook figures out that you have a good post, because it's getting a lot of likes, comments or shares, then it sends it out to a lot of people. If it gets a lot of activity from the people who liked my page, then Facebook sends it out to the rest. It seems like if I post Sunday at 3 am when presumably not a lot of people are online, it's still going to send it out to the same 5% of people who like my page. It will just spread it out over a greater period of time, so I just don't think that the time you post is a factor, and that's something I had to learn on my own.

Webcam

I've performed magic for more people than anyone else in the world the past 3 or 4 months because

of webcams. I get bothered by people who attack "webcam magic" or "webcam magicians." I think this is a valid, great new form of sharing magic. Everyone says everything is fake. It's frustrating because I'm not actually doing camera tricks. I'm accomplishing this with sleight of hand, but I can't tell people how I'm doing it. I want to be like, "No, it's not fake. I usually put it in this hand," but you can't say to them how to do the trick, so I'm just left with telling people, "No." It's true that some people who perform on their webcam cannot perform live. They don't have good rapport, but that doesn't mean that this is an invalid medium for sharing the art form. This is an incredible medium.

Bicycle Standard Index Playing Cards

So much of magic is card magic, and what I've been doing with my channel and with sharing my magic is figuring out ways to take the principles behind card tricks and apply them to things that aren't cards. I had one video a couple weeks ago that it got 10 million views, where it was this old card trick from Jim Steinmeyer called "The 9-Card Card Trick." Other people have tried to do videos with it, which is great, and it's an interactive trick, which means the

person watching needs to have cards in their hands. What I figured out to do is instead of telling viewers "Go get 9 cards," I told people, "Go get a piece of paper and a pen. Draw a tic-tac-toe board. Draw a different symbol in each quadrant. Rip it up." Now, it's like everyone had 9 cards in their hand. I'll often use simple Bicycle Rider playing cards because I think people are less likely to think that it's a trick deck of cards.

Performing Under Pressure: The Science of Doing Your Best When It Matters Most

I liked the book because they had a ton of strategies for combating performance anxiety. About ten of them were good for me, so I would go through them in my head every day, and that, plus a couple shots of alcohol before I went on stage did the trick. This helped me out. I wrote the authors to thank them.

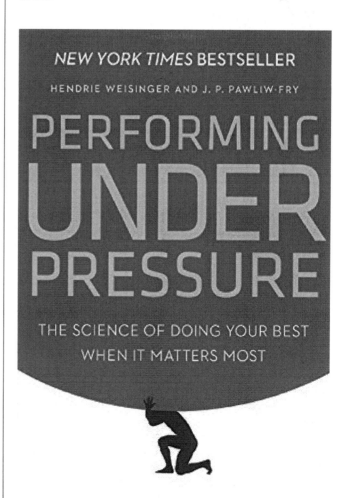

NEW YORK TIMES BESTSELLER

HENDRIE WEISINGER AND J. P. PAWLIW-FRY

PERFORMING UNDER PRESSURE

THE SCIENCE OF DOING YOUR BEST WHEN IT MATTERS MOST

Steven Leckart
Investigative Journalist

Steven Leckart is a writer, director, and investigative journalist. He has written a handful of documentaries, including SILICON COWBOYS, and has contributed to various magazines including Wired, Esquire, Men's Health, Maxim, and Popular Science. His most recent story is featured in the February issue of Chicago Magazine. Steven is also the co-author of Cabin Porn, a New York Times bestseller about hand-built architecture. (Published 02/1/19)

DEEP GROOVE TO SUPPORT SPINE

Wood Back Roller

I have a theracane, which is wonderful for self-massaging shoulders, as well as a trigger point foam roller for legs/hips. This roller is ideal for performing myofascial release along your entire back. It features two ridges that are intended to be situated on either side of your spine. You just lay on top of it and roll slowly, using your own body to control the pressure. My pilates instructor first turned me onto this, and now I do it every few days. It's 15-inches long, so I can travel with it. There are other versions, but this one features rubber rings on both ends, which prevents slippage and scratching hardwood floors.

Patagonia Black Hole Duffel

Since 2015, I've traveled around the globe with this 45-liter backpack/duffel for as long as 27 days at a time. Plenty of pockets. Comfy shoulder straps. Made from sturdy ripstop polyester. Water resistant. I've walked through downpours and my gear stayed dry. Small enough that I've never once had to check it on any size plane: Always fits under the seat if not the overhead bin. I chose all black, but there are brighter, bolder colors.

Contigo Autoseal Stainless Steel Travel Mug

Hot coffee that stays hot for a long time is a boon, especially while traveling, which is why I can't believe more folks don't pack a good vacuum-insulated mug. After four-plus years of abuse, my 16-ounce mug is dented and the paint is chipping, but it still keeps coffee hot for hours at a time. It's never leaked. It fits in most cup holders on planes, trains, buses, and rental cars. I chose black, but color options abound. Worth noting: Newer entries in this space are intriguing. Zojirushi's SM-SA mug reportedly offers superior heat retention, but it's also more expensive than my Contigo.

Trint

This automated transcription service uses AI to generate a rough transcript in a matter of minutes. The rough transcript populates an online page akin to a Google Doc with time code. You can click on any phrases that don't look correct, and

the audio will instantly play. If the text is wrong, you can amend it on the fly. The service is not super accurate throughout, but it's ridiculously fast and super cheap. Fifteen dollars for 60 minutes of audio, which is a fraction of what a professional human-based service will charge. I used to pay $60 for 60 minutes, which felt like a good deal. Also, if you hear yourself conducting interviews, you will improve. This requires you to listen but reduces the effort and time necessary to self-transcribe an entire file.

The Bicycle Thief

I've published a nearly 10,000-word narrative magazine feature in the February 2019 issue of Chicago Magazine about a serial bank robber who was once an Olympic-hopeful track cyclist. Over a four-year period, he robbed 26 banks in three states — and always used a bicycle as his escape vehicle.

Elan Lee
Co-creator of Exploding Kittens

Elan Lee is a professional game designer. He is a co-creator of Exploding Kittens, the most-backed crowdfunded project in history. And before that, he was Chief Design Officer for Microsoft's Xbox.
(Published 11/2/18)

Blank Playing Cards

I am a firm believer in that you just never know where the next great game idea is going to come from, but you can be pretty sure that if you don't at least record it and prototype it somehow, it's going to be gone forever. So these are literally just a deck of cards, blank on the front, blank on the back. I travel around with these things everywhere I go, and just a bunch of Sharpies. And the basic idea is, any rough idea I have — I used to take all this time to meticulously document them and outline it and figure out the rule sets — and what I figured out is it's so much easier and so much more effective to go straight to paper prototype. And this is the absolute best tool to do so. If you have a card game idea, jot

down a bunch of cards and quickly see if it works. If that game needs dice, figure out how many sides you want that die to have and pull out that many cards and start drawing numbers on the cards. They're great to create characters, they create inventory items. Literally any game competition imaginable can be created with these things. So I carry them around with me everywhere I go.

Don't Shoot the Dog

Don't Shoot the Dog isn't actually about dog training. It's about positive reinforcement, and the psychological aspects of shaping behaviors. And what it all really comes down to in game design is picking a core game mechanic that you want, and a way that you want those players to behave around that game mechanic, and just molding it, reinforcing it, and shaping it as much as you possibly can. I love this book. I recommend it to all new game designers, not to learn how to train dogs or horses or any of the other animals in there, but basically to learn how to model behavior and reinforce the kinds of things you want to see your players perform and make them feel great about interacting with you and those behaviors.

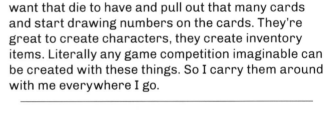

Cosco Retracting Box Cutter

In my workshop, I mostly deal with paper. I mostly am building paper prototypes all day, every day. And involved with that is a whole lot of cutting paper. And I was just making a mess. I was cutting my clothes and cutting my body with these stupid box cutters, because I'm not a very organized, careful person. This thing is so simple. It's just a handle, and when you squeeze the handle, a small blade comes out, allowing you to cut paper or cardboard or whatever it is that you need to cut, and when you let go of the handle, the blade retracts into the handle, making it a perfectly safe thing. So as I cut, and then stuff the thing in my pocket, suddenly I don't have to worry about tearing holes in my clothes or fingers or anything else. It's super light. It's all made of plastic. It's actually not the sturdiest of devices, not to say the one I have has ever broken. But it has needed some repairs from time to time. Because of the price point, every time I open a new workshop anywhere, I immediately buy about 10 of these things.

Retractable Charging Cable

This is a Lightning cable. It's actually also a mini USB cable. I travel a ton, and the problem I have with all cable organization is I'm just too lazy to adhere to it. The cases and the straps and all the things that I need to keep my cables organized, I end up abandoning. So this solves that problem for me. What it is is a small plastic case, maybe about the size of four quarters in a stack. And it has the

front and back ends of the cable poking out of it. You pull them, and suddenly, you have a two-foot-long, in this case, iPhone cable. Pull them again, and they're spring-loaded, so they retract back into the case. I travel around with four of these things, and whatever adapters I need, and then just a USB brick that plugs into the wall and has four ports. So when I set up in any hotel, I plug all of these things in. I can charge all of my devices overnight. And then the next day, when I need to pack up, I literally, one fist, grab everything out of the wall, yank on both ends, they all retract into a single, very neat pile. I drop those into a pocket in my backpack, and I'm done.

Aquanotes Waterpoof Notepad

This is one of my favorite things. This is a waterproof notepad. I don't know why it is, but all my good ideas show up in the shower. I'm sure there's all kinds of writing about why, but I don't know. All I know is, every day, I take a shower and that's where all my best ideas pop into my head. And for whatever weirdo reason, when I step out of the shower, like waking up after a really lucid dream, I've just forgotten everything. So my solution was, I found this great, super cheap waterproof notepad. It attaches to the wall or tiles of your shower via suction cup, and it ships with a totally standard No. 2 pencil that also attaches via suction cup. And it's waterproof. So the pages have a slight waxy coating to them that. They're hydrophobic, but the pencil markings work perfectly. So I jot down all my ideas in the shower.

Andrew Leonard
Writer

Andrew Leonard is a journalist who writes features for San Francisco magazine, Men's Journal, Rolling Stone and other outlets. He previously wrote for Salon.com between 1995 and 2014 where he covered technology, business, Internet culture, science fiction, and economics, among other topics. (Published 10/9/15)

that people have been doing for millennia. It's the perfect match of tool and activity.

Garmin Edge GPS Bike Computer

There's an intersection between geek and serious cyclist that has everything to do with the data. People want to know how many miles they've done, what their average mile per hour is, how many feet they've climbed, what the gradient is that they're currently going up, and I think the Garmin computer

Wok Chuan

I think the best way to describe it is as a weaponized spatula. It has little folded edges at the side, so it's not like a flat spatula. It has these edges that make it into a scoop. It is what happens when you spend three thousand years stir frying in a wok and you evolve the perfect tool for that activity. You hold the wok with one hand, and you hold this with the other and it just feels like you're doing something

really captures this. If you go to one of these Century rides in Northern California and look at people's bikes, you will see that ninety-five percent of them have some kind of bike computer hooked to the handlebars. The vast majority have Garmins.

The Way and Its Power: Lao Tzu's Tao Te Ching

This is the classic Taoist work supposedly written by a guy named Lao Tzu in maybe the fifth century BC. I have seven translations because that to me is in tune with that first line, "The way that can be spoken is not the true way." There's this post-modern aspect to the very first line that has always intrigued me as contradictory and amusing. Everybody comes up with different translations. Every time I dip in, there's a different way of hearing it.

Reporter's Notebook and Pilot Precise V5

There's just something about writing it down in hand and then crossing it out when it's done that encourages me to actually get it done. It's just a basic psychological thing. It seems like the old

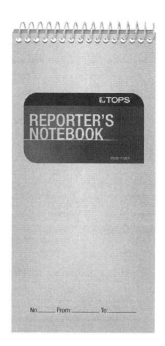

writing by hand on paper makes it more meaningful than a digital, virtual to-do list and it works for me. I use a classic reporter's notebook. It's called a reporter's notebook because it's perfect for going out and recording. I like the extra-fine rolling ball pens from Precise. I guess they're the V5 model. What are they called? They're pilots, so yeah. They're pilot pens. I write different things down in different colors just to amuse myself and keep myself engaged.

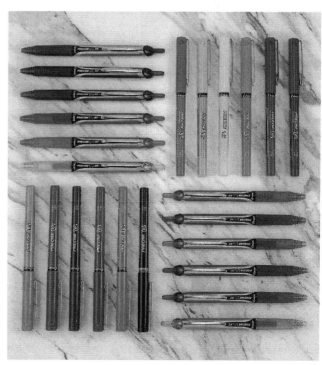

Steven Levy
Editor at Large at WIRED

Steven Levy writes about technology. He's editor at large at Wired and his books include Hackers, Crypto, Artificial Life and In the Plex. (Published 09/21/18)

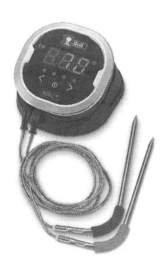

Big Green Egg and Weber iGrill Thermometer

The grill that I find that is the best is a thing called the Big Green Egg. It's the variety of grill that's called the Kamado grill. It's a ceramic thing. It's unlike the Weber things, which are made of metal and basically just cook things over the coals. It has the convection angle as well. When you close the big ceramic thing, the temperature as well as the charcoal and the grill cooks it up there. So you can kind of control the temperature within the egg. The thing's shaped like a big green egg, as the name implies. There's a cult of the Big Green Egg. There are Big Green Egg nerds that, you know, share secrets and endless accessories you can buy. And so I find that the Big Green Egg is best used when you have a way not only to monitor the temperature inside the egg — it comes with a thermometer that enables you to do that — but to also monitor the

internal temperature of whatever you're cooking. I use this thing called iGrill. It's made by Weber. And basically it's a device that sits outside the grill with a bunch of probes that would go on the meat. You close the cover over it and you can monitor up to four different pieces of meat or fish or whatever you're measuring in there. It's USB, so it goes to your phone or even to your watch, so you're walking around and your watch might buzz and tell you it's got five minutes to go. You can monitor from there. It's fool proof, especially with something like fish where you don't want to overcook. It's really great to monitor it. I've never really screwed anything up with this combination.

BookBub

This is an app that I've been using the past few months. I think that e-books cost too much. The value proposition isn't any where near what you can get for a hardback book that you keep for life and you can read it without a light source, and there's the physical pleasure of it. Though e-books certainly have their virtues, it's great to have and I love traveling with my Kindle or my iPad, I use both, full of books. So I'm never worried about not having something to read. A BookBub sort of plugs into that idea —maybe a model where books are so cheap, you'll buy one on impulse and just have it around whether you read it or not, turns out to everyone's benefit there. As it turns out, every so often, even the books you want to read, get on sale at Amazon and other e-book purveyors, and I'm talking about costing $2 instead of $12 or $10. So BookBub keeps track of all this stuff and first, you fill out some forms or say what kind of books you like, and it figures out the kinds of books you might be interested in and it reports to you when books are on sale. So everyday you get an email with about five books that you may want to read that cost between $1-3. And I find maybe once a week, I'll buy a book. I'll say "Oh, that's cheap. I've always wanted to read that." Or "Here's a great version of Don Quixote or here's a thriller by an author I really like" or "here's Joan Didion's Slouching Towards Bethlehem. Wow, I have that on my book shelf, but I'd love to carry it around with me in case I want to read her essay about Jim Morrison on a plane ride." So I use this and I have probably 50 books now, some of which I'll probably read, some of which I won't read, but I'm happy just to have them. So I think that it's a great model. Some of my books have been on sale for a couple of bucks, and I've bought them on there too.

AeroPress Coffee and Espresso Maker

I actually met the inventor of this and his name's Alan Adler, and he's a guy up in years. He got interested in coffee and tried to figure out what the best way to

do a cup of coffee is, and he invented this thing, this vacuum tube. It looks like something you might give an enema with really, and you put some ground coffee into one end and it comes with this little round filter, you get like a thousand for $7, and you heat it up. Adler is very specific in saying, don't do it to boiling, 175 degrees is the perfect temperature. But I find, you don't have to be that precise. You pour in the water, you give it a little stir, and then just push the tube down there, push the plunger in, and it gives you an amazing cup of coffee. And as it turns out, the Coffee Geeks have rated this on a level with $4,000 espresso machines, and some boutique coffee shops actually have rows of AeroPresses. That's the way they make your coffee. They have annual AeroPress contests. For me, it's just a great cup of coffee and it's super portable. I have AeroPresses in three different locations. My personal advice is three full scoops, don't skimp on the coffee. And it's fantastic. The other great thing about the AeroPress is it's self-cleaning. When you push the plunger down, it cleans itself. All you have to do is give it a quick one-second rinse, and pow, there it is. You don't have to worry about scrubbing it out.

Temi

I had a period where my transcriber was gone, and I needed to get transcription. Temi is done by AI and it's 10 cents a minute and it turns it around within a minute. They give you the transcript, and then you edit the transcript, you're encouraged to edit the transcript to fix it online and they're watching what you do. So they're getting better and better and better. So over the past few months, the thing has gone to virtually unusable to pretty good, like about 70 percent, I'd say, of normal transcribers. I'm finding it better and better and better, and it is so incredibly cheap and fast that I'm pretty much taping now, just to get a raw transcript.

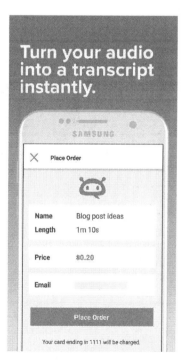

Steve Lodefink
User Experience Designer

Steve Lodefink is a Software User Experience Designer by day, and a tinker and maker of things by night. As a contributing author, Make and Craft magazines and blogger, Steve has written and shared numerous how-to articles. He enjoys exploring new tools and methods as well as learning the old ones. (Published 08/31/18)

Everlast PowerTIG

TIG stands for tungsten inert gas. And what that means is, these are both arc. MIG and TIG are both forms of arc welding. In a TIG you're holding a tungsten electrode, and your power supply is creating an arc between that tungsten electrode and your workpiece. And it's being shielded by typically argon gas. So that keeps it from oxidizing. So you're holding a torch that's just an electrode. It's a cleaner process, and it's just a lot nicer for a bunch of reasons. I tell people to start with TIG welding if they're not going to be needing to go outside to weld.

Grizzly Dial Indicator

This is a tool that typically machinists use. It's a precision measuring tool. It looks like a stopwatch, kind of. It's got a dial and a little probe sticking out of it, and that probe is sensitive to measurements of a one thousandth of an inch. So the dial's calibrated, or it's notched off in thousandths of an inch. You can measure just minute tolerances and take minute measurements of motion, essentially. So if you're truing a wheel, you could put this on — and usually you can true a wheel just by sticking a nail next to it in a pair of vice grips and seeing if it wobbles too much — but this lets you really get down to take fine measurements.

Zenith 591 Stapler Plier

Everybody's probably got both a regular desktop-type stapler where you slide some paper under it and then wack it or press it hard. And then the other common one everyone's probably got is like a T51 stapler-type of tacker, for tacking your fliers on the telephone pole. This one is, they refer to it as a plier staple, because you kind of hold it in your hand like a pair of pliers, and it squeezes the base of the stapler — the anvil of the stapler — into the business end. You typically have something in one hand and then you've got this grip in the other hand and you can sort of articulate both hands to position the thing

where you want it rather than just a one-hander. It just feels good to use it. I just have it hanging on the back pegboard of my workbench where I do most of my stuff, and use it mainly for reclosing packages.

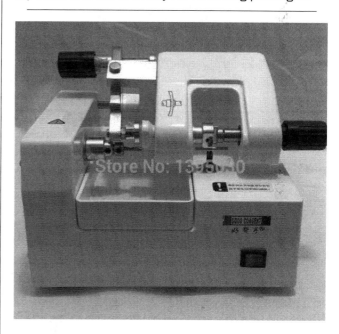

Eyeglasses Lens Cutter

This is definitely one of the more esoteric tools. This allows you to cut new lenses for your eyeglasses. It's essentially a flat parts duplicator where you have a pattern or an existing eyeglass lens, and you put that in one side, and it rotates using that as a cam. And on the other side there's a little spindle that's got essentially a rotating drill bit, and it'll duplicate the shape of that lens on to another lens.

Michael Lorsung
Transmedia Artist

Michael Lorsung is a transmedia artist based in Snowmass Village, Colorado. He is a practicing artist, tinkerer, and experimenter who also works full time managing the sculpture program at Anderson Ranch Arts Center. His work investigates human questions through the lens of industrial production and technology.
(Published 11/23/18)

Mitutoyo 3-Part Hardened Combination Square Set

I use this set for layouts across a variety of media. Being able to indicate angles and lines with a high degree of precision makes tasks like the layout of sheet metal components, scribing indications for machining operations, and setting up machine tools a pleasure. I have used Starrett as well as Mitutoyo and find them to be comparable.

Ideal Industries Stripmaster

I have used a lot of wire strippers, including a handful of "automatic" strippers. This has proven itself time and again to be one of the best. It grips

the insulation while pulling the part to be stripped from the bare wire in a single hand motion. Aside from being a lovely piece of engineering, it does its job reliably and consistently, something I appreciate when stripping lots of small jumper wires for soldering to perfboard. The best part is that they are still being made, and used older models are often great flea market finds. Cheap too.

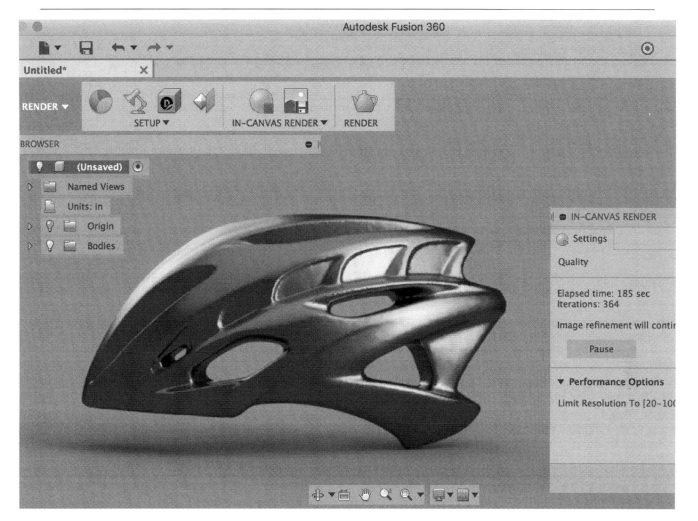

Autodesk Fusion 360

I began 3D modeling in 2012 using Rhinoceros 3D. I found the interface to be unintuitive and a bit clunky. I was also dismayed to find that there was no integrated CAM software, and the Rhinocam was going to cost me another $600-2,500, depending on the version. I was introduced to Fusion 360 in 2014, and I found the interface to be much more intuitive, and the features it included to be incredible, especially given the price tag for students, educators, and businesses making under $100k/year. I now use it to design parts that are 3D printed, milled in a variety of metals, woods, and plastics, as well as profiles for plasma and waterjet cutting.

4 Mil Single Matte Drafting Film

I do a lot of drawing, both sketching ideas and drawing assemblies, before I produce them. This drafting film has a fine-toothed side that takes pencil and felt-tipped pen well, and also allows for the erasure of both. I find it to be a pleasurable drawing surface, as well as one that allows for the layering of drawings, making it useful in drawing parts with multiple assemblies or pieces.

Om Malik
Partner at True Ventures

Om Malik is a partner at an early-stage venture firm, True Ventures. Prior to becoming an investor, he started GigaOm, a technology blog, and covered technology and its impact for over two decades. Om loves technology, its possibilities, and writes about its impact on his blog, Om.co. He can be found @om on Twitter and Instagram. (Published 3/22/19)

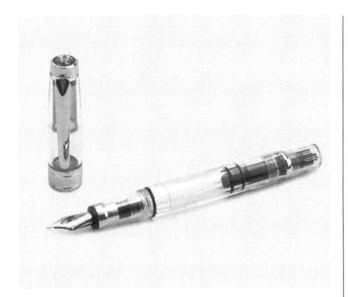

TWSBI Diamond 580 Fountain Pen

I use a fountain pen and a notebook to write most of my thoughts and notes from interviews whenever I meet companies. The reason I do that is I find the process slows me down a little, makes me think, and I like the way the fountain pen's nib makes the noise when it moves across paper. I feel a tactile connection with the words which are coming into my ears, into my brain, and then out into this piece of paper. The pen I use a Taiwanese-made pen, and it's TWSBI Diamond 580 Fountain Pen. It is a piston filler — a piston filler is a way of filling ink into the fountain pen. The reason I use it is because it's actually a really well-made fountain pen, it has a steel nib. So if you put too much pressure on it, it doesn't bend as easily. More importantly, it's a very well-made high-quality pen. I have used it for close to two-and-a-half years and I've never had a problem

with it. It is a demonstrator pen; since it's transparent you can actually see the ink. The ink sloshing around in the container makes the whole feeling more organic, that the pen becomes almost a living thing, and that's what I love about it.

Muji Organic Cotton Mix-Pile Sneaker-in Socks

These are sneaker socks made for wearing with sneakers, and I have tried many different versions of these socks which come up to your ankles. They are basically made for people who wear sneakers, however, I like to wear proper Italian-made leather shoes but I don't like wearing long socks. I want to show some of my ankle and I feel like I'm a little bit Italian — not really, but I just like the way they look and I just love the quality of Muji. I would say I have washed these socks about 50 times and they still are exactly the same as the day I bought them. For a $5 pair of socks, I have never met any product that good. With 50 washes, even the best socks lose shape, they lose the shine, they become dull, they stretch. But these are just perfect, the elastic is great, the fabric has softened a little bit but there are still no holes in those socks. I just wonder how they have done it? There must be some magic there.

Dsptch Heavy Braided Camera Strap

Dispatch is a local San Francisco store, and I constantly kept changing cameras and I needed an easy way to find a camera strap which I could just replace, like move from one camera and put on the other without having to mess about. The guys from Dispatch made this great system in which you basically buy a strap and number, and depending on the number of cameras you have, you get ties for those cameras. The strap just plugs into that tie, and when you want to use a different camera, you take off the strap and put it on to the other camera which has the same camera tie. It's just a braided nylon cordura kind of material. It's very strong and the tie and the plug are also super well designed and extremely strong. I have a very heavy camera and

that has never been an issue. It is also handmade, and made in San Francisco. It's almost like a net kind of a braid and it's just so beautiful and so elegant.

Corpus Natural Deodorant Sticks

I like this brand of deodorant sticks called Corpus. It's a natural deodorant, it doesn't have any artificial ingredients, and the reason I know about them is because the company was founded by the founder of another brand which I like called Baxter. Baxter of California makes men's products. Shaving creams and beard oil and stuff like that, and he sold the company then started this new company called Corpus, and I found them to be just way better than the Baxter products. The Baxter products have a slightly alcoholic feel to them and you can feel there is something artificial about it. Whereas these ones just feel so much more natural. They're almost invisible, and the scent on the deodorant sticks is pretty low key and pretty muted and I just like it for that reason. I've been using it for about six months and have had no allergic reactions. I just feel if we use less artificial things in our lives, the better we are. There's no logical reason to use one deodorant stick versus the other except personal choice. This one just clicked with me. I will recommend that people should try their product because it's such a high-quality product.

Jane Metcalfe
Co-founder of Wired

Jane Metcalfe started Wired Magazine with her life partner Louis Rossetto. More recently, Jane was the President of TCHO Chocolate. She's currently at work on a new startup about how advances in science and technology are conspiring to improve our health.
(Published 05/17/16)

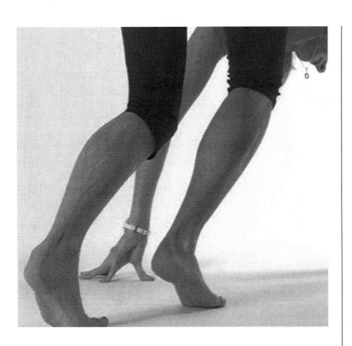

Kinesio Tape

The tape accelerates the healing from an injury or from inflammation, and it also can be used to support muscles that have been inhibited in some way. It's not that thick, and it's a woven tape. It's got a special acrylic adhesive on it that allows it to stretch with your skin. It actually slightly pulls the skin away from the lower dermis, which basically operates on the principles of osmosis. It allows the fluids to move from the high pressure into the vacuum created when you lift the skin away, into that low pressure area, and it enables your lymphatic and your venous drainage systems to literally pull the fluids away and to help drain swollen and bruised tissues quicker. I can wear this for 3 to 5 days. It works starting instantly.

Game Ready

I've had minor injuries before. They always say, "RICE. Rest, ice, compressing, and elevation. RICE." After the trauma of an injury or a surgery, the ice is really, really critical. If you hit it hard and diligently, immediately, you're going to have better results. Game Ready makes it so easy and so comfortable. It's beyond just a soothing relief of the coolness on your hot, swollen tissues. It's also got this compression, which is mimicking the natural muscular response of your own body. They have this thing called ACCEL Technology. You have a machine. You fill it up 3 quarters of the way with ice and a little bit of water. It's a digital interface, and you dial in your program, which can be 30 minutes on and 30 minutes off, or you can just do 15 minutes at a time, whatever you might be looking to do. Then the wrap goes around pretty much my entire leg, from my thigh to just above my ankle. It starts to inflate so it inflates and then, it has waves of little minor compression. It inflates and freezes your leg in that one position. It is amazing. I can't wait. I'm just happy to just sit on the couch and, "Oh. Good. Here it starts again."

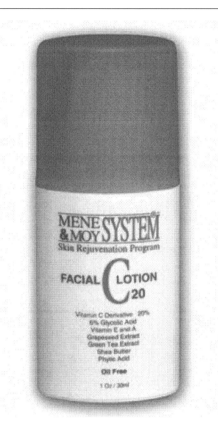

Mene & Moy Facial Lotion

I have to tell you, this product really was a game changer for me. People started saying, "What have you done to your skin?" All I'm doing is using this vitamin C lotion. In fact, the vitamin C is combined with a glycolic acid found in sugar cane. The glycolic is a type of alpha-hydrolic acid, and it is the smallest molecule in the alpha-hydrolic acid family. It's used in all kinds of things, including as a dyeing and a tanning agent. It's used in adhesives and plastics. It can be used for flavoring or preservatives. It's use in skin care is to basically dissolve the upper layer of cells on your skin. It gets at the tired, sun damaged, expanded pores, and it can lighten the discoloration that you get from the sun. It can help clear up acne and black heads. There's claims that it can actually

regenerate your collagen or thicken the epidermis. The thing that I keep noticing is it just evens my skin tone. That, combined with the vitamin C, which has protective effects for UV photo damage, are really radical, really noticeable. My sister sent it to me. She gets it in France. The company's called Mene and Moy. They're based in Britain. When I first looked at it, it was like $200 to get it over here. But there are now distributors in the United States and you can buy it online. I think $44 price is the going price at the moment. You put it on, you cleanse your face in the morning, you put it all over your face after you dry your skin, and it tingles a little bit. That gives you a sense that there's something actually starting to work. Then, you put your moisturizer on top of that, and your sunscreen on top of that.

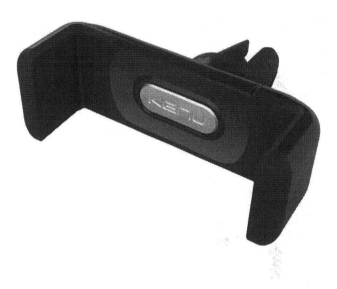

Kenu Airframe+

I love this device. It is so simple. Literally every time I get in my car and put this in my little air-co vent, it just brightens my day. I have not yet upgraded to the Tesla so I don't have a sophisticated in-car navigation system. We started buying cars that had that but then I don't change cars as fast as the technology changes. I got my iPhone and I had a Velcro-ed thing that was working pretty well, but it just aged out. It timed out. Then, the phones got bigger and heavier. I recently got an iPhone Plus and god bless Kenu, they were right there with an Airframe+ for me. What it basically is, is a bracket that you can stick into your air condition vent, that will hold your iPhone at eye level for you. You can literally just glance. You don't have to turn your head at all. You can just glance at your navigation.

Robyn Miller
Computer Game Designer

Robyn Miller co-founded Cyan Worlds in the late 1980s, where he designed and directed the landmark video games Myst and its sequel Riven. In 2010, he co-founded Zoo Break Gun Club LLC, with producer/filmmaker Mischa Jakupcak. (ZBGC) has produced several films and has projects in development for film, television and virtual reality. (Published 02/7/17)

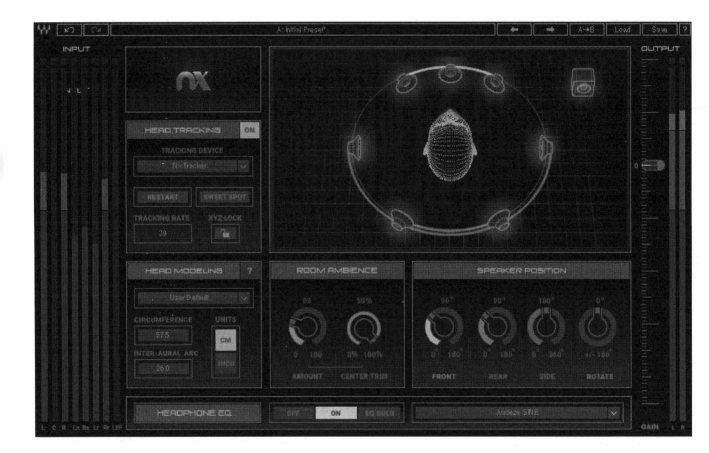

Nx Virtual Mix Room over headphones

I found out about this through Waves kickstarter. They're a company who have been around for a long time and they've created a lot of great plugins — they know what they're doing. This hardware and software combination allows you to hear three-dimensional audio from any pair of headphones. I'm waiting for someone to use it with virtual reality.

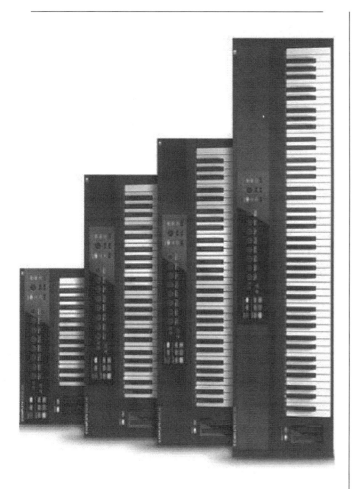

Komplete Kontrol S-Series

I've used a variety of MIDI controller keyboard before but never anything as smart as Komplete Kontrol S88. It helps that my go-to software synthesizers are made by Native Instruments and work seamlessly with this keyboard. Without touching my computer, I'm able to adjust parameters from the S88 (or record my adjustments over the course of a song). This isn't new — I've had MIDI controllers before — but this is the first controller that speaks the same language as the software synths I use. This comes in four different sizes.

Hurricane Harps S32 Student Melodica

I don't see a lot of people playing melodicas and I don't know why. They're a blast! It's a reeded

instrument (you blow through a tube to create the sound), but you play on a keyboard to choose your notes. So you have the opportunity for tons of dynamic, but it's easy to play. It ends up sounding like a poor man's English horn.

PDF Expert

I'm sure many have heard of this app. In fact, there it was rotting away on my iPad and I never really touched it. But when I bought my Apple Pencil, I revisited PDF Expert and was stoked. I'm now able to edit manuscripts and screenplays exactly as I would on paper with a red pen. Now, no more printing out 200-page documents just so I can scribble all over them with a red pen.

Craig Mod
Writer

Craig Mod is a writer and designer. He's worked extensively with Silicon Valley and Japanese startups. He spends about two months each year walking the old pilgrimage paths and ancient highways in the mountains of Japan. (Published 09/27/17)

Moulton Bicycle

This is a funky British bicycle, designed by Sir Alex Moulton, and part of his claim to fame was working on the suspension systems for Mini Coopers back in the original Mini Cooper days. He wanted to find this, kind of, more efficient bicycle form and he built the Alex Moulton bicycle. Alex realized, "If I use a tiny wheel, but really high pressure, I get all of the benefit of the bigger real bikes, but I get more maneuverability in cities and faster acceleration." I bought the cheapest Moulton I could get, which was about $1,500 and that was a single speed.

Suica Card

This is a really old thing, the Suica. It started as a electronic ticket system for the subways. The Japanese subway system works where you pay an entry fee and then depending on how far you go, when you leave on the other side, you have to pay again, you have to tap out. You have to make sure you have enough money on there to get out the other side. This card is an auto-fill card that's connected to your bank account. I have it set that if it drops below $40, basically, 4,000 yen, it will add another $100 automatically. Basically, you never have to worry about if you can get out the side or if there's enough money on it. You can also use it in cabs and in the convenience stores. It just saves you from having to think about coins and all that stuff.

WaniKani

Japan is like a lot of countries that have a language that isn't spoken by a lot of people outside of the country. It can be kind of impenetrable and then

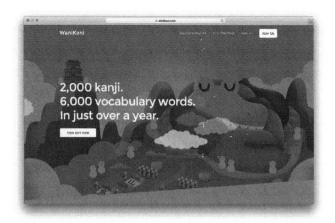

Japan has this other layer of weirdness in a increasingly global society where Japan has decided not to get good at English. If you go into the countryside, people in Japan really don't speak English at all. If you know the language, you can go onto a mountain in Japan and you can walk through these rice paddies and rice fields in the middle of nowhere and you can connect with the people and you can have these conversations and you can learn about lives in ways that would otherwise be impossible to learn about. It's just fun and addictive and it's this self-inspiring loop. Today, I think there was a lot of tools that didn't exist when I was studying way back in the day. There's a tool called WaniKani. I've had a lot of fun playing with it. It's better than Anki because the mnemonics and the cards are already prepared for you. They put a lot of thought into the system of giving radicals a consistency so that these mnemonics stories makes sense as you go through.

Magnetic Chalk Board

I just love blackboards. I like quiet technology. I got a really big one and actually, it's funny when you go into this universe of trying to find blackboards, basically it breaks into two stratospheres. There's one where it's for hipster restaurants and cafes, and the other is for esoteric, country schools. This blackboard is two meters long, it's like three meters high, it sits against a wall in my living room/studio, and it doesn't call attention to itself like a whiteboard would. It kind of sits back there. There's just something really satisfying about having a blackboard. You can use magnets on it, and I find the combination of note cards with the magnets with little notes written on them allows me to move them around real easily, so I don't have to erase things and then redraw it or whatever. I'm able to move stuff, shuffle stuff around easily. Then

what I do is I use the full-touch chalk to kind of add metadata around all of the note cards and group things. I find that works really well.

AirPods

Again, I like technology that doesn't draw attention to itself in the sense that you don't have to interact with it much, you can just kind of use it. I think when you have your AirPods in, you look like a fool and you kind of draw attention to yourself that way, but I like the user experience of it and the object itself and the charging case that it comes with, and then the way the AirPods stick into the charging case using magnets, and the fact that the case itself is a battery.

Eric Moore
IT Manager at Institute for the Future

*Eric Moore is the IT Manager at Institute for the Future in Palo Alto, California. He previously worked for Apple in its Information Systems and Technology Department. Having grown up on a farm in Georgia, he's a tinkerer by nature who loved to break things and put them back to together to learn how they worked.
(Published 01/19/17)*

Anker Compact Car Jump Starter

I have an old, classic '72 Chevy Blazer that I have in storage. It was in storage for over a year. I took it there and changed out the fluids and was getting ready to start it and obviously the battery was dead, but I connected this thing to it and without hesitation it started it up, and when it died a couple of times, each time I connected that thing to it, it started it, no problem. It has a fast charger port, a higher voltage as well, flashlight, emergency SOS signal for the flashlight as well. Usually when your battery dies, it's kind of at the most inopportune times. A lot of times it's late at night for some people, so add in to the stress of trying to connect it correctly once you do. If you connect this wrong, you get the red light and a beep, and when it's done correctly you get the green light and then you just start it. This thing is awesome.

After Credits

After you sit and watch a movie now they usually have teasers at the end — if there's a teaser to the sequel or outtakes or gag reels or whatever. This app lets you know whether you need to sit around and wait after the movie to see additional content. Also, based on the actual people that have viewed the content, lets you know if it's worth waiting around for it as well.

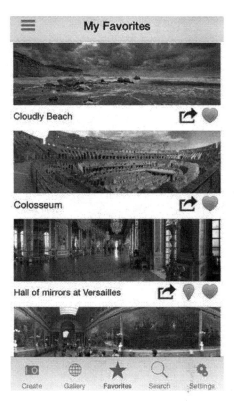

Cloudly Beach

Colosseum

Hall of mirrors at Versailles

Create   Gallery   Favorites   Search   Settings

or any type of VR hardware, you can basically load that picture up and it's like you're walking around in that picture. Basically, it's a fully encompassed 360 picture.

Breville Milk Frother

This is one of the best pieces of hardware that I own. This thing basically takes your milk and it steams it, so you don't have to buy that really, really expensive machine with the frother wand on the end. You dump it in there and it has a couple of discs in there that spin— one that has more teeth to it if you want that extra froth, and one with a flat disc for a cappuccino or what have you. It does everything for you. You push a button, set your temperature and walk away from it.

DMD Panorama

What this does is, it allows you to take 360-degree spheric panorama pictures, so you can share those pictures with friends. It's a different level of immersion depending on the venue. I have pictures from Hawaii and Waimea Canyon with this thing. You can zoom in and just spin around the picture itself, and then also for people that use Google Cardboard

Ricoh Theta S

This camera is super small, super compact. You can have it in your pocket and most times you won't even notice it's there it's so small. It takes 360-degree pictures as well, but the awesome thing about this is you can live stream.

Meara O'Reilly
Sound Artist

Meara O'Reilly is a sound artist and educator, most recently in residence at the Exploratorium in San Francisco. She is co-creator of the Rhythm Necklace app, a musical sequencer that uses two-dimensional geometry to create rhythms. Her collaboration with Snibbe Interactive on sound-based cymatic concert visuals for Björk's Biophilia album was included in the world tour.
(Published 04/4/16)

Making Music: 74 Creative Strategies for Electronic Music Producers

This is a really great book by Dennis DeSantis. I love it because it fills a gap that's often left between personal creativity and highly technical software manuals. It kind of pays a bit of an homage to Brian Eno and his Oblique Strategies in that you can almost pick up anywhere when you're feeling stuck and looking for a new approach or idea. There's sort of just different sections that you can flip through. The format is set up as a collection of kind-of problems and then solutions and it covers everything from basic music theory to different ways to beat procrastination, so it's both practical and kind of philosophical in a way.

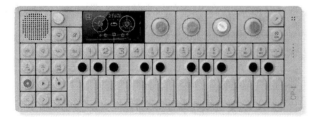

OP-1 Portable Synthesizer

I have to say that the OP-1 is one of the best new instruments that's out there. I found it to be simultaneously complex and accessible. Essentially, it doesn't sacrifice complexity but it has great design constraints that allow you to make something right away. It's not a full octave and the keys are not full size. There's all these buttons on it that, at first don't make any sense and they sort of just have numbers or whimsical little designs on them, and when you press them, all of a sudden there's this advanced functionality.

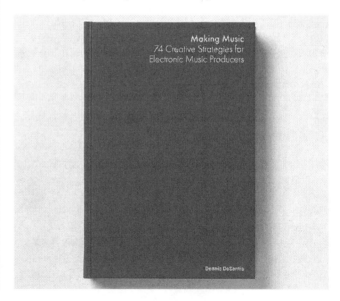

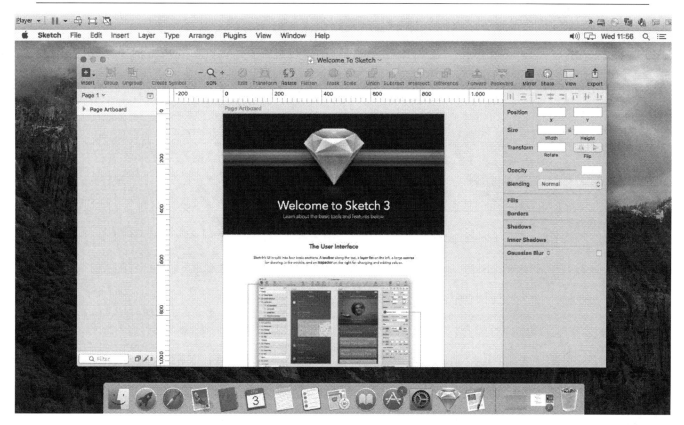

Sketch

Sketch is now kind of my go-to design tool because it's such a focused piece of software, in terms of, it was focused specifically on what I was trying to do, which was basically prototype how something would look on a iOS device and be able to immediately export things and put them in code and put them in action, as opposed to having to do lots of jumping through hoops to export stuff. It's definitely great as just a basic graphic design tool, whether it's doing a mock-up for a web page or just making a poster or a flyer or something. It does everything that Illustrator does on the basic level.

Complete Honda 4 Stroke Bicycle Motor Kit — 36 Spoke

I've been living in San Francisco for the last three years with all the hills. Whenever there's been a day that's kind of rainy out or cold, it makes me get on my bicycle because I know that I will have an assist. I was able to just to attach this kit to my mountain bike and it's a one-time purchase essentially. You don't have to keep replacing batteries, which are expensive over time. The engine is tiny and it costs about $2 to fill up, at most. It's really cost effective once you have it and it's also incredibly efficient.

Windell Oskay
Co-Founder of Evil Mad Scientist Laboratories

Windell Oskay is the Co-Founder of Evil Mad Scientist Laboratories, a Silicon Valley company that has designed and produced specialized electronics and robotics kits since 2007. Evil Mad Scientist Laboratories also runs a popular DIY project blog, and many of its projects have been featured at science and art museums and in Make, Wired, and Popular Science magazines. He's the co-author of the recently published book, The Annotated Build-It-Yourself Science Laboratory. (Published 08/2/15)

Rotring 600 Mechanical Pencil

The Rotring 600 is a beautiful instrument. It has a hexagonal body that's a lot like the size and shape of a traditionally yellow pencil, except it's made of nice heavy brass. The part where you actually hold it has a cylindrical, thoroughly knurled grip, also made of brass. This is kind of a no-frills but perfectly made pencil. It doesn't have a retractable tip or cushion or self rotating lead or most of those other nice fancy things that we see on modern pencils.

Aluminum Brazing Rods

Brazing is where you take two metals and you heat them up and you join them together with a third dissimilar metal. When you solder a copper wire to a copper wire using some tin lead or lead free solder, you're doing a brazing operation. You're taking those two metals and joining them with a third metal. You heat up your metal and then you wait until the brazing rod melts as it touches the surfaces. It starts to wet to the surface. Then you can just bond your metals together. It works on aluminum, magnesium, galvanized steel, brass, and copper. It's shockingly easy and strong for what it does. It's sort of like a low-budget welding technique for people who don't do a lot of welding.

RoboGrip Pliers

I've got several sets of these pliers. Some of them 20 years old, and as far as I can tell they're completely indestructible. Just a joy to have. Frequently somebody is asking, "Where's the RoboGrips, because we need them." You can get a two pack of these for usually $30-$40, and they come in a couple of different sizes. They are just unbelievably strong and great at getting a grip on something. They of course self-adjust to the size of the object.

OneTIME Tool® - Fat Head Hook Rule - 2019 - Order Deadline August 19, 2019 | OneTIME Tool® - Deluxe Trammel System - 2019 - Retired August 5, 2019 | OneTIME Tool® - ClampZilla 4-Way Panel Clamp - 2019 - Retired July 29, 2019 | OneTIME Tool® - Straddle Square - 2019 - Retired July 15, 2019

OneTIME Tool® - Stair Tread and Shelf Gauge - 2019 - Retired July 1, 2019 | OneTIME Tool® - Stainless Steel Step Gauges - Retired June 24, 2019 | OneTIME Tool® - Clamp Rack-It Mobile - 24" - 2019 - Retired June, 17 2019 | OneTIME Tool® - Sharpening System - 2019 - Retired May 20 2019

Woodpecker's Page of One-time Run Tools

Woodpecker's makes some unbelievably beautiful machined jigs for doing woodworking operations. I have a ruler from them, and it's just a 12-inch ruler. It's made of quarter-inch-thick aluminum machined on every side, and laser-engraved. In a sense it's absolutely overkill, but on the other hand it's just the most beautiful thing that I've ever called a ruler. It's just a joy to own. Their collection of tools, they're all one-off tools that just a few specialized people need. They have this page where you can go and browse through these one-time tools.

Metcal MX-500S Soldering System

The Metcals are the legendary great soldering irons. They work on a really interesting principle that regulates the temperature at the tip, not by using a thermostat but actually by using radio frequency power that is sent down to the tip. You can imagine this a little bit like a greenhouse that you want to regulate a specific temperature and you have a set of lovres on the roof that are either clear or metallic. When the temperature is too cool, you let them be clear. When the temperature is hot you make them metallic and they reflect all the sunlight away. The Metcal tip works just like that. It has a temperature-sensing element that absorbs power when the temperature is too low, and reflects power when the temperature is too high. The instant you touch the tip of this iron to whatever you are soldering it goes from being exactly the right temperature to still being exactly the right temperature, rather than dropping precipitously like a regular soldering iron tip does.

Jennifer Pahlka
Founder of Code for America

Jennifer Pahlka is the Founder of Code for America, a nonprofit dedicated to proving that government can work for all people in the digital age. She served as the U.S. Deputy Chief Technology Officer under President Obama, and founded the United States Digital Service dedicated to the same idea. (Published 12/1/17)

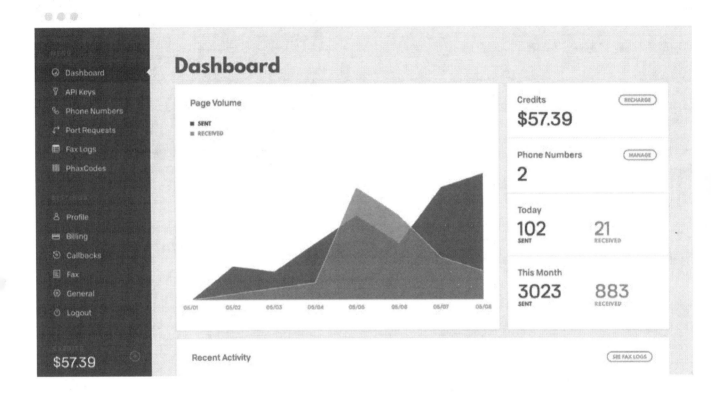

Phaxio

I will have to admit upfront, I'm not actually a coder, but I do work with our coding teams here at Code for America, and what I like about Phaxio is that it's sort of a hack, not just on sort of services, but on government. What we do here is we try to make services that work much better than the government services as it's offered. For instance, if you want to apply for food stamps in California and you want to do it online, you'll go through an application form that's over 50 screens long. One of the things we started doing was just making a better online form and then having that form create a fax and then faxing it into the office. It turns out the place where faxes are still really, really useful is in government services and in government offices. I never would've said, 10 years ago, that fax was key, but it really is for the work that we do, and it really helps us hack bureaucracies.

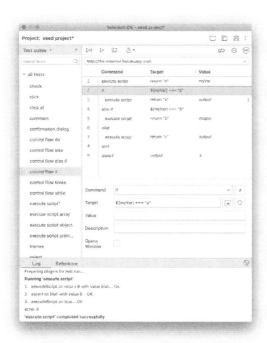

Selenium WebDriver

I'd say this is like the next step in making services that can sit on top of government services a lot easier to use. Now, instead of creating a fax that goes to the office, we just drive that data using Selenium right into the system of record. It doesn't entirely close the loop because at the end of the day, what you want to do is actually redo those systems of record to be much simpler and have clearer, easier front ends and ask fewer questions and have fewer data problems. For now, this is a very effective way that you can hack online applications to government services and really anybody can do this. The way I describe it to folks who aren't developers is that this is like little robots take the data that we collected from the people and then put them in the online form that actually exists.

Lyft hack

I'm a big fan of Lyft, and one day when my daughter was calling from her school and it was raining and she wanted me to come get her, I said, "Well, I'm not going to come get you, but I'm going to send you a Lyft." I just used my finger to move the map to where her school was, dropped the pin there and called the car. Then for a minute I thought, "Oh my gosh, is this dangerous?" But I realized I could actually watch the car arrive and pick her up, watch the driver drive

her here and knew exactly when she would arrive. The great thing is I can also do that when I'm in New York and my kid is stranded and needs to go home, and when I'm in another country, I can get her a car whenever she needs one.

Japanese Copper Tamagoyaki Pan

This is just my favorite thing in my kitchen just because it's kind of unique. Tamago is basically egg that you get at a sushi restaurant. It comes sort of nigiri style, there's like a little slice of scrambled egg, essentially, but it's done in a very Japanese way. To make Tamago, you have to have a small rectangular pan. This one happens to be copper. It just looks beautiful, it has a wooden handle and then this beautiful copper body. Basically what you do is you make this mixture of egg and dashi and a little salt and a little sugar, and then you have to sort of pour it in bit by bit and then roll it up, sort of sticking it at the end. What it makes is this very rectangular piece of egg that you can then slice and it looks very pretty when you lay it on the rice.

John Park
Professional Maker

Our guest this week is John Park. John is a professional maker. He builds creative technology projects, tutorials, and videos for Adafruit Industries. John hosted the Emmy-nominated Make: Television show on American Public Television. Prior to joining Adafruit, John worked in computer graphics, including 12 years in animation at Disney. John is an amateur circus aerialist, and a synthesizer enthusiast. (Published 01/25/19, 04/15/15)

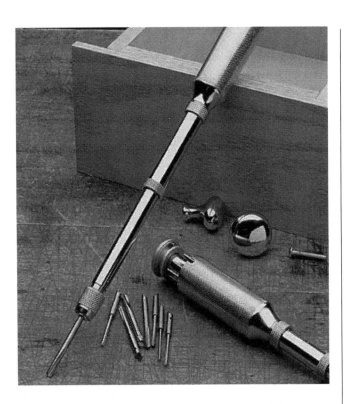

Garrett Wade Yankee Push Drill

This is so much better than a small hand drill or electric drill. I've got a couple of old ones in my workshop and I love them. For precision work making holes in small parts or tight places, I use these instead of a drill. They're much easier to control thanks to the parallel double fluting vs. a spiral drill bit, and they usually come with a good assortment of bits stored in the handle. This Garret Wade model looks nice, and very similar to my old Goodell-Pratt No. 185 (patented 1913). You can also hunt these down at yard sales and on eBay.

Copper Napier Jigger

This is an excellent measuring jigger for making drinks, with stepped gradations from 1/2 oz. to 2 oz. in 1/2 oz. increments. It's an obsessive, respectful modern remake of a classic art deco drink jigger from Napier company by Standard Spoon. They crowdfunded the manufacture and offer some improvements over the original, such as solid copper (which feels good and makes me happy), two extra internal engraved lines for 1/4 oz. and 3/4 oz. Plus, they dropped the handle, so you can stack them, and they don't get tipped over. I have a few originals I've collected over the years (OK, five of them at last count) but this new copper model is now the one I use most when concocting beverages. Also available in milliliters.

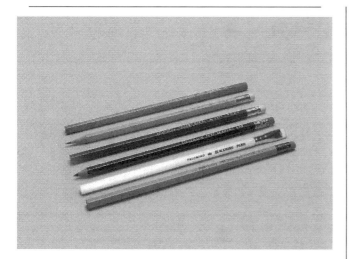

Crossword Puzzle Sampler Set

I love crossword puzzles. I work digitally on the daily NYT puzzles, but Sundays I do it on paper, as well as the spiral-bound collections. This curated set of pencils are great for crosswords on paper, newsprint, and that horrible, shiny NYT Magazine "paper." They are hard enough to avoid smudging, soft enough to erase. The General's Test Scoring 580 made in the US is my choice for the magazine. Any of the others — Camel HB from Japan, Cara d-Ache Yellow School Pencil from Switzerland, Mitsubishi Office Use 9850 HB from Japan, Palomino Blackwing Perl, and Tombow 255 B made in Vietnam — all are great on newsprint. It's a fun little luxury to dig into my crossword-specific pencil pouch, select a pencil, and remove the metal pencil cap (these work well and tuck into a crossword puzzle).

QuickRes

This is a little dock icon that lets you pick the resolution on the Macbook screen. You can pick any of a dozen resolutions that are good for the retina display, or you can set it up so that at the press of a button it will flip between two or three different presets that you've chosen.

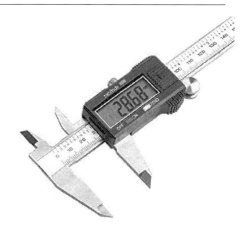

6" LCD Digital Caliper

I don't know why I went so long without having these, but I got them a few years ago. It's a really cheap set of digital calipers that can measure up to six inches of inside diameter, or outside diameter, or the depth of something. It has a depth gauge tail that swings out as you roll the head of the thing along the shaft. It has a digital read out. You can switch between inches and millimeters.

John Park's Workshop

I do a live stream on Thursdays at 4pm EST/1pm PST. It's live here in my workshop, and I usually do a couple of smaller projects, and tips, and tutorials. Then I'll have a larger build of a project that I'm doing for that week, which I then create a full learn guide tutorial for the website for Adafruit. We stream on the Adafruit YouTube channel as well as Twitch, Facebook Live, and Periscope.

Bob Parks
Freelance Writer

Bob Parks is longtime fan of outsider technology and was once an editor for Wired magazine. He writes articles for magazines like Popular Science and Businessweek about engineers, designers and inventors who work outside of their formal area of training. (Published 04/2/15)

Sawstop with Mobile Cart

These are the saws that have an electrical system that automatically stops the blade once your finger touches it. It stops in five milliseconds, so that you only get a little nick on your finger. I'm working with my children a lot around the saw, because I want to teach them safety and also it's a very exciting tool to use to build big stuff, and so I think it's a must-have at this point.

Ellipse Half Mask Respirator

When I'm looking for gear, I'm often checking out wood-working shops. Right now Ellipse just sells in the U.S. the particulate filter. So it's just for sawdust

and vapors. This is super low profile on the face, you can put your glasses or your hood over it. If you're welding you can put a welding mask over it. It doesn't feel like anything. And I also hate when I'm using a good respirator, the feeling of the straps pushing into my glasses, my safety glasses, and this one seems to have solved that ergonomic challenge. I love the feel of it on my face. They've figured out how to put the cartridges much closer to the face, so it doesn't hang out so far, and then it also has much less material, so it comes in much closer to the mouth. It's basically not like a gas mask that goes over the whole face. It is like a dust mask, but it has that respirator quality that the neoprene presses against the skin.

Fernco Wax-Free Toilet Seal

I've replaced five toilets so far in my renovation projects in my house. And each time you have to put in a new toilet, you have to fight with those wax seals. It's about six or seven inches and it sits around the drain of the toilet and it forms the seal between it and the floor. So that as you finally press the toilet into the floor, it crushes it into a shape that fits right around the toilet and you don't get any fumes or material coming up through the drain. Fernco came out with this maybe 10 years ago, and they've started to sell like hot-cakes to plumbing fans. This is a neoprene adhesive and it's sort of a different process. Typically, it's very awkward when I've got the wax seal on the floor, I'm grabbing this incredibly heavy toilet, my knees aren't that great, so I'm swinging this thing over the hole, trying to land it in the middle of the wax ring. And the first time I usually miss and crush the side of the wax ring, and have to start again. This is a different process. You turn the toilet over and you press this wax-free ring, the adhesive, into the toilet drain. And now you've got this long, four- to five-inch plastic throat and this adhesive piece stuck to the toilet. So it's completely stuck, you can basically lift the whole toilet with the plastic throat. Then you'll turn the whole thing around and then you kind of guide it into the hole and it's got these friction-sensitive plastic fins that press

it to the toilet flange. And you've got your three-inch, four-inch toilet flange, either of those work, and you press it in. And you're good to go. It even gives more stability to the toilet, if you're on one of the ceramic floors where there's a little bit of unevenness, it'll hold you in there a lot better.

Sawyer Mini Water Filter

This is an example of where technology and design completely recreates the market. Water filtration while camping used to be a huge pain in the butt and the devices cost from $100 to $400. And now this little device, that is now 1.9 oz, fits right in the palm of your hand, and can filter 100,000 gallons of water. They give you a half-liter pouch that you put dirty water into, and then you squeeze the water through the filter into your water bottle. I think that the more expensive filters still have a use when you have a big group and you're cooking and you need a gallon of water really quickly. But they're still awfully heavy and expensive and this one you can use as you go, each stream you come to you can top off your water bottle, with no problem. I've found that I use PVC tubing to make my own hydration system for running, I don't have to bring water with me. If I'm going on an easy run that might last two hours with some exploring, I'll just leave the house with Sawyer and just pull from any stream. It has the 0.1 micron filter, so it's the one with the highest filtration along with the top-of-the-line models.

Arion Paylo
Design Director at Blue Bottle Coffee

Arion Paylo is the son of an artist and carpenter. He was initially drawn to the keyboard instead of the table saw. After 11 years at Apple, he's gone from thinking about how Genius Bars work to how coffee bars work. At Blue Bottle Coffee, he strives to create cafes that foster memorable moments with delicious coffee.
(Published 11/22/16)

of getting rid of those used blades so easy so there's just something so beautiful about that. I love looking at all the scuffs, dirt, and crusted epoxy on it and thinking about all the cool stuff my father made with it.

Fiberglass-Reinforced Ratchet Lock Utility Knife

I use my father's decades-old Japanese Olfa breakaway utility knife all the time. My dad was a fine wood worker, a carpenter of all sorts, and as a kid growing up I always saw this utility knife in his shop and it has this real practical purpose to it. It has a little ratchet on it and you can slide the blade up and actually crack it off, so it's like a strip of blades that are connected to each other and you kind of just snap them off with a pair of pliers or whatever you have handy so that you always have a fresh blade easily at hand. As someone who cares about design and utility, there's something so amazing that this thing is decades old. It works really, really well. You know it's gonna last decades longer yet the actual core of it is so ephemeral. It's just these blades that can go away. It makes the act

Porlex Mini Stainless Steel Coffee Grinder

This tool has been one that has really saved the day for me in dire moments, which is when I'm traveling and I don't necessarily have access to good coffee or good coffee tools in a hotel or a friends house or wherever I'm staying. This is a small, very portable, conical, burr grinder that allows for a very consistent grind in a really, really tiny package. I don't know if they actually designed it this way, but it will actually fit on the inside of a Aeropress so when you're packing your bag you can take your Aeropress, which is another awesome coffee tool. Your filters can fit in there. You have a bag of beans with you and you can be making delicious coffee. Just recently I was traveling from Washington D.C. and in the middle of the terminal I was waiting for my plane that was delayed. I had all my gadgets out. I went to a shop to get some hot water and I brewed my coffee, and people probably thought I was making a bomb in the airport, but I've got to have something a little better than your average airport terminal coffee, so it's a lifesaver.

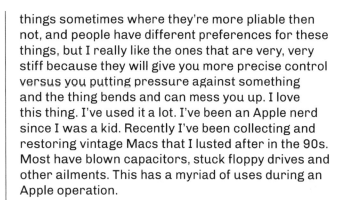

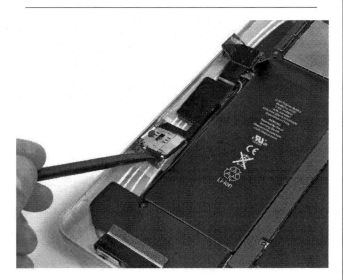

Universal Black Stick Spudger

Yeah. This is a really simple tool but extremely versatile. It's a piece of nylon that comes to almost like a pencil point at one end and a chisel tip at the other end. Near the chisel side there's a little notch that's sort of angled a little bit. It's anti-static, or static safe, and you can use this to do things like pop up little clips on a logic board really gently or put them back in place. You can use the little hook to move a tiny cable out of the way or use the chisel tip to stuff one back into a channel where it belongs. It has a lot of value when you're repairing tiny electronics, but I've used these for all sorts of things because, literally, it's just like a pointy stick. If you buy a big pack of them, then you're not too worried about messing them up. The key, though, is finding them. There have been generations of these

things sometimes where they're more pliable then not, and people have different preferences for these things, but I really like the ones that are very, very stiff because they will give you more precise control versus you putting pressure against something and the thing bends and can mess you up. I love this thing. I've used it a lot. I've been an Apple nerd since I was a kid. Recently I've been collecting and restoring vintage Macs that I lusted after in the 90s. Most have blown capacitors, stuck floppy drives and other ailments. This has a myriad of uses during an Apple operation.

VanMoof Standard

This thing is such a joy every time I use it and so much of it is because of how well thought out the components of it are and it kind of distills into this really great tool to get you around. It's a single-speed VanMoof bike. They're based out of Amsterdam and they make a bunch of different bikes, but the one I have is almost the simplest one you can get from them. It's a really simple bike but it has a couple of really really special things on it. One is it has an integrated lock, so all you have to carry with you is a key. You always have the lock and it always is kind of neatly tucked away in the bike when you're just riding around. It's got the lights and the brakes, all that stuff is just integrated. It's a pedal brake and the lights are driven by the hub so there's no cables, there's no buttons, there's no nothing. You just get on the bike and you go. When I first got it I was like "Oh this is like what I had when I was a kid. That seems like maybe not the right solution for a bike." It turns out, it works really well and if you're not riding really fast, if you're not going up and down hills everywhere it's extremely effective. That is just the coolest tool to me is one that doesn't need an interface because it's already solved all the interface problems so well it just gets rid of them, so all you have to do is get on and pedal.

David Pescovitz
Co-editor of Boing Boing

David Pescovitz is Co-Editor and Managing Partner of Boing Boing and a research director at Institute for the Future. (Published 11/9/16)

Okki Nokki Record Cleaning Machine

This is built like a tank. It looks like a big, heavy record player without a tone arm. You put a record on it and squirt some cleaning solution on it. Then you turn it on and the record spins. You scrub it gently with a goat hair brush. Then, you turn on the vacuum feature and it sucks up all the fluid and dirt in a couple revolutions. It's amazing, really, how clean it makes the record.

Mobile Fidelity Original Master Sleeves

My son and I always joke that we can take a record that he's dug out of the dollar or $5 bin, give

it a good cleaning, put a new inner sleeve to replace whatever moldy thing is in there, and it would be for sale at one of the hipster record stores in San Francisco Mission District for $25. I buy these sleeves in bulk.

ZeroDust Stylus Cleaner

Getting dust on your stylus of your turn table can be really annoying because then you start to hear the sound muffled and it's really bad, and it's not good to touch it. You can blow on it, but that doesn't usually get it all off. This is a luxury, admittedly,

because they're like $35 and it comes from Japan. It's this little square plastic container with this lump of solidified gel. It feels kind of like Jello, but a little firmer. You basically dip the stylus into the gel and lift it back up, and whatever was on the needle is then held in suspension in the gel. I've had mine for three years and it's basically as good as new.

Classic Style Popcorn Maker

We got this because my daughter, who's seven, really digs popcorn. She would eat it all day long if she could. My wife actually came up with this idea as a Christmas gift for her. The way it works is you put in the kernels, and then you put in the oil.

We use peanut oil, it tastes really good with it. You turn it on and it just starts popping. The popped corn pushes the lid of the kettle and falls into the hopper. It tastes good. And it's super easy to clean. There's this little tray at the bottom of the hopper and you just brush all of the unpopped kernels into that and take it out and dump it. Then you pour like a half a cup of water into the kettle and turn it on and it boils very quickly. It just gets rid of all the burned on stuff, if there's any, then you wipe it out with a cloth.

Celestron NextStar 5SE Telescope

This has a computer and motors so you don't even have to program anything. You turn it on and use a handheld device that looks like a phone handset to steer the telescope to objects in the sky. You can pick an object out of the database and it'll move the telescope to point at that object. You can point the telescope yourself and it'll tell you what it is that you're looking at. It gives you a whole new relationship to the night sky.

Daniel Pink
NYT Bestselling Author

Daniel Pink is the author of four New York Times bestsellers on work, business, and psychology. His books have won multiple awards and have been translated into 39 languages. Dan was also host and co-executive producer of "Crowd Control," a National Geographic TV series about human behavior. His latest book is When: The Scientific Secrets of Perfect Timing. (Published 01/18/19)

3M Ear Soft Earplugs

I'm a big fan of earplugs because I find that I work a lot better if I just block out sound. And a lot of times, what will happen if you have expensive noise-canceling headphones, the battery will run out, or you'll forget them, or I will actually always worry about losing them. And so, I buy this box of earplugs. They come in these small, individually-wrapped pairs, and I use them for everything. There's something, to me, that when you put in earplugs, it just blocks out the rest of the world and signals that you're in it. I basically keep a fist full of them in my backpack. They're very good in hotels, too. Because a lot of times in hotels, it's like, "Oh, I have the room next to the clanging ice machine. Oh, I have the room next to the elevator and there are 3,000 Kiwanis from Buffalo, drinking all

night and coming in late at night." And so, all of which is to say that I don't have many friends, but I have a lot of earplugs.

Faber-Castell Jumbo Grip Pencils

Over time, I'm not sure how it happened, I really like using pencils. As a writer, as a note taker, I still find — maybe it's delusional —but I find that I think better if there's some tactile element to what I'm doing. I almost never take notes by computer on my laptop. I prefer to take notes by hand. And there's actually some evidence that aids in retention. I just did it because I liked the tactile-ness of it, and I love pencils. I love the sound of pencil on paper, the scraping that it makes. I like the way that it looks. I tend to doodle and sketch a fair bit, and so it's much better than pens for that, because pens often have that little dollop of ink sometimes that will gum on there. And as I've experimented with pencils, the ones that I settled on were these things called Jumbo Grip Faber-Castell pencils. And what they are is that the barrel is thicker than a typical kind of No. 2 pencil. That's one thing about it. The other thing about it is that the barrel isn't really a barrel. It's not in the shape of a cylinder, as most pencils are. It's actually in the shape of sort of a rounded triangle. And it also has these small raised plastic dots that are akin to braille in their texture, and what they do is they allow a firmer grip. And it turns out that they're often used in elementary schools — for like first graders, second graders — especially boys, who struggle a little bit with fine motor skills, because it gives them a little bit more grip. I ordered these pencils by the case, and I sharpen them, and I grind them. I'm literally holding one right now. So, I love these pencils. And they're totally cheap.

MasterClass

MasterClass is a set of classes conducted by like the best people in the world at what they do. So, if you look at basketball skills, they have Steph Curry. If you look at screenwriting, they have Aaron Sorkin. You look at acting, they have Helen Mirren. They have a lot of writers. For comedy, they have Steve Martin. It's very, very well produced. And so, what they are is a series of classes, but the classes are more like interviews. They're not as purely didactic as somebody standing in front of a class and telling you precisely how to do something. At least, not the ones that I've watched and enjoyed. But you get to see people who are really, really great at something explain how they do it. And as I said, it's very well produced, and they're divided into videos. They vary in length, but the videos can be anywhere from three minutes to sometimes 20 minutes, and they're divided into certain sections based on what the person is trying to teach. Helen Mirren has a

very short video about how to walk onto a stage. Something that you wouldn't think about, but you're like, "Whoa, that's actually a big thing. Like how do you walk onto a stage if you're an actor?" Margaret Atwood has one about novel writing that was fantastic. But what I think is interesting — like in the class on wine with James Suckling — it was "How do you hold a glass to examine the color of a wine?" It turns out I was doing it completely wrong. I think it's a great investment. I think it'd make a super cool gift, too.

Hell's Handle Fish Spatula

I'm not much of a cooker. But if it involves cooking outside, that's my domain. And so, we've ended up grilling a lot of fish, because we have three people in my house who don't eat meat. And fish is actually really hard to grill, because it's very different in consistency from a beef steak. A lot of times the fish, particularly when you cook it on the skin side, it sticks. And I was always frustrated, and my wife found this spatula that is the greatest spatula I've ever seen. And I'm not exaggerating. I mean, it is so great. And so, all the sudden, I'm able to up my grill game significantly because of this spatula. It sort of has this beveled edge to it, and it has this handle, and it's exactly the right level of flexibility. You can get underneath the fish in a way you can't with a regular spatula, and it has some give, so you can actually, with fair amount of confidence, say take a hamburger and literally flip it in the air. This is the first time in my life I've been excited by a kitchen tool. So, if you grill fish at all, this is perfect. I mean, it's just a great, great product. And the brand name is kind of cool, too. It's called Hell's Handle by Mercer.

Charles Platt
Contributing Editor to Make:

Charles Platt has written science-fiction novels, computer books, and books about electronics, including Make: Electronics, which is a best-seller in its field. He was a senior writer at Wired magazine, and has designed and built prototype equipment for a California laboratory. (Published 06/8/18)

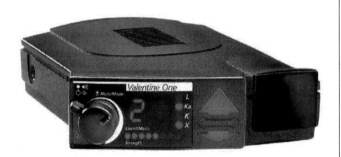

Radar and Laser Detector

I've had a Valentine One radar/laser detector for many years, and although it's the most expensive detector on the market, it certainly has saved me about ten times its price, which of course is an indictment of me for not driving slowly enough, but there it is. The radar component is still useful because a lot of highway patrol guys seem to get lazy and they just don't use instant-on radar even though they have it. They just leave it on all the time, which is really very helpful and I would like to thank them for that. The advantage of the Valentine One is that it has two arrows that show you whether the source is in front of you or behind you, or sometimes to one side or the other. Another advantage is they upgrade the firmware on a regular basis. So now that people are driving cars with radar built in, to help you become aware of hazards in the car, my detector was recently upgraded to ignore those signals, which, as far as I know, some detectors still pick them up and give you false positives.

Hygrometer

A hygrometer measures relative humidity, and for those of us who have sinus trouble — which seems to be an increasing number of people — if you are traveling and you bring your humidifier with you, as I do when I travel by road at least, it's nice to know when you need it and when you don't. Because if the humidity's relatively high, you don't have to go through all the hassle of unpacking it and plugging it in. I just bought the cheapest one, which is under $3 and has no batteries, I don't know exactly what's inside it, some sort of bi-metallic strip or something, and it's very light, so it's easy to carry anywhere.

Miniature Table Saw, 4" blade

Table saws are scary devices. I almost broke my arm with a table saw once when it kicked back; it hit my bicep fortunately and not the joint, and I decided that I wanted the versatility of a table saw and less risk, so I decided that a smaller one would probably be a little safer, and then I discovered that it's actually much nicer to work with because it's so precise. So this a half-sized table saw, which I think is really intended for people who make models of ships, is a very nice little thing to have. It's good for wood up to an inch thick actually, so it's not as limited as you might think. But very precise and

I bought mine from a guy in Florida who actually makes them himself in a basement workshop using his own lathe. It's just a beautiful thing to have.

Capacitance Meter

While multimeters often have the ability to measure capacitors, they don't have a very wide range. A dedicated capacitance meter does a better job and doesn't cost much. The great advantage is that it has a much wider range than the capacitance-measuring capability of a regular multimeter. So you can see it as kind of an indulgence, but it's nice to have an additional meter on the bench so that you don't have to disconnect your volt measurement in order to make your capacitance measurement, and having indulged myself, I found it was actually very useful.

NeilMed Sinus Rinse

Irrigating the sinuses with a saline solution can be just as effective as antibiotics and is also helpful for

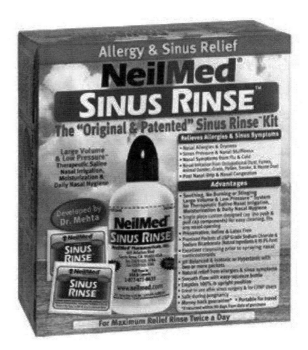

allergies. Some people use a neti pot, but the Neilmed system is more convenient. A simple squeeze bottle, sold with little packets of saline powder.

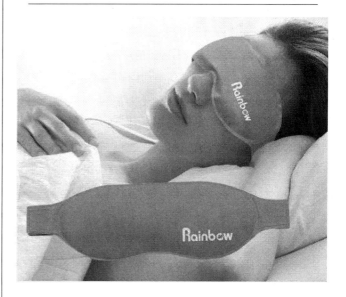

Hot Mask Eye Compress

During allergy season, I get itchy eyes. My ophthalmologist recommended a mask containing granules that absorb and hold the heat. You microwave it for 30 seconds and wear it for two or three minutes. The heat opens glands that release oils around the rims of the eyes. Antihistamines are not good for itchy eyes because they dry the eyes, making them more itchy in the long term.

David Pogue
Founder of Yahoo Tech

David Pogue is the Founder of Yahoo Tech. He is a technology correspondent for CBS News Sunday Morning, a columnist for Scientific American, and a technology columnist for The New York Times.
(Published 05/27/14)

BusyCal for Mac

My life revolves around the calendar. What's neat about BusyCal is that it builds on the same database as Apple's own calendar program. So, you get all the benefits of all the work Apple has done to, for example, synchronize your calendar between your phone your tablet and your computers, but they've added more features and a better design on top of it. On any other month-view calendar, today's date is where it would fall if it were on a wall calendar, which might be on the bottom row, but by definition you're looking at a calendar to plan ahead. My favorite thing about BusyCal is it has the option of having today's date be at the top of the calendar even if it's the last week of the month. It's a perpetually scrolling month view and it makes so much sense, so you're always looking ahead.

Nomad Charge Key

There's nothing worse than realizing that you've lost your charging cable for your phone. I've stumbled upon something called a charge key. It's a tiny, rubberized, two-inch strip. One end slides into your USB jack. The other end slides into your iPhone and it's a safety charging/syncing cable that's two inches long and can go on your keychain. I'm a big believer in having that as a backup. It's saved me more than once.

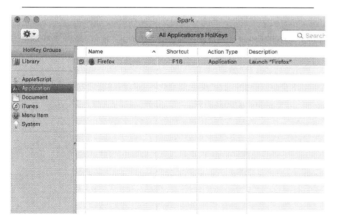

Spark for Mac

This is a really great macro program. I don't use the dock ever. I open everything with keystrokes: "Control W" for Microsoft word, "Control B" for BusyCal, "Control E" for Evernote, etcetera, and then I've set up the the top left escape key to be the left-handed delete key, and it is life-changing.

Anchor TrueSeal Food Storage

My wife turned me onto these things. They're these indestructible, heatproof, wash-proof, drop-proof bowls with airtight rubberized lids. My fridge looks like a commercial, it's so organized and beautiful.

Chop2Pot

This is a cutting board that folds in thirds so once you're done cutting the thing you fold up the wings and make a chute so the food slides into your bowl without falling off.

Snuglet for Mac

This — some miracle of physics — amplifies the magnetic grip of the MagSafe magnet power connector so that it does not fall out unless you really kick it or trip on it.

Dean Putney
Founding Software Engineer at Glowforge

Dean Putney is the founding software engineer at laser cutter startup Glowforge in Seattle. Previously, he wrote software for organizations like Reddit, IDEO, Boing Boing, and Cool Tools. (Published 02/2/18)

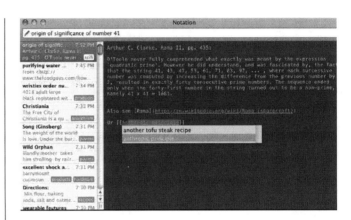

Markal Lacquer-Stik Paintstick

These are sticks of a thick, oily paint. Their purpose is to fill in creases or engraved areas, then you can wipe away the excess leaving a crisp and bright painted space. We use these with the Glowforge a lot — it's extremely convenient for making labels on projects. Text on colored acrylic looks especially good. I used these sticks recently to label all the bonus squares on a Scrabble board I made with the Glowforge. The Markal brand sticks are the best because they rub in very smoothly and easily. Other sticks are harder paint, making them much more difficult to rub into the crevices. You can use isopropyl alcohol to dissolve the excess for easy wiping without affecting the paint in the cracks.

Notational Velocity

Notational Velocity is a basic text editor for Mac meant for taking quick notes. This answers the question of "Where can I write this down?" for the computer. I use it to plan my day, write down quick information if I'm on the phone, and keep important snippets of text or code right at hand. nvALT is a fork of the original Notational Velocity that appears to be more frequently worked on. You can access it via a global keyboard shortcut. Its search is quick and accurate. It doesn't do images or files. nvALT has become the go-to place for me to drop almost all my thoughts and insecure details. You can use SimpleNote to sync your notes to your phone or elsewhere.

Node-RED

NodeRED solves the same problems that If This Then That or Yahoo Pipes try to tackle. While IFTTT tries to hide a lot of the complexity, simplifying to very pure one-to-one connections, NodeRED lets you build a "flow" or network of connections. It handles regularly scheduling updates and checks, has a fairly large library of components and tools you can choose from, and is relatively easy to work with. While it's originally meant to run Internet of

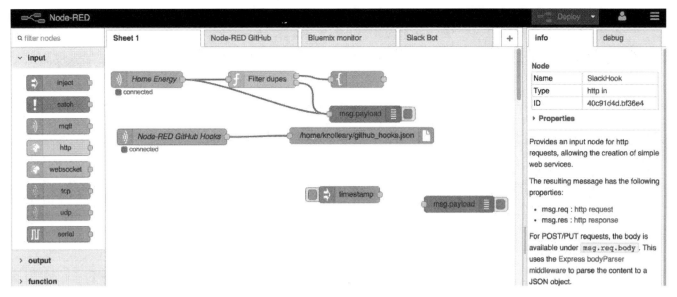

Things devices, it's perfectly capable of controlling more complex systems. I am using it to collect albums from Bandcamp and organize them so I can post them to my music blog. NodeRED can be set up on a Raspberry Pi fairly easily. It's also available as a Docker container, very quick and easy to set up.

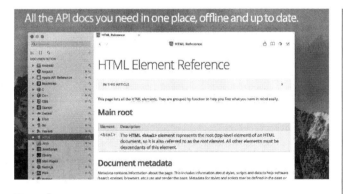

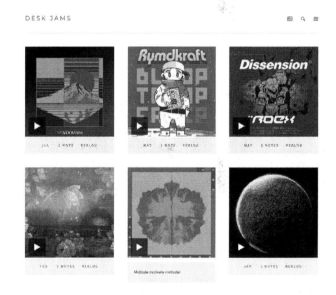

Dash

Dash is a code reference tool. Its primary purpose is to search and read the manuals for different programming languages. This alone is extremely valuable, as reading the manuals online or in a PDF can be extremely tedious. But Dash also makes adding manuals easy, stores them offline, and is accessible in a global keyboard shortcut. Dash can also manage global snippets. This is great for things you type a lot, like your address or certain quick responses to things. An unexpected use for Dash is as an always-open web browser. You can search Google and Stackoverflow with it, but even power users may not know that you can add custom search for websites you use frequently. I added our internal JIRA tracker and Confluence to Dash, allowing me to keep the documentation and tickets I'm working on close at hand without having to dig through dozens of browser tabs.

Deskjams.com

The purpose of Desk Jams is to provide music that is good for working, to kind of get you into a flow state where you can concentrate on something, you're not being distracted by anything, so in general that means that I'm looking for albums or mix tapes, that kind of thing, that are album lengths, so they're about half an hour to an hour and don't have any distracting lyrics and kind of provide a smooth feeling to work to.

Simon Quellen Field
CEO of Kinetic MicroScience

Simon Quellen Field is a chemist and former Google software engineer and is the author of over a dozen books, including Gonzo Gizmos, Return of Gonzo Gizmos, Culinary Reactions, Why is Milk White, Elements Vault, Why There's Antifreeze In Your Toothpaste, Electronics for Artists and, most recently, Boom!: The Chemistry and History of Explosives. He's the author of the science toy website SciToys.com and several novels. (Published 10/20/17)

Taylor Wharton LD10 Aluminum Liquid Dewar

I'm often asked to demonstrate scientific toys and things at different science conventions, like the Google Science Fair, and one of the things that they love is when I show off all of these fun things that you can do with liquid nitrogen. And, of course, it lasts a lot longer if you keep it in a big Dewar. So I've got this thing, it's about 2 feet tall, about 10 inches in diameter, and holds 10 liters of liquid nitrogen,

which I get locally from a place called Nitroderm. And we do all kinds of fun things with it. Put some liquid nitrogen in a bowl and squirt some whipped cream out of a spray can into it, freeze it really hard. Kids pop it into their mouth and crunch on it and fog comes out their nose like a dragon.

Mastercool 90066-B Vacuum Pump

I have a vacuum chamber, and this vacuum pump, this one does six-cubic-feet per minute, which is pretty good. It used to be that vacuum pumps were really expensive, but once the smog dealers needed them in order to take the Freon out of your air conditioner for environmental reasons, everybody needed one and they got cheap. But, with this vacuum pump, I can put some liquid nitrogen into a small thermos and put it in my vacuum chamber and start sucking the air and the nitrogen vapor out of that chamber. And after about a minute or so, you get solid nitrogen, and then you disconnect it and let the air rush in and in about 3 seconds, it's liquid again.

Tekpower TP3005T Variable Linear DC Power Supply

This has got a nice LCD display on it and you can set the current or the voltage to be constant. And what I use it for is electroforming. You take a solution of copper salts and a few other magic ingredients. Usually, it's a proprietary mix, they don't tell you exactly what's in it. But you can start electroplating something and if you let it go, it will make a thicker plating. So, for example, suppose I took an egg. I could paint conductive paint in a pattern on the egg, like a filigree or a tree or whatever. And then I could submerge that in the plating bath and plate it for 20 minutes or so and get a thick-enough copper plating that I can dissolve the egg away and now I can hold this filigreed Fabergé egg-like thing in my hand. I also use this for nickel plating.

Baofeng Ham Two-way Radio

I picked this up recently, when I was going up to see the eclipse up in Oregon, and we knew that there would be so many people in these little towns that only had cell phone bandwidth for a tenth as many people as were going to be there and so, we wanted to stay in touch and be able to chat with other HAMs on the road about traffic conditions, which we also expected to be a nightmare. And this little gadget has 128 memories that you can easily program with all of the repeaters for all of the HAM radio repeaters on the mountains and stuff and it just works. It does everything you want and it's tiny. It's probably good for anywhere, 5 to 20 miles. But once you hit the repeater — the repeaters are networked —so I can talk to people in Portland, Oregon or in San Diego.

Sean Michael Ragan
Former Editor of Make

Sean Michael Ragan is the author of three books, including The Total Inventor's Manual, which is on sale now at Costco, Sam's, and all major book retailers. He's also a former editor of and longtime contributor to MAKE Magazine and MAKE online. You can find him on Amazon, Medium and Instagram. (Published 5/17/19)

3M Stikit Gold Paper Sheet Roll

When I use sand paper I find it's not very useful as just loose paper. There are a lot of clever sanding blocks out there and sanding solutions, but 3M, as far as I know, is the originator of this idea where you just sell sand paper on a roll and you put a peel and stick backing on it, which if you've ever fiddled about trying to attach sandpaper to a wooden block for sanding or to a piece of glass or a surface plate for lapping, is obviously a smart idea.

Kant Twist Clamps

These work kind of like C-clamps, except better in almost every way. I say "almost" because these are a lot more expensive than C-clamps. But the advantages I

think are worth it. The cantilever mechanism means the screw you turn to tighten the thing is actually perpendicular to the applied clamping force, instead of directly in line with it. The jaws sort of lever sideways to give you more mechanical advantage than you'd get from turning the same size C-clamp handle. So you can clamp harder without working as hard to do it. The gripping pads or jaws are plated in copper to keep them from marring up your work, and because the screw doesn't directly impinge on them they can rotate to align with the faces of your part. Also you can spin them around to one of several different gripping faces before you tighten the clamp down.

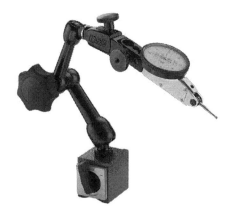

Noga NF Dial Indicator Holder

If you want to do any kind of precision work with a drill press, lathe, mill or other machine tool, you need to have a dial indicator and a way to position it where you need it. Thing is, a dial indicator is really not that complicated from an engineering perspective, and for most applications all you're doing is trying to minimize movement of the needle along a toolpath or around a cutting axis. So a cheap import one works fine. It's better to have a good one, but if you've only got so much money to spend, it makes more sense to buy other stuff first. So here's a case where it actually makes sense to spend more money on the mount for the instrument than on the instrument itself. These arms come on a switchable magnetic base so you can stick them to ferrous metal surfaces, and the Nogas in particular are just awesome when it comes to being able to quickly position them where you want them and lock them down. With a Noga, you can basically loosen one knob, pull the end of the thing where you want it to be, and tighten the knob back down, and the whole arm locks up rigid. So it's quick and reliable and a real pleasure to use.

Fireball Forged Bench Vise

I picked this vise for lots of reasons. First of all, it's the only commercial vise I know of that can be ordered with solid copper jaws. Usually if you want a set of copper jaws, you have to make your own. And copper jaws are so much better for most things, and in so many ways, than the hardened steel jaws that most vises ship with. A) Copper's soft and so it doesn't leave marks or scratches on stuff, even if you gronk down really hard on it. B) Copper is malleable, so it actually conforms a bit when you grab down on a part and grips it better than hard steel, so it's less likely to slip. C) Copper is a great

conductor of heat, so if you're using a torch or a soldering iron on a part you've got clamped in the vise, copper jaws will help keep it cool. D) Finally, copper is a great conductor of electricity, so if you're doing some kind of arc welding process on something you've got clamped in the vise, you can count on the copper jaws to make good electrical contact with it for your ground electrode. Apart from the jaws, this is just a badass vise in general. It's forged instead of cast, so it's stronger, and it's got a separate set of round pipe jaws underneath the flat jaws. It's got a little anvil on it. And it's got a bolt hole pattern in the base that fits the fixture holes that are standard on BuildPro welding table fixtures, which means you can mount it on your table quickly and take it off just as quickly. Plus I think it's really pretty, too. I like the kind of crystal blue hammertone paint a lot. Finally, Fireball tools is a cool little US company owned and operated by a maker in Washington state. His name's Jason Marburger and he's got a really interesting YouTube channel.

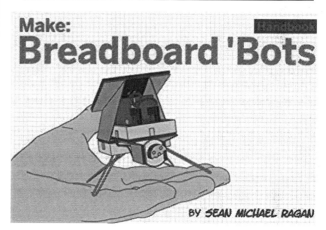

Breadboard Bots!

I just finished up my third book, which isn't out yet, but hopefully will be soon. It's called "Breadboard 'Bots" and it's a series of robotics projects that can be put together without soldering or programming anything by building modular circuits on those little mini breadboards and then interconnecting them mechanically and electrically in various ways. If you all remember the whole BEAM robotics thing, the designs are a lot like that, except without all the fancy freeform soldering. I always liked BEAM because I like the game of trying to get these little robots to have the most complicated possible behaviors using just sense-and-respond kind of analog electronics and clever mechanical design instead of programming a microcontroller or microprocessor.

Trey Ratcliff
Photographer

Trey Ratcliff is a photographer, artist, writer and adventurer. Each day, Trey posts a new photo to his website, StuckInCustoms.com, the #1 Travel Photography blog. His images and stories capture the beauty of exotic travel destinations as well as the humor of bizarre situations he often finds himself in. There is always something new, unexpected and beautiful to see.
(Published 11/19/18)

The Untethered Soul

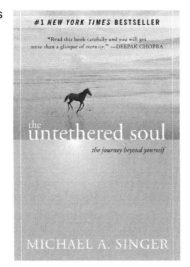

I think tool aficionados will especially enjoy this because as humans, we use our prefrontal cortex to envision what a project will be like when you're working on it and what a project will be like when it's done. Well, this allows you to use your brain as a tool. And each chapter is a different thought experiment. And you can envision your brain doing different things. It's really a book about Zen and letting go of the ego and creating things for the pure joy of creativity. Not necessarily so worried about the end result, but sometimes if you start with these right premises, the end result will come about on its own. And this book is not, of course, just great for the idea of building things, but it's great for your whole life. It's brought a lot of meaning and solitude and serenity to my life.

Google Tasks & Keep

I've gone back to the old Gmail, which has been upgraded. The two cool upgrades I like with it are Google Tasks, which is a very simple to-do list, and Google Keep,

which is a very simple note taking tool. Both of these are now integrated into Gmail, so whenever I want to update my to-do lists on my phone, it automatically goes into my Gmail. It's all nicely integrated. I have a few to-do lists. I like to keep it simple. I have a list called To-Do Soon, and I put the most important things toward the top. And then I have another list called like Books to Read, Movies to Watch, these sorts of things. And it's just right there in Gmail watching me all the time. And then Google Keep is nice for keeping very simple notes. It's very elegant. I switched to that because I was getting sick of Evernote. Evernote was giving me all these pop-ups all the time, always trying to charge me more money. And I had a subscription, but I don't know what was going on. It was giving me this threatening message that I was going to lose access to my notes. And that upset me. I felt like, "That's a little too sales-y, Evernote. I don't like where you're going with that." And I just trust Google more. And my notes are not that complex. It's a few words there, it's a URL there. And that's really like 99% of all I need. So I'm kind of going all-in on Google.

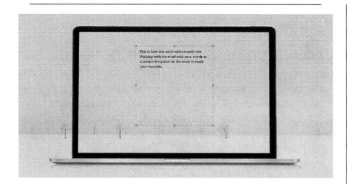

Ommwriter

This app is only for the Mac and it's nice because as soon as you launch it, it goes full screen. You can't see any of your other apps to distract you. And you just start writing. And there's like 10 different backgrounds. On the bottom there's white snow with some barren trees. Other ones have a yellow background with a stucco wall. And you can turn on kind of like this weird ambient music and there's different typing sounds. Or you can turn both of those off. And you just start typing. It's just a stream of consciousness. A very small thing that I like about it is that it doesn't give you any red squigglies. So when you misspell stuff, which I misspell all the time, it doesn't tell you. You'll find out later when you copy and paste it into something else. When you put it in Google Docs, it'll tell you. You can fix it. I think when you're writing, you're full of self-doubt. "I don't know if this makes sense. Are people gonna understand what I'm saying? Should I rephrase this?" And all of a sudden you get a red squiggly and it's like a little punishment, like a teacher. Like a nun hitting you with a ruler. Okay, maybe I don't know how to spell that word and I mess it up every time. And it just starts to fill all that self-doubt that you try to ignore. This doesn't do that.

Insta360 ONE X 360 Camera

This is a very small camera. Like a big lipstick. And it shoots 360, 4K, and it auto-stabilizes. There's a firmware update, so make sure you get the firmware update. It's so smooth. You can attach it to a dog and a dog will run and the final video looks like a drone flying one foot off the ground. So it's amazing. You can attach it to a Selfie

Stick and you can kind of stick it out right in front of you, like a few feet away. And one of the coolest things about it is that when it stitches together the video, it will erase the Selfie Stick. So it's almost like this little orb is just floating there in the air before you. Currently, no one is making any interesting 360 videos. I think most of the day is totally banal and boring and full of chaos. But whenever you have some kind of moment of order or something interesting. It's almost like a blog entry. You can record it and this is some amazing information. It's not just the audio of what you're saying but it's the entire sensorium of everything around you. And I think that's pretty cool.

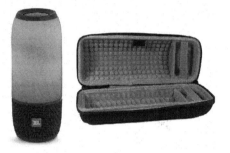

JBL Pulse 3 Wireless Bluetooth Speaker

This is a Bluetooth speaker. It's waterproof. You can use it outside. You can throw it in the hot tub. I personally love music, and I am often in situations where I am outside with a group of friends and we're talking or having some drinks around a campfire. And I like to have music around me all the time. And so this speaker allows anyone to connect to it with Bluetooth and it has the most incredible sound. When you're outside with friends and you kind of pass it around. You start playing a song and someone else says, "Oh, I love that song. Can I play a song?" And then they jump on YouTube and they Bluetooth connect it and they play their song. And it's just kind of a really fun thing. It glows in like millions of different colors. It has all these different colors that light up as LEDs on the outside. So it's kind of just fun to like sit in the middle of the group. And everyone just kind of stares at it, especially at night. I think people like campfires. We're not that far away from our ancestors where we would all sit around campfires. But very rarely do we have fires around us anymore. So this is kind of like a little digital fire. And it also plays music and it's just kind of a fun thing that brings joy to people's lives.

Rob Reid
NYT Bestselling Author

Rob Reid is the New York Times bestselling author of novels including Year Zero and the recently released After On. A longtime entrepreneur, he founded Listen.com, which created the Rhapsody music service. Years ago he was a Fulbright scholar in Cairo, and he still speaks better Arabic than you'd think. (Published 08/16/17)

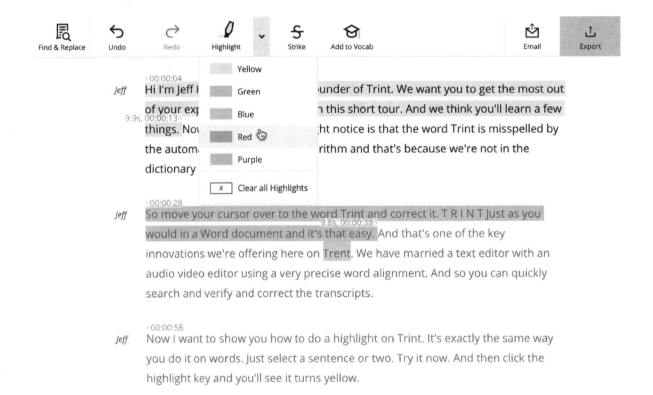

Trint

Trint is a transcribing service. What happens is you upload your conversation and you hit a button and it thinks for a few minutes, and it transcribes it voice-to-text. And then you click anywhere in that transcript, and it starts playing at precisely that moment. It's dynamically linked to the conversation. You click on a word, and it starts playing there. And you cross words out. Like for instance, let's say somebody "um-ed" a few times, or they stammered, or they said something and they didn't like the way they started and they said it again. You cross out that stuff that wasn't meant to be there. And it's not professional-editing quality, but you hit the play button and it skips that stuff, so you end up getting a very, very, very rough cut of what your editor might create.

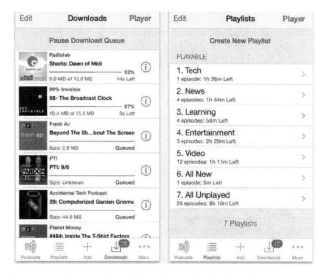

Zoom H6 Six-Track Portable Recorder

This thing is very rugged. It's a beautiful piece of industrial design. It's got a very nice heft to it. It will take up to six inputs with four XLR jacks, basically you can patch in four microphones of any arbitrary quality that you happen to have access to. It takes SD cards, so you can go up to 128 gigs and have gazillions of hours of capacity. The battery life is good. It's about 20 hours on a few AAs, which is neat. I've been lucky enough to conduct six of the seven interviews I've done so far face-to-face, and so being able to field produce and get out there and bring a couple microphones with me and this tiny-but-magnificent piece of electronics and get something that is near-studio quality is very, very precious for me. It's about the size of a guitar pedal or a chunky glasses case. It's really, really portable.

Downcast

So instead of using the built-in Apple player, which I think is okay-ish at best, I use something called Downcast. It allows you to listen up to 3X speed with a lot of granularity as to how fast it is. I'm sure others have come up with a term. I call it "fast listening." And it is particularly important to me as a podcaster right now because I have this need to listen to lots of stuff, but I think it can be valuable for anybody. We need our downtime and our zen space and time to just reflect, but we all have many hours of stuff to do each week where our brain is way too engaged to allow true creative thought or deep relaxation, yet nowhere near enough engaged to be anything other than bored, whether it's doing dishes, packing, walking the dog, exercising, walking through airports, the whole bit. And certain information is to be savored. An audiobook that is a magnificent performance, it would be a crime to listen to it at 2 or 3X speed, but some things you really want to inhale that information and get it into your brain as quickly as possible, and if you've got a zippy brain, as I'm sure most of your listeners do, the ability to inhale it as quickly as the circumstances allow, it's just a dial you have in your hand, and why not have that dial? So that's why I like Downcast.

After On

It's set in an imaginary start-up, set in present-day San Francisco. So it's very much about the entrepreneurial world and the way that we do entrepreneurship and start-ups today in Silicon Valley. But at the center of the story is a rather diabolical social media company called Phluttr, and it kind of embodies everything that's wrong with social media dialed up by maybe about 20%. And this'll sound like a spoiler but it's really not, because you'll see it coming from page one, but about midway through the book Phluttr attains consciousness. But rather than going all Skynet and trying to kill us all, it takes on its character from that which it is, which is a social network, so it basically becomes a hyper-empowered, super-intelligent 14-year-old brat.

Howard Rheingold
Author and Artist

Howard Rheingold is a critic, writer, teacher, and artist; his specialties are on the cultural, social and political implications of modern communication media such as the Internet, mobile telephony, virtual communities, digital media and learning, and online co-learning. (Published 06/11/14)

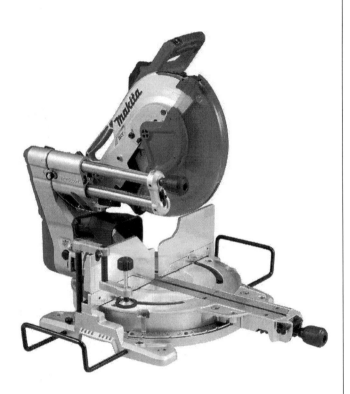

Makita Compound Miter Saw

I've got a Makita compound miter saw, which is invaluable. Compound means you can move it in an angle in the horizontal plane, but you can also move it at angles in the vertical plane to make bevels. That's very useful, especially if you get a blade with more teeth on it so that you can make finer cuts.

Copy Paste Pro

Copy Paste Pro will remember up to the last 200 things that I either cut or copied to my clipboard. You remember how scary it was the first time that you wanted to move something by cutting it and pasting it? So you cut it and it disappears to a place you can't see; this makes the place you can't see extensible and visible. Then you can go back and re-paste anything. Also you can make a key combination. I make it "Command + Shift + C." or "X." and "Command + Shift + V.," so you can copy, copy, copy and paste, paste, paste. If you're blogging or you're programming, anything in which you have to copy a lot of things and then paste them again. It's intensely useful. And it doesn't matter what medium it is, so you can copy images as well as words to it. Copy Paste Pro is kind of a freeware product. You buy the $20 version and you're set for life. I highly recommend it. Like I said, I use it a hundred times a day.

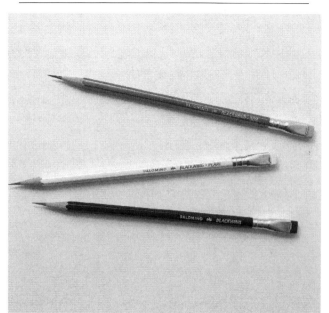

Felco Pruners

In my garden this is probably the thing that I use the most. It's got a holster. You wear the holster for a while and it gets this nice sheen from your hand. I just use them for cutting up anything that's basically smaller than your thumb, and there's a lot of it in my garden. If you've got fruit trees or you've got bushes or blackberries or ivy, anything like that, you'll use it a lot. It is a dangerous tool and you've got to be mindful of that. You don't want to drop it on your foot as I did once and ended up paying $1,300 to my emergency room to wash it out and give me a Tetanus shot and put a couple of drops of glue in it. They didn't even have to stitch it. They glued it, but I'm always mindful of it. Also when you are using those and you've got you hands up in a bush and you are cutting, please make sure that your hands are not in the path of that because you can clip your finger off with it. Anyways, it's very useful. I use it a lot. I think dangerous tools are a call to mindfulness. You just need to pay attention. It forces you to pay attention.

Palomino Blackwing 602 Pencils

One thing that Boing Boing turned me onto are Blackwing pencils. I've got those out in the shed. I've got them in my sketchbook here in the office.

Spoonflower Fabrics

If you go to Spoonflower.com you can upload any image and they'll send you fabric.

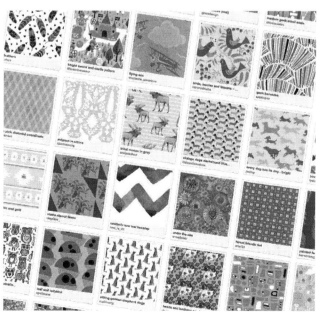

Rich Roat
Co-founder of House Industries

Rich Roat is the co-founder of the graphic design firm House Industries. He is also co-author of a stunning new book House Industries: The Process is the Inspiration with Andy Cruz and Ken Barber. (Published 08/2/17) Note: Rich Roat sadly passed away since doing this interview.

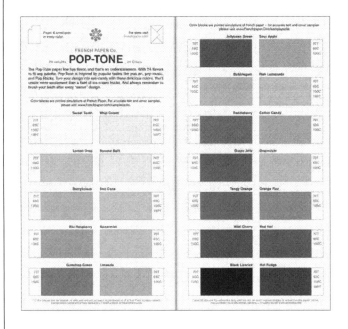

Kraft Tape Dispenser

This beats any tape gun. You just load it up, fill up the water reservoir, and pull the lever. It even cuts the tape for you, to the length you specify with the lever pull. We're always packing up samples, gifts, and general goodies to send all over the world. Plus we have this online store too, so we need to ship that stuff too. If you don't mind getting a skidload of the tape, you can get your logo printed on it too. It sounds pretty mundane, but we always get great comments on it.

French Paper Co.

In the old days of graphic design, premium printing paper was a B2B thing and you had to buy the stuff through a print shop who had to buy it through their local distributor. When Andy and I first started House Industries, we were in Delaware and no Delaware distributors carried French, so we posed as a print shop so we could order their paper direct from a Baltimore distributor and have it shipped to another printer, sort of like the CIA set up a shell corporation to buy titanium from the Russians that they needed to build the SR71 blackbird during the cold war. We were friends with fourth-generation owner Jerry French, but at the time, it was verboten for paper mills to sell direct to designers. Still, Jerry would see that some "fell off a truck" every once in a while to fuel early House Industries font catalogs. Then the internet came along and fucked a bunch of shit up, but also eventually made it okay for French to sell direct to consumers. About the paper itself — unbeatable color palette and delicious textures, mostly attributed to hero graphic designer Charles S. Anderson. Their swatch books are more valuable than a PMS chart, and if you have a pernickety printer who doesn't feel like doing a little sourcing, you just get out your credit card and order it yourself. French is also a really cool company, surviving as an independent mill in a time when most other such businesses are long gone. And they were generating their own hydroelectric power, recycling and being environmentally friendly before those kind of things were cool, like almost 100 years ago.

stack them around the studio. We didn't like any of the designs that were available, so we made our own boxes. We even got a design patent for the box die.

S & S Machine

These couplings make it possible to break a full-sized 700C bike down into airline-checkable luggage. I'm a cycling nut, and I like my bike. When I travel, especially to bike-friendly places like most of Western Europe, Seattle, San Francisco, etc., I like to take my own bike along because it's all dialed in, fits me perfectly and doesn't make any strange noises. I just break it out of the box, assemble, and ride out of the front door of the airport. Seattle even has a bike assembly area for idiots like me.

House Archive Boxes

Shameless self-promotional plug here. We're good ol' American hoarders and we work in a building without much closet space, so we wanted somewhere we could dump all of the valuable junk that piles up on our desks that also looked cool when we

Son Dynamo Hub

There are other dynamo hubs out there, but none quite as beautiful as this one. I ride my bike to and from work every day, and in the winter it's often dark both ways. USB-powered LED lights are nice and all, but there's something cool about being able to throw a leg over the bike and not having to worry about remembering to recharge. This may sound weird, but the hub also makes this great little vibration that gets slightly more pronounced when under load. I just keep my lights on all the time because I like the feeling of generating electricity when I'm riding.

Dave Rome
Gear Editor at CyclingTips.com

Dave Rome is a gear editor and content strategist at CyclingTips.com, a premium online cycling publication with the mission to share the beauty of cycling. Dave was a previous editor at the UK publication BikeRadar.com, and has been involved in the bicycle industry for over the past decade. As a bike mechanic, Dave is a self-confessed tool nerd, and often writes in-depth reviews and features about hand tools for DIY cyclists and mechanics. (Pubished 06/14/19)

PB Swiss Tools Rainbow Hex Keys

It's a Swiss company that make these. Basically when you're working with bicycles, hex keys is sort of the number one tool that you need to use. Much of the bike is built with Allen key bolts and you get a lot of use out of these tools. PB Swiss in my opinion makes one of the finest options. They do one which is powder-coated in basically a rainbow of colors. You can pick the size that you need without really having to look. You can just sort of know the color that you want. For example, I know that the five millimeter, which I use, is orange and the four millimeter is yellow and the six millimeter is red. It's really easy and quick to grab the one you need and just get to turning those bolts. I've yet to break one. Amongst a lot of pro mechanics they're commonly considered the most durable hex key going, so you know I've had my set for five or six years, whereas in the past I'd normally only get a year or two out of a set of hex keys. They are not cheap, but they should last a lifetime. I mean they are made in Switzerland, they're made with a very high-quality stainless steel, and they're lovely to use.

Dynaplug Racer Bicycle Tire Repair Tool

This is an American-made product; Dynaplug is the brand, out of California. Basically they're like these little CNC aluminum machines. Maybe like a pen knife in a sense. They're very small, they fit in the palm of your hand and basically what they're designed to do is you jab them through a tire in the event of a puncture, and it leaves behind a little rubber worm that fills the puncture. These are designed for what we call tubeless tires. If you imagine a bicycle tire, it normally has an inner tube inside of it. That inner tube is a rubber balloon, and normally when you get a puncture you only puncture that inner tube and it's a matter of replacing that tube. For tubeless tires it's much more like a car or a motorbike system, where the tire itself is airtight and is holding the air inside. If you puncture a tubeless tire, all you've punctured is that outside tire and normally it's quite easy to find the hole, because you'll just see the air escaping. More commonly people will use a liquid tire sealant inside their tires, so you'll actually see the liquid coming out or foaming out of that hole. This tool comes along and you just pull the end cap off and stab it through the tire and pull it back out and it leaves behind a plug.

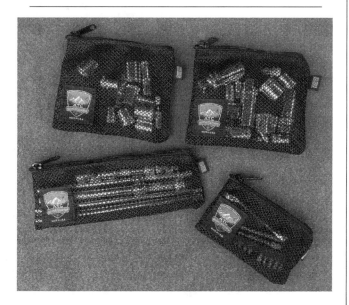

Adventure Tool Company Mesh Organizers

These are from an adventure tool company out of Colorado. They're American-made and basically made to military specs. All the little pieces on them are super durable, and basically they're my favorite way of carrying whatever small item I need to keep track of. I know there are a lot of these products for various storage of USB cables or headphones or whatever they may be, and this is what I've found to be the best. They're mesh so you can see through them, but because of the material used they're extremely durable, extremely light and not overly expensive for what you get. I've got one with all my cables for travel, I've got a hard drive in it and a backup battery, and I just keep that and I can transport it, transfer it from bag to bag in a rush, and I don't have to think about what I'm packing. I've got another one which has my camera card reader

and another backup drive in it. I've got it fairly well organized, but it's just a nice little mesh item and better yet, I can use them in the toolbox as well, because that's what they're really made for.

Dualco Grease Gun

I've had one of these for I'm going to say 12 years now and I'm still on the first one. Basically it's a small, handheld grease gun that you fill up with whatever grease you like through the bottom and it's got a little pump-action button that when you press the button, the grease comes out of this needle-like tip. It's a very precise applicator for whatever grease you want. It's not too large, it doesn't take a huge amount of grease, but I've found it to be just about perfect for where you need to put grease into a tight spot without making a mess. You can get different-size needle tips for it as well; you can get a longer one if you need it. It's an all-steel construction and I've found it to be extremely durable, very easy to use.

CyclingTips Podcast

I've just begun working on a series of podcasts with my company Cycling Tips, and we're basically going to deep dive into all worlds of tech. We are currently doing a podcast about what bike weight means — for those that count grams of their bike — that's sort of what I'm getting hyper-focused on at the moment. It's been wonderful for my inner nerdery.

Rebecca Romney
Rare book dealer

Rebecca Romney is a rare book dealer at Honey & Wax Booksellers in Brooklyn. She got her start with Bauman Rare Books, managing their Las Vegas gallery. She is known for her appearances on the HISTORY Channel's show Pawn Stars, where she evaluates books as the show's only female expert. She recently published a book on books called Printer's Error: Irreverent Stories from Book History with HarperCollins. (Published 10/6/17)

Mylar Film Rolls

This is an archival uncoated polyester film used by antiquarian book dealers, librarians, and archivists to add a layer of protection to an object for storage or handling. It's added to dust jackets, cut into sleeves to tuck in individual sheets of paper, etc. You also see this with displays. When people are displaying things open, they will use these little strips of mylar, if a book is open to a signature or something like that. These strips are things you get in rolls, and these rolls are part of your book fair kit, so when you go to a book fair you're all ready to pull out your strips of mylar and "mylar" things open for show. It's always a problem if you forget your roll, but the person next to you is going to have a roll of mylar too, because everyone has a roll of mylar, so you can always bum one off of someone else. It's pretty ubiquitous in the trade. This idea is

that it's archival, meaning there are other types of transparent film you could use in order to put things in just to protect, but in the long term you need something that doesn't have any chemicals or agents in it that might be damaging. For example, sometimes you see this terrible book sin, which is people put Scotch tape on their books in order to repair the spine or something, and Scotch tape has a very high acid content. If you see a book that was taped 20 years ago, today it has that icky orange color, which is really gross. That is the acid deteriorating the paper. Something archival is really what you need when you're protecting, because otherwise, in the end, you're actually doing more harm than good.

Cliplight (both LED and UV)

The tool that I always have in my bag is what's called a cliplight. It's essentially a handheld light that I use to backlight paper. It uses LED light. It's not very hot or anything like that. It's kind of the shape of a pen, or maybe a highlighter, because it's about eight inches long and it's a little thick, like three-quarters of an inch. It just has a button that you click on and off to turn the light on. In order to see clearly the watermarks and chain lines of a book printed on handmade paper (generally before 1800CE), you need to backlight the paper. Watermarks and chain lines are important evidence of how to identify a book — its format, any repairs, when it was printed, whether it has been messed with by an unscrupulous seller, etc. I use the UV light for things like offsetting of ink that's normally invisible to our eyes. I've used this with autograph authentication specifically, but you can use it for printing too. A good example of this is one time we were authenticating a signed first edition of To Kill a Mockingbird. This book in the dust jacket, even not signed, is like a $15,000 to $20,000 book. It's an expensive book. If it's signed, then you're looking at $35,000, $40,000. You've taken a book that's already very expensive and you've doubled the price with the signature. When we're offered something like this, we're doing our due diligence very, very carefully. Looking at this book with the naked eye, everything seemed right, but then you put it under this UV light and you see that the offsetting is wrong. If these pages were next to each other for 50-plus years, you get a ghost of the title page design on the blank of the page in front of it, and under UV, you can see this. When we turned on the UV, you could see, in fact, that it didn't match up, that it was still To Kill a Mockingbird, but it was a different title page design from a later edition. What had happened here is they had gotten a book that was authentically signed, the signature was right, but it was a later edition. The person knew that the single leaf that you needed to say it was a first edition was the title page with the copyright on the back, so they took that page from a first edition and inserted it into this book. And the way we were able to tell was from the UV light.

these about half-an-inch to an inch away from the focal point, and it provides magnification generally in the lower end, like 5-20x magnification. I'll keep that around in a pinch for easy things.

White Gloves as the "Anti" Cool Tool

I would love to take a moment to debunk the myth that I should be wearing white gloves when I handle printed books. From the British Library to the Houghton, none of the major conservators and rare book curators recommend these. And for good reason: with gloves, you lose your tactile sensitivity and are much more likely to damage the book while handling it. Just wash your hands first and you're fine.

Magnifiers

I use a few different magnifiers, depending on the circumstance. The easy go-to is frankly just a good old jeweler's loupe. These are generally doublet lenses, which are a single piece of glass that has been ground into a lens on each side. You can flip them open. They're really small, about the size of a dime, at least in width, and then they're obviously thicker than that. You just keep it in your bag and you can pull it out. The idea is you keep

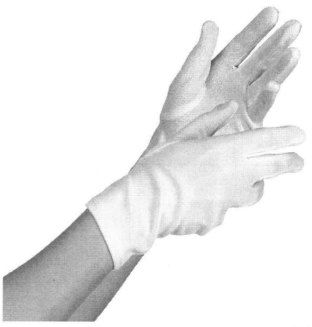

Kevin Rose
Serial Entrepreneur

Kevin Rose is a serial entrepreneur and product builder, having founded the social news site Digg in 2004. Later, Kevin pursued a career in venture investing, investing in companies like Medium, Ripple, and Blue Bottle Coffee while at Google Ventures, and is now investing at True Ventures. (Published 02/8/18)

Peloton Bike

I had taken a couple stationary bike classes and the ones that you actually have to go in person. Then I had a buddy of mine that was like you don't understand, these Peloton classes are a lot of fun, they really motivate you, you can do it in your house, and for me that just sounded like, okay, I'll give it a shot. And I went and tried it at a friend's house, and I got hooked and purchased one. And for a geek it's awesome because you get all the really detailed analytics on the screen there post-workout, and then it's all live streaming classes, so when you're in a class the instructors will call you out by name sometimes, and there's all different types of instructors depending on your music style and likes, so I've just found it to be a great way — if you have an extra half hour — to just jump on for 20 minutes and get a work out in.

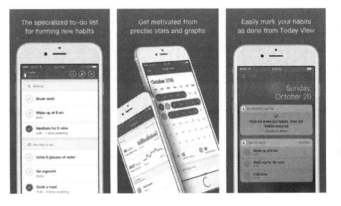

Habitify: Habit Tracker

I've been into habit tracking apps, but they always kind of fall off, but as a data junkie, and kind of a geek, I really like to see and be held to certain habits. I like to see a completion rate, and progress indicators, and little charts and graphs. This is just a really beautiful and simple habit tracking app. So for me, I set up daily habits that would be, say, "meditation" and there'll be habits that I want to happen three times a week, like "cardiovascular exercise," or taking certain vitamins three times a week, things like that, and so this is just my go-to app for all things habit tracking.

Ledger Cryptocurrency Wallet

I've tried both the TREZOR and the Ledger, and I wanted a place to have a physical device that is required to unlock your wallet, so that means, if I lose my laptop, or wherever I'm storing my cryptocurrency, you have to have this device

and things of that nature, but it's always kind of a pain. It's difficult in that these things are expelling gases, and you always have to keep everything submerged the right way, and this was a device that I had found probably a year ago called The Easy Fermenter that really makes it easy. You buy these little glass weights that sit inside of any standard mason jar, so it keeps all of your vegetables submerged beneath the brine, and then all you do is just screw on this lid that has an automatic exhaust valve to allow the gases to escape, and it's as simple as that.

Oak Meditation

I launched a meditation app called Oak. I wanted to kind of go back and teach more traditional meditation techniques so that people could come in, get trained up, and then really be set free to practice on their own in the unguided mode. The app starts off by teaching you general mindfulness meditation. We have mantra-based meditation, and then we have a loving kindness meditation, and so these are all going to be things where you take these courses inside of the app, and then you use our timer, which has chime reminders and things of that nature, and background sounds just to practice on your own, but I just wanted to give something away, and build something for free. So this entire app, and the courses — it's all free. There's no subscription or ads or anything like that.

along with a PIN code to authorize any transactions, or any sending of any of your coins or tokens. The reason I went with Ledger versus TREZOR is just the amount of companion apps and kind of built-in coins that they support. Right now, they support close to 30 different coins, and that was more than TREZOR.

Easy Fermenter Wide Mouth Lid Kit

A little hobby of mine is fermenting vegetables, and I've done this with a whole variety of different stuff. I started with sauerkraut, and I've done pickles,

Zander Rose
Executive Director at The Long Now Foundation

Alexander "Zander" Rose is the Executive Director of The Long Now Foundation, which was founded in 1996 to become the seed of a very long-term cultural institution that fosters very-long-term planning. He was hired to build their clock that lasts 10,000 years. He's also the founder of the Robot Fighting League, and a contestant on the ABC series Battlebots. (Published 07/26/15)

Knipex Parallel Plier Wrenches

Knipex is a European brand that makes some of the nicest things like adjustable wrenches, but they recently came out with this type of parallel wrenches. The funny thing about them is that you would look at them and you'd go, "Oh, well, this is like a normal kind of sliding adjustable wrench." But until you use them, you don't quite understand how amazing they are. You can adjust them but then when you actuate them, they have flat jaws that stay totally parallel. They're way more powerful than a crescent wrench even though they look like a set of pliers. They don't damage the flat surfaces that you're working against. Let's say if it's a nut that's an offsize or something that's custom-flat on it, you can adjust it to that size and it won't damage it. We used these in a lot of the construction of the 10,000-year clock project because we end up making a lot of custom fasteners and things with custom flats for tightening. These just are indispensable. We have them in every toolbox that we use.

Gear Drive Case Ball End Hex Keys

These are by Wiha, another European company. They make excellent tools. The thing about this particular set, is that there's these little gears in the actual case that gear them all together so when you grab one wrench and you turn it, they all turn out together, and so that you can pull one wrench out and then relock them all back in. People who've used the most common brand, Bondhus, will know that you spend a lot of time wrestling with two hands trying to get these things in and out of the case. As soon as they're out of the case and you don't know that size you're reaching for, it's a total pain. This is an optimization of the way to hold wrenches so that they come in and out of their case much better and have just become a total favorite.

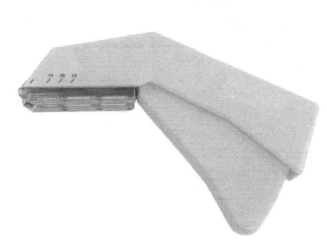

Skin Stapler

Normal people are not good at suturing, but if you want to close a wound and get somebody back to pavement and it's going to take several hours or a day, then a person with very little experience can actually close that wound back up with the skin stapler. There's lots of YouTube videos. You can practice on an orange at first and then you could go get some pig's feet and cut those. Put a nice wound in the pig feet from the butcher and close it back up. Pig's skin is apparently very close to the human skin. That's what doctors usually practice on.

3M Scotchcast Plus Casting Tape

I find that most of those first-aid kits have things like a bandage and some Band-Aids, but if you have an accident in the backcountry, mostly what you're trying to do is get somebody back to pavement. One thing generally missing from those kits is a water-activated resin cast material. You basically open up the package. You get it wet with some of the water from your water bottle and you can make a cast or a splint right then and there on the person. Unlike most of the air splints, this is a small, tiny roll of what looks like gauze but it's actually a resin-activated cast material, and then you can custom make it to any shape, if a bone is sticking out, you can work around that. If you have climbing tape with you, which generally we do, you can just make a splint up one side of their leg and then wrap around that or at their arm and wrap around that with the climbing tape and then it doesn't have to be cut off. If you don't, you could wrap it around the person's limb but you will have to cut that cast off when you get to a doctor. That's definitely the best material for stabilizing a break or a sprain when you're in the backcountry. It's the lightest thing you can carry as well, way lighter than the air splints and other backcountry splints.

Yuba Boda Boda Family Cargo Bike

There's a lot of cargo bikes out there that are extremely long, by both Yuba and Xtracycle. The problem with those is that they don't fit on bike racks. The Boda Boda by Yuba has a little bit longer wheelbase than a normal bike but still fits on normal bike racks.

Louis Rossetto
Co-founder of Wired

Louis Rossetto co-founded Wired with his life partner Jane Metcalfe. During his five years directing Wired, it won the National Magazine Award for General Excellence twice and was Adweek's Hottest Magazine of the Year. Wired also pioneered commercial web media, launching HotWired, the first website with original advertising and Fortune 500 advertising. Since Wired, he's pursued different obsessions, from real estate to helping start and run the high-end chocolate company TCHO, to writing his new novel Change is Good. (Published 08/23/17)

DxO OpticsPro

I kept looking for something that would allow me to process images faster and better, and I ran across this tool called DxO OpticsPro. Basically there's a plugin that goes into Lightroom, you can export photographs directly out of Lightroom into DxO, and then inside of DxO you can do the kind of image polishing that you'd like to do in Lightroom, but that Lightroom isn't totally adapted to. Maybe that's because they don't want to dent Photoshop. In DxO OpticsPro, there are a whole bunch of tools which are seemingly more intelligent than just a slider. Things that just make the whole process of arriving at a really good image easier. For example, you can pick spot reading and then look at a face, select the face on the image, and the program will adjust the lighting for the face itself and for the rest of the image. So it's not just lighting the face and then lighting the rest of the picture, it's lighting the face and making sure the rest of the picture stays in the right color in Lightroom.

Botvac D3 Connected

This is a normal looking Botvac but the nice thing about it is that it runs off an app. Once you set the whole thing up, then you can just press a button or even have it run off Alexa and tell your Botvac to start cleaning. It starts at the docking station and then it starts to take off and go around and vacuum the floor like all of these things do. The one thing about this particular robot is it doesn't just randomly run around the room; it actually it has a laser probe or something that's looking out and it's setting the parameters of the room and stuff in the room and then it goes around and tries to systematically, go up and down as much as it can go and vacuum that floor rather than the kind of crazy pattern that you might otherwise get by a robot that went, banged into something, and turned around and went the other direction or another direction again. So it's more efficient in that sense, and then when it's all done it runs back to its docking station, it sort of wiggles its back up against the dock, and sends you a message. It says, "I'm done." And turns itself off.

Philips Hue Lights with Yonomi App

When we first left Wired, I wanted to just put in state-of-the-art lighting in our place, and among the solutions that came along have been Phillips Hue system which started out as sort of colored lights. But there was the implication there that there was something more that could be done, and finally Phillips came along and it has a bridge that connects to your Wi-Fi or your network and then there's an app to run it. They finally realized this could be its own little ecology for lighting, and pretty soon they started introducing just plain white bulbs and then they introduced motion detectors and wall switches. For a few hundred dollars, now you can get the starter pack of the bridge that connects to the light bulb, so you get a bridge and two bulbs for around

60 bucks. With the app, which is free, you can then turn those bulbs on and off, you can set a schedule for them, you can connect them to motion detectors, you can connect them to switches. For a few hundred dollars then you can build a whole house lighting system that does about all the stuff that my multi $10,000 lighting system used to do 20 years ago. I think that's kind of remarkable ,and of course it's gone beyond that as home automation has gotten to be a new field.

Foundation Wailer 99

It used to be that you needed multiple skis if you were a dedicated skier or you just liked skiing at all. You'd have to have one set of skis for powder skiing, and another set of skis for barreling down the front of the mountain, and maybe another set of skis for all mountain skiing, where you'd also go on rough parts of the mountain. I got a pair of these a couple of years ago, and it certainly changed my sense about dealing with the whole mountain and all the different experiences that you can have on the mountain. There were whole parts of the mountain that I would never go near because they were not groomed or they just seemed spooky, or they were just too deep or whatever. And now with these kind of skis — they are good for the entire mountain.

J.D. Roth
Founder of Get Rich Slowly

J.D. Roth started blogging in 1997, before "blog" was even a word. In 2006, he founded GetRichSlowly.org, a site devoted to common-sense personal finance. He sold Get Rich Slowly in 2009, then bought it back in 2017. His mission in life is to help everyday people master their money and achieve their financial goals.
(Published 02/23/18)

National Notebook

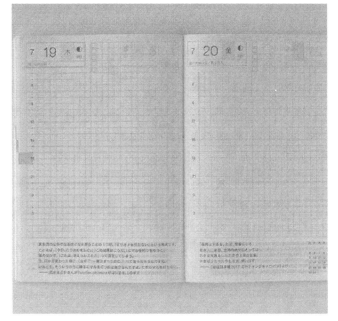

Cristal ballpoint pens. I buy them by the case from Amazon.

I am a writer, and I do most of my writing on a computer like most writers do nowadays, and that's not very exciting. Everyone has their favorite computers. But I also do a surprising amount of writing by hand, and I have my own favorite cheap notebooks. I use a couple of the models from a company called National Brand, and basically there's this legal supply store here in Portland, and I go down there and I stock up on these notebooks. They're a little more expensive than Mead spiral notebooks, but they're also a heavier-quality paper. And then I buy Dixon Ticonderoga pencils and BIC

Hobonichi Techo Planner

This is a Japanese calendar. It's A6 size. It's by a company Hobonichi, and instead of having all sorts of lines and times and all that, it's basically just a big blank slate. Each page has a date, and it shows noon, and it shows dinnertime, and other than that it's just squared paper for you to jot down your thoughts or to jot down your schedule. And for me, it works like a charm. Until my girlfriend convinced me to go digital, this was my source. I carried this with me everywhere.

Tom Bihn The Maker's Bag

I am a bag nerd. I have probably a dozen backpacks and messenger bags, and I use all of them. I like Filson bags, but they're expensive. For the past two years, my daily bag is the Maker's Bag from Tom Bihn. I like it because it's not overly complicated, for one. It'll hold a 15-inch laptop, but not much more than that. And then it will hold several books and magazines, plus there are maybe a dozen pockets. Maybe I'm exaggerating, but it seems like there's tons of different pockets and zippered places so that I can tuck all sorts of different stuff in there. I tend to travel a lot for work, and so on the plane I want to be able to have all of my stuff compartmentalized, and with the Maker's Bag I'm able to do that, and yet it's not overwhelming.

SleepPhones

So, this is something I originally got for travel. So what SleepPhones are is an elastic headband and inside is a set of earbuds, but they don't actually go in your ear, they just kind of rest outside ear. That's what SleepPhones are, and the kind I have are wireless. You do need to plug them in to charge them, although I think they have a model now that uses induction charging. So at night, when you're getting ready to go to sleep, if you want to listen to something you put the SleepPhones around your head like a headband — or I actually use it to double as an eye mask to keep out light — and then you listen to whatever you want to listen to. And like I said, I originally got them for travel, but because my girlfriend and I both have trouble sleeping, we now both use them to listen to stuff at night.

Icebreaker Merino Clothing

I am a huge fan of Icebreaker merino wool clothing. I discovered this stuff in 2010, and have been hooked ever since. It's warm when it's cold and cold when it's warm. It itches, but only a very little. The best part? Wool does NOT retain odors. That means you can wear an Icebreaker shirt (or a Smartwool shirt) over and over and over again without washing it and there are no consequences. This makes wool clothing ideal for travel. I know people who travel for months at a time with only two Icebreaker shirts. They take two because it does help to alternate them, to air one out after you use it — especially if you've been running in the shirt. No specific Icebreaker item to recommend. I just love their stuff.

Tina Roth Eisenberg
Swissmiss

Tina Roth Eisenberg is a Swiss born, raised, and trained graphic designer. In 1999, she came to New York City for a three-month design internship and never left. Over the past 13 years, Tina started numerous side projects that have organically turned into businesses. A creative co-working community called FRIENDS, a global monthly lecture series called CreativeMornings, a simple to-do app called TeuxDeux, and Tattly, a high-end temporary tattoo shop. She lives in Fort Greene, Brooklyn, with her two kids, Ella and Tilo. Tina is often referred to as Swissmiss, after her popular blog. She likes that. You can find her on Instagram and Twitter @swissmiss. (Published 04/26/19)

FREITAG Zippelin Inflatable Travel Bag

I really love the ZIPPELIN inflatable travel bag by FREITAG. FREITAG, for those who don't know it, is a Swiss company. They make bags out of truck tarp and they started I think over 30 years ago. If you're not familiar with truck tarps, in Europe, most trucks are not made out of metal, but they're made out of this really, really solid tarp. They turn these recycled tarps into bags. They're so cool. They last forever, and the two founders, the Freitag brothers, they're really incredible humans. They just keep reinventing this thing, and they just came out with this travel bag that has an inflatable bike tube inside, which is the frame for the travel bag, so you pump it up and that makes it solid enough to be a large travel bag. When you're done traveling, you can let the air out and roll this bag up and take the wheels off and it's tiny. Imagine you have a giant suitcase, but you can roll it up. It's waterproof as well, and it looks good and every single bag looks different because they use truck tarps, so a lot of these tarps are also printed on.

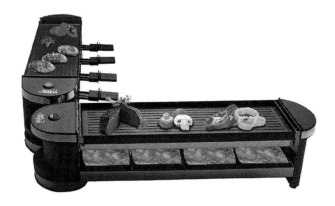

Artestia Electric Raclette Grill

Raclette is a very traditional meal you eat in Switzerland. You have it a lot on Sundays or on special occasions. It's this little grill that comes with teeny tiny sort of Teflon pans where you can put a slice of Raclette cheese; it's a certain type of cheese that melts really beautifully. You put that in, and then you put it on this grill and you wait, and that cheese melts away and you chit chat, and so everybody sort of cooks. It's a bit like the Korean barbecue of Switzerland, and while the cheese melts you can grill meat and vegetables on top of the grill. I've had many of these and it's a really cool communal way of having dinner because everybody chips in. You just sit there and you help each other grill the meats, and then when the cheese has melted, you scrape it over soft boil potatoes and put some Swiss spices on it. It's delicious. It's my favorite way of entertaining. As the host, you don't have to run around. You prepare everything ahead of time, and then everyone sits and cooks, and you smell cheese.

For Extra Volume
hold longer at the root

Revlon One-Step Hair Dryer

Anyone that knows me knows that I'm actually not a very girly lady, but my downstairs neighbor, I saw her put a box out with this blow dryer. It's a blow dryer and a round hair brush in one, and I saw her put the box out and I noticed that her hair was amazing, and I thought she was constantly getting blowouts. I was like, "Wait a second. You're not getting blowouts and you use this thing?" She says, "Yeah, it's incredible." So I got this thing and it's totally life-changing. If you like long, shiny, straight hair, this hair dryer/hair brush all-in-one is really a game changer.

U Konserve Stainless Steel Tumblr

We call it an insulated tumbler. Where you can keep your hot and cold beverages at the temperature that you poured it into, and this one is just really beautiful. I think it's great that more and more people bring their mugs in the mornings. I see a trend now here in New York. A lot of people don't want to do the throw-away cups so they bring their own. I found this one and it looks a bit like a stemless wine glass just out of metal and white at the bottom, so it's super sleek and super modern. I actually found it in California while I was in a supermarket. I was like, "This is just so pretty that I don't mind walking around with this on the street." Now I have like five of them. I keep three at work and two here and it's just a really pretty, sleek tumbler. When I sit on the stoop in the summer I drink out of it, and I have my wine in it and nobody knows I'm drinking wine on the stoop.

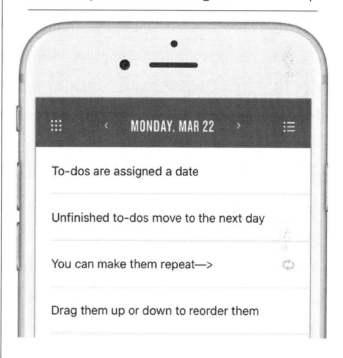

TeuxDeux

My Studiomate Cameron Koczon and I built this because I was lamenting the world of to-do apps in 2010, and I said, "I just want it to be as simple as a paper list of digital." We sort of took that as a joke.
I was ranting about it over lunch, and he said, "Just design it. I'll build it for you." It took me three hours and I was done, and then 48 hours later we had a working prototype and I was using it and then we were like, "Let's give it away. Let's just give it to the world." It's very simple, but it's so useful.

Adam Rubin
NYT Bestselling Author

Adam Rubin is the New York Times bestselling author of Dragons Love Tacos, Robo-Sauce, and half a dozen other critically acclaimed picture books. He is also a world-renowned inventor of illusions and was recently named Director of Puzzles and Games for ArtofPlay. com. (Published 08/9/17)

Pilot Frixion Erasable Blue Ink Pen

This pen is not actually marketed as a disappearing ink pen. It's marketed as a Frixion Pen, and its intention is to be an erasable pen. It's a normal-looking pen and on the back of the pen is this sort of rubber or plastic nib. And if you write with the pen and you rub the nib over the ink, the ink goes away. But, the true nature of the pen is that it's heat activated. So if you heat up the ink, it disappears. That could be with the nib that's on the back of the pen, or that could be with the flame from a lighter, or that could be in a microwave. So basically, what you have, is you have a pen that writes with ink that you can make disappear with fire. And that is a pretty cool tool to me. One of the cool things about it is that you can use it sort of as a fun science thing to do with kids because, you don't necessarily need to use fire. If you draw on paper and you put it in the microwave for about 15 seconds, you can watch the ink visibly disappear with nothing touching it, which is a really fun experiment with kids.

Ultra-Sil Day Pack

The Super Scrunch Backpack — It's a rip-stop backpack. It's like 20 liters and it stuffs down into a pouch that's smaller than your fist. It's super strong.

It's super reliable. And I keep one in all of my bags. My backpack, my carry-on, my duffle. I always have an extra backpack that takes up less room than a pair of socks. When you unfold it, you actually have a little mini-pocket inside if you want to put your keys or your headphones in there. So, when you're on the road, you want to put some laundry in there or you want to put extra souvenirs or you just want something for hiking to stick into your larger backpack, it's a totally awesome product.

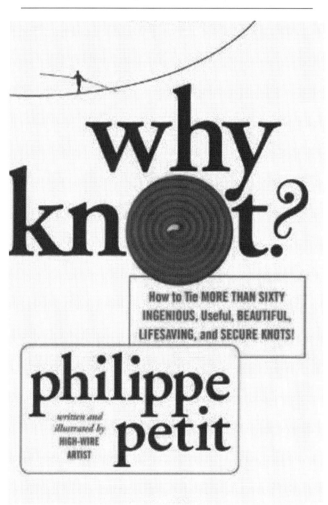

Why Knot?

Why Knot? is an illustrated guide to knot tying that was written by Philippe Petit. He is the famous subject of the documentary, Man on Wire. Where he tight-rope walked between the Twin Towers before they were finished being built. An amazing guy. Like a total Polymath. He illustrated and wrote this book himself, which is pretty amazing because he is definitely a guy who is very dependent on knots. So, he's super passionate about the history, and he's really good at explaining the different kinds of knots you might need to use for sailing or for camping or hiking. And he's even got some magic trick-type of knots in there, and there's some really cool decorative knots as well. I learned how to tie a monkey knot, or a monkey's fist, from the book.

Black Ergonomic Stool with Foot Ring

I was in the advertising industry for 10 years, and I quit my day job almost two years ago now to write full-time and work from home at design, and I was worried that I would just spend the whole day sitting in a chair and just kind of slouched over. So, I was looking for something to help me overcome that problem and I found this stool. It's an adjustable height, rotating, rolling desk stool and it is so perfect for me. I like it because it gives me a couple of options, like I can sit my feet flat on the floor and get that upright posture for a while, and then sort of switch to more of a perched position like a little bit more on the edge of the stool with my heels up on the base ring. I'll put it up all the way or I'll sink it down, depending on what I'm doing, if I'm drawing or if I'm typing or something like that. I like the stool because, I think for me, it helps me sit up straight more frequently. I mean you could still slouch of course, but in a chair I find I would slouch back more often and you cannot do that in a stool so, it keeps me upright for longer.

Paolo Salvagione
Visual Artist

Paolo Salvagione is an artist who works at the intersection of engineering, participation, and levity. He has sent his studio visitors out one second-story window and back into another on a 900-pound steel wheel, and created scent-based sculptures that use smell as a touchstone for memory. He worked, for over a decade, as lead engineer on the 10,000 Year Clock of the Long Now Foundation.
(Published 10/27/16)

Greenlee 45000 Wire Stripping Tool

I feel like anyone who's worked on electronics projects has kind of run into this tool in their drawer full of things. They kind of look like pliers that are punitively for stripping wire and all they kind of really do is they notch the conductive elements. They occasionally will strip off the insulation. Often they will even pull the insulation over the wire and kind of extend it out so you have to cut it again, and then when you do that you end up with the insulation pulling back. About 2 years ago I was working with a collection of people on a project and I stumbled on the Greenlee 45000, and not only does this thing allow you to kind of quickly adjust what wire gauge you want, but it also allows you to quickly adjust what amount of stripping you want to do on that wire. It will even let you gang up four or five wires at a time. It's unbelievably nice.

FastCap Glu-Bot Glue Bottle

Glu-Bot is designed by the wood industry to put down glue in a really nice way on things that you're gluing up. One of the things that no one talks about when you're doing adhesives is something called drool, which is when you're trying to lay down an adhesive, depending on the viscosity you get to that moment where you want to stop but the glue bottle doesn't and so you end up with little drips on the floor, on your hands, on the part of the wood that you didn't want the glue, which can be a real bummer. What's neat about this bottle is that they've designed it so that it takes the glue from the bottom instead of the top, which means that you don't have to worry about the skin or the viscosity difference between the bottom and the top of the whole thing because oxygen slowly usually dries things out.

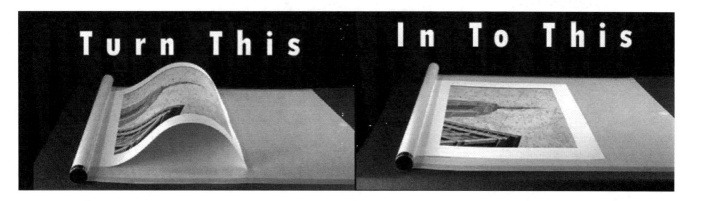

De-Roller Paper Anti Curl Device

This is one of those things where somebody should make the Boy Scout badge which is just somebody hitting their forehead with the palm of their hand kind of like "Aw, I should have thought of that." This is amazing. In the arts, I often transport things, works that I've purchased get rolled up, and there's always this challenge of like how do I de-roll it and this is a company that makes a device that someone introduced me to and I'm just smitten with it. It's super simple. It's a piece of plastic that's got foam running on both sides and a metal tube and basically you roll it out, you set the object that needs to be de-rolled in it in the opposite direction of roll, and then you roll it back and then maybe engage the Velcro for a minute or so, and then unroll it and the object is flat.

Marson Ribbed Rivet Nut Kit

This feels very much like you're using a pop rivet but what you are actually doing is you're installing threads in something. I first ran into this in the bicycle industry where I wanted to add another water bottle cage to my bike, and so what it does is it allows you to drill a hole in a tube and then you can put this thing in here and with the thing that looks like a pop rivet gun, you basically insert a nut in a way that it won't spin and then you can screw on your additional water bottle cage. Since then, I've used it to basically add nuts to the side of my refrigerator and put nuts inside of the trunk in my car. You can screw a series of things into that sub-assembly. It's really nice in the sense that it allows you to kind of put something in place that allows you to kind of almost breadboard a bunch of ideas in different locations.

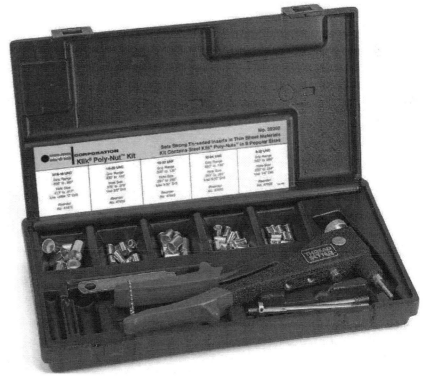

Anita Sarkeesian
Feminist Frequency Radio

Anita Sarkeesian is a media critic and the host of Feminist Frequency Radio. She has a new book called History vs Women, which she wrote with Ebony Adams. (Published 09/28/18)

Calendly

I found this app called Calendly and what it is is you just send a link and then the other person finds the time on your calendar and just automatically schedules it. It's like heaven. The way it works is you put in your calendar constraints. If you want to have availability open from nine to five, Monday through Friday, you do that. You can also change it and be like, "Oh, I'm not available from one to five or whatever might be." It's very customizable, and then it only shows the other people the dates and times that you are available. It's awesome. I think there's premium versions where you can send to more people at once, but in my experience I'm just using it one-to-one. I've also seen people use it who work in a customer service scenario where they're scheduling meetings to introduce new clients to their product or what have you, and so they set it up and then they're just like, "Here, pick your time that works." I've seen people use it for events. So, if you're at a conference and you're scheduling a bunch of meetings, you can use it that way for that week to make sure that everyone can just schedule in and it's not all these back and forths.

Instant Pot

The Instant Pot is a slow cooker, pressure cooker, rice cooker. It's a multi-tool thing in your kitchen that lets you cook kind of everything. It is remarkable. I actually had the instant pot sitting in my house for a couple of years and never used it, and I finally pulled it out earlier this year, and I don't know why I waited so long. You can make so much with it so quickly. You can sauté in it. You can do roasts in it. You can make soups. I boil eggs in it. You could put 20 eggs in it and it will be absolutely perfect every time, because it's the exact same pressure and there's no juggling when did the water start boiling and all of that stuff. I come from a family where my mother has every single kitchen gadget known to humankind. I somehow end up with all of these kitchen gadgets, and this is a one-stop shop. I'm seeing more and more cookbooks coming out. I just got "25 Affordable Easy Instant Pot Recipes." So we're seeing more and more experimentation and more and more options of how to use it.

Eagle Creek Packing Cubes

I am a little bit neurotically obsessed with packing efficiency. I am constantly looking for more efficient ways of bringing the least amount of things, especially when I'm going on month-long, multi-city trips. So, packing cubes are one of the things that I started introducing into my travels. They're basically like little bags, and instead of just folding your clothes up and throwing it in the suitcase, you fold your clothes up and you stick them in these little bags, and it lets you pack in more, more efficiently. You can make them sit in whatever ways, which is this nice tidy collection. So, if you do have to pack a little bit more and don't want it sort of popping out everywhere, these bags help contain it. The brand that I use is Eagle Creek. They're a little more stable and structured in size as opposed to ones that are more flimsy. You can pack them, you can just fold your clothes as you would and stuff them in, or you can roll your clothes. There are lots of different ways to use them.

The Gender Knot: Unraveling our Patriarchal Legacy by Allan G. Johnson

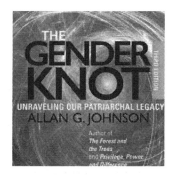

This is a book that I always have. Once I read it for the first time, I was like, "This is foundational and instrumental to my feminism, to my activism work," and the reason I love it so much is because it takes these very big concepts of systems of oppression. In this case

specifically, it's talking about patriarchy and distills it down into very easy to understand language. It takes it out of the theoretical, academic realm and explains it in ways that's really easy for folks to understand, and I found it to be so instrumental in my understanding, or the early days of understanding feminism, that I highly recommend it to everyone who wants to get a better sense of what is patriarchy. What are systems of oppression? How do they affect you? How do they affect our world, and what do we do about it? It doesn't make it any simpler. It just makes it more accessible. It uses language that we can understand. It makes it more available to more people instead of keeping it trapped in these academic spaces.

History vs Women: The Defiant Lives that THEY Don't Want You To Know

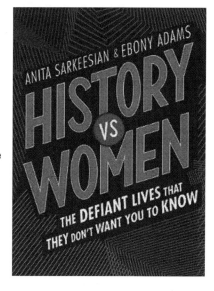

We profiled 25 women who have been erased from history. The book actually came out of a series that we did at Feminist Frequency called the Ordinary Women, where we told the stories of five women that we thought were very interesting and that we wanted other people to learn about. So, with History vs Women,

we obviously got to tell more stories and dive in a little deeper. I think one of the things that this book does is we're trying to root the fact that women have been written out of history and the erasure of women's experiences, women's lives, women's contributions to our contemporary time and the way women are treated today. So, we write in the book about why you should care about these women. Why you should care about these forgotten stories and how it affects us today and in the future. It was really important to us to be intersectional in the way that we approached the women that we chose. It is intergenerational, so we tried to do a very wide span of history, and we tried to look as globally as we could.

Adam Savage
Tested.com

Adam Savage has spent his life gathering skills that allow him to take what's in his brain and make it real. He's built everything from ancient Buddhas and futuristic weapons to fine-art sculptures and dancing vegetables. Today, Adam hosts and executive produces MythBusters Jr., as well as a brand-new series, Savage Builds, which airs on Science Channel. He also stars in and produces content for Tested.com, including behind-the-scenes dives into multiple blockbuster films (including Alien Covenant, Mortal Kombat and Blade Runner). His most recent book is called Every Tool's a Hammer.

(Published 05/31/19, 06/24/16)

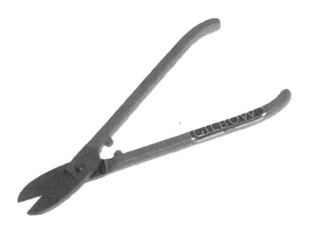

Gilbow G56 Straight Jewellers Snip

These are Gilbow nippers. I found out about these while working on a suit of armor with Terry English in Cornwall, England. Terry is the armorer for Excalibur. He pulled one of these out to cut through some fairly heavy aluminum in this precise way to get around this thing. I was like "I love the idea of a non-power tool making these tiny little precise cuts in aluminum to do the shaping he was doing." He made these things really sing in his hands. They're more rugged, and they're made with a tolerance. You can really clamp down and you can feel it just wants to cut through a fairly reasonable gauge of aluminum. The pair that Terry was using was probably 35 to 40 years old. I was really pleased to see that Gilbow is still in business, still making tools, and they seemed every bit as awesome as they always were. I always like finding an old tool that's still being made by the same company.

USB Digital Portable Soldering Iron

The tool is a sort of a twin tool. At the business end is the newest kind of soldering iron that I have encountered, which is effectively a USB powered soldering iron that when you connect it up to a power source, you can literally plug this from this power input to a USB. This thing heats up to its full heat in about 10 seconds. Its heat is highly adjustable. I have never found a bench top soldering iron to work for me, to stay hot enough. What I've plugged it into is a power supply that connects right up to one of my DeWalt FLEXVOLT 60-volt batteries. There's been this whole new thing lately of add-ons for power tool batteries. Not only USB power supplies for powering your phone and external power supplies for powering things like this, but also, and Tom Sachs introduced me to this, there are main market and aftermarket adapters for any battery to almost any other cordless system.

Hobart Battery Powered MIG Welder

This is a battery powered MIG welder, which means this pelican case is all that you need to lay down a weld bead. You don't need gas. You don't need to connect it to anything. I bought this during MythBusters, and there were a couple of times it saved our ass. We carried it to the top of a crane to take care of something that we couldn't have taken care of any other way. On the new show I have coming up on Science Channel, Savage Builds, this thing was a completely mission-critical tool on almost every episode. This also can be hooked up to gas if you want to, but in general I keep flux core wire in it so that it creates its own gas envelope. What I also love about this is I just watched Aliens the other night for the first time in a few years, and it's still a perfect movie. There's all these points at which the marines are like, "Close that door and weld it." They're welding the door shut, and I'm like, "That's not science fiction." You could carry this welder on the back of a marine and weld the door shut behind you. This would be, along with a generator, one of the most important parts of my bug-out kit at the end of civilization, which might be a couple of weeks away.

Ammoon Convex Thumb Plane

This is a plane with a convex bottom. It's got a hardened steel blade that sticks out of a flat on the bottom. This is meant for planing out the inside of the back of a violin. This comes about from I'm always on the search for industries that are using things I haven't seen before. I've been watching a lot of luthiers and violin makers over the last couple of years on YouTube, because I just love watching that precision, the slow, methodical pace. I've been over the last couple of years becoming more attuned to finer woodworking, to gluing all my joints, to making the joints rabbeted, or doweled, really making things last. It's a totally different mindset. This is part of that program. I have collected a larger collection of planes and spokeshaves and things like that. I'm really bringing them more into my process.

19" Forged Alloy Nail Puller

This is a really ancient tool and it's a cast iron nail puller. It's got a little beak at the end like a octopus' beak or a squid beak, and that's the part you put around the nail. You use the handle to hammer the beak and the beak clamps in and grabs both sides of the nail. Then you pull back on the handle using the lever to the side of the beak and it yanks a nail right out of the wood. I use this tool maybe once every couple of years, but every time I do there's no other tool that would have done what this does. You could have a nail that's missing it's head and this thing could still pull it out. Try and find me another tool that could apply that much physics to the problem of pulling a nail. It feels right out of a Sears catalog or a Montgomery catalog from the turn of the last century.

Jen Schachter
Multimedia Maker

Jen Schachter is a multimedia maker and a mastermind of interactive art projects, including a giant light-up sign for the Obama White House, a wooden parking-validation robot, and a monumental 3D-printed sculpture of Rosie the Riveter. You can find her product reviews in Make Magazine, her epic collaborations with Adam Savage on Tested.com, and her tool manuals in fabrication shops in Baltimore. (Published 01/11/19)

RZ Reusable Filtration Mask

This is an excellent alternative to the rubber respirators that are standard in most shops. It's a breathable cloth filtration mask with one-way air vents that prevent condensation from building up inside. It's comfortable to wear, doesn't suction to your face, and the straps are a lot easier to get on and off. They have four different kinds of filters available for dust, fumes, smoke, chemicals and stuff, down to .1 micron. The fact that it's so comfortable means I'm not constantly ripping it off so it's actually doing its job — saving my sinuses, my lungs, and probably my life in the long run.

Dovetail Workwear Pants

These work pants are a game changer for women in trades. They fit really well, have lots of deep and specialized pockets, reinforced knees, and tool loops. They are made of super-thick, rugged denim that stretches. You can literally do squats in them with full mobility. The other thing I love, apart from the name and the function, is the company was founded by three women, and their marketing is really diverse and inclusive of different body types, skin colors, and gender expressions. I have a pair of their Maven Slim Stretch back from when the brand used to be called Moxie and Moss, and it's pretty much all I wear in the shop. They have other cuts and styles, overalls, shirts, and other gear too. My one complaint is they are always out of stock because they're in such high demand.

BLACK+DECKER The Matrix

I've had a Craftsman Bolt-on tool for six years and it's probably the power tool I reach for most. It's a cordless, interchangeable multi-tool with one drill-type handle and a whole set of attachments that snap on and off. Unfortunately Craftsman discontinued them, but Black+Decker's version, The Matrix, looks about the same and it has 4.5 stars and 400+ reviews on Amazon so it's probably a safe bet. Theirs has attachments for a drill, sander, jigsaw, oscillating tool, router, and impact driver all in the base kit. You can also get a trim saw or a reciprocating saw. I use the heck out of the drill, trim saw, and sander on mine. It's definitely not going to replace a serious router or circular saw, but it's great for quick and dirty projects or anyone who has limited space or budget.

Yongnuo 300 Air LED Light

This is a low-profile, lightweight-but-high-powered LED light that's designed to be mounted to a camera, but really versatile in how it can be used. I'm a novice when it comes to photography and video, but I've been researching and starting to up my game when it comes to documenting my work.

This light is inexpensive, and you can attach it not only to a camera, but also a light stand or tripod, it has adjustable brightness, color temperature, for tungsten or daylight, and it can be powered with AC power or a rechargeable battery. Adam Savage used a very similar LED panel to build a custom shop light. One piece of advice: it doesn't come with power supply, battery or charger, so shop around for a good deal on one.

We the Builders

I work with a group called We the Builders that makes crowdsourced, 3D-printed sculptures, and what that means is we take a digital file or we scan an object. We bring that into the computer and slice it into sections, so we basically separate it into a grid, and then each of the sections is exported as a file for 3D printing. And you can go onto our website, download that file, and print it at home, and then you send us the part, and we collect parts for the whole sculpture. And in the end, we get a few hundred or, in some cases, a few thousand parts. We assemble them all together into the shape that we initially started with.

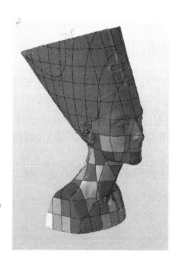

Joshua Schachter
Creator of Delicious

Joshua Schachter is the creator of the social bookmarking site, Delicious, the creator of GeoURL, and the co-creator of Memepool. (Published 05/2/16)

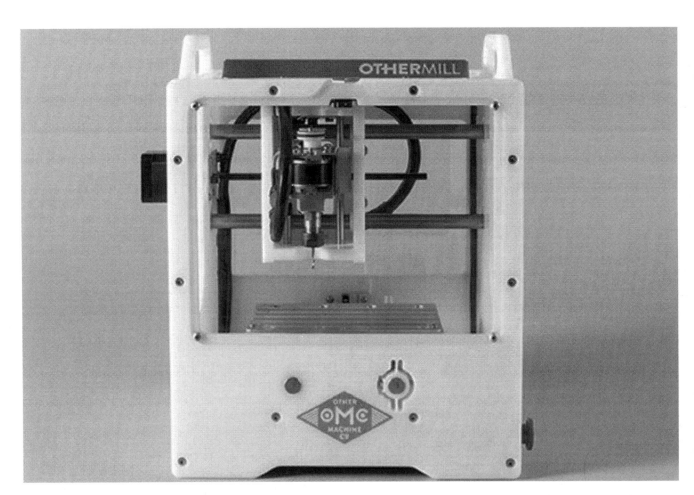

Othermill (Bantam Tools)

This is basically a 3D remover. The examples it comes with are mostly targeted around designed PCB, PC boards, so it comes with copper-clad boards, and you etch away and drill through the places where circuits and chips would go in, parts would go in, and be soldered to. It's not too expensive, it's easy to machine. Other Machine has made software that's actually pretty good if you have 2D shapes you want to cut out of materials, it can go directly from SVG to machine, and when I'm in a hurry I often do that. It's a tiny CNC machine, but it is a real CNC machine, so it's not dumbed-down in any particular way.

that kind of stuff. One of the things I like doing is infusing tomatoes with balsamic vinegar, so the vinegar goes inside the tomatoes.

Extruded aluminum rail, 80-20

80-20 is a series of rail used for industrial and scientific use. It's pretty inexpensive. You can get pieces of it on Amazon. Basically, they're long slots of aluminum with a channel in them so that you can easily bolt, unbolt, and rearrange the parts. The nice thing about aluminum is you can actually cut it on woodworking tools. And it's not irreplaceably expensive, so you don't feel too bad when you mess with it or change it up a bit.

VacMaster VP122

A vacuum chamber sealer is often used for sous vide in professional kitchens. It drops the pressure down in a chamber with the bag of food, seals the bag, and then returns the pressure. It basically seals it in a vacuum. The vacuum is powerful enough that when you put fruit or vegetables in there, the vegetable cells contain a tiny pocket of air called a vacuole, and the vacuum sealer will burst the vacuole, so for some things like watermelon or some fruits it will change texture entirely. You can also put liquid in there which will get pulled into the cells when the vacuum releases. You can make pickles in a few minutes. You can infuse pickles with vinegar or with brine. You can also infuse fruits with alcohol,

Deli Cups

Deli cups are these little polypropylene little containers that, when you get Chinese food and the soup comes in one it's got a little top. They're super cheap. I think it's like $50 for 200 on Amazon, cheaper if you shop around, but I use it for a ton of things. When I take stuff apart, I use it to sort the parts, the screws, the little bits that come off of things. I've heard people say they use muffin tins to organize parts for when they take stuff apart. I use deli cups instead, because you can seal them, put them away, etc. I use them as parts bins for new parts when I'm building stuff. I use them for mixing chemicals quite a bit because the polyethylene or polypropylene does not react to much, so it's a great thing to mix stuff in.

Elon Schoenholz
Commercial Photographer

Elon Schoenholz is a former guest editor of Cool Tools and has been working as a commercial photographer documenting art and architecture in L.A. for the past 20 years. He's a husband and father, gardener and an avid cyclist, and a founding member of the LA County Bicycle Coalition. He raced cyclocross for three seasons without ever breaking the top 10. (Published 2/22/19)

Gitzo Series 5 Carbon Fiber Tripod

I've had a lot of tripods over the years. Gitzo is known for making the best. I believe they're a French company. But this tripod is special in that it's considerably taller than any other tripod I'm aware of. I think with the center column it gets up close to 11 feet. I actually use it more than you might expect at its full height for shooting exteriors and also for getting over very large pieces of art. Sometimes I'll photograph rugs or tapestries and have to get really high up. There's really nothing else in the game that even competes with this one.

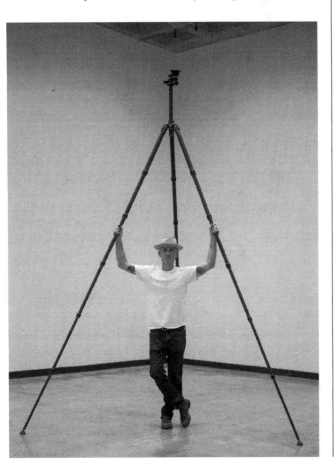

VSGO Camera Sensor Cleaning Kit

I recently started shooting with the Sony a7RIII that came out within the past year or so, and it's been a revolutionary camera for me. But it's a mirrorless camera, and so therefore, there's no barrier between the sensor and the open air when you switch lenses. So I found right when I bought it and started using it, I was getting lots of dust on the sensor, and besides the expense of paying $50 to have a camera repair place clean the sensor, I couldn't be without it for 24 or 48 hours. So I looked into cleaning it myself and was pretty afraid to touch the sensor, but I went for it and got these inexpensive swabs by a company called VSGO. I found it on Amazon, pretty well reviewed, and I watched some YouTube videos. And I did it myself very effectively with a little bit of optic cleaning fluid that comes with it in a kit.

Krane AMG500 Tilt Cart

Almost more important than my tripod is my cart, because a lot of times I don't have a budget for an assistant but I'm carrying a ton of gear. And for a while I was using a Magliner, which is like what a UPS driver uses. It was just a little bit overkill. And the Krane model that I found at Samy's Camera in LA is just a perfect in-between for me. I easily get 250 pounds on it, and it's just great. It folds down very small, so it's much more portable than a Magliner would be, but it carries more than twice as much as what one of those little folding carts would carry. It has two basic setups. You can have it set up so that the bottom of it is flat, or you can angle the bottom of it. Even when the bottom's angled, it's still rolling on all four wheels. I have a Pelican case with lenses, a big backpack with my Profoto lights, another backpack with my camera bodies and laptop, a tripod bag, and then another bag with light stands and umbrellas, and that all fits. And then two sandbags, and that all fits on the cart, and I'm able to move it myself without assistance.

Iron Gym Total Upper Body Workout Bar

One of the most useful things I own is a pull-up bar that can be taken down anytime. So as opposed to the traditional, old-school pull-up bars that would screw and torque into a door frame, this rests on top of the door frame. Some door frames have sort of the equivalent of a window frame, where there's a little ledge. And so a piece rests on that, and then sort of due to leverage and gravity, it's very, very stable. So you can take it off, and you can put it up or take it down in just a moment, and I particularly like that because I like to have it in the kitchen. If we have company over, I take it down. But I do a lot of my work from home, and getting away from the computer and hanging, as I believe I may have heard Tim Ferriss talking about, that's something that I find is enormously helpful for my back when I'm at my computer all day.

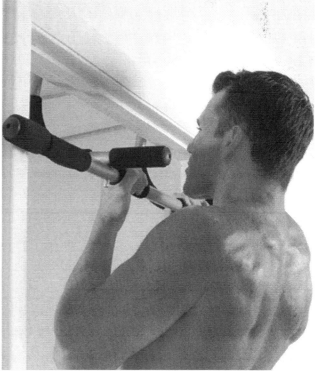

Nik Schulz
Illustrator

Nik Schulz wears many hats. He's contributed illustrations to magazines including Wired, Fortune, and Popular Science. He was actually the first illustrator for Make magazine. He's also a furniture maker, automotive illustrator, and an overlander. He lives and works on Orcas Island in Washington State. You can find him on Instagram at @nikschulzillustration.
(Published 08/30/19)

Map Measuring Wheel

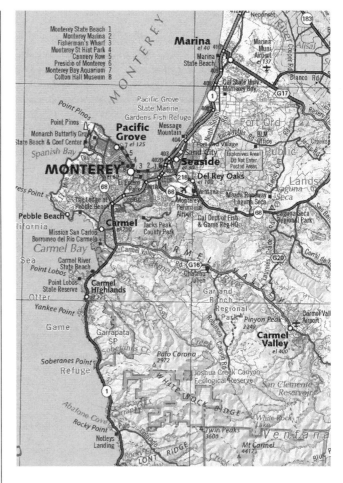

This device is used for measuring non-straight-line distances on paper maps. Google Maps does a great job in most situations, but when you get into the backcountry Google doesn't always know what is a road and what isn't. And you might not even have an internet connection. Using a map measuring wheel is a satisfyingly direct alternative to measuring distances online. Mine is a vintage Keuffel & Esser from Switzerland. Minerva is another vintage brand. Alvin makes a new one.

Benchmark Maps Road and Recreation Atlases

Each of these paper atlases covers a single state. The front section divides the state up into regional maps that list recreational opportunities — for Washington there are about 10. Though

the real beauty happens in the detailed "Landscape" pages. Each spread (19"x13.5") shows an area about 60 miles x 50 miles. They're exceptionally clear and easy to read. In places like national forests, the maps will delineate the difference between a trail, 4×4 road, dirt road, or paved road. In my overlanding experience they're much more useful and easy to read than USGS maps.

244

interchangeable jaws so that you can crimp other terminal types like flag terminals (connector and wire at 90°) or terminals with built-in heat shrink.

RIDGID 12-Volt Lithium-Ion 3/8 in. Cordless 2-Speed Drill Kit

I bought the previous generation of this drill. At first blush this looks like an unassuming drill driver but it's really one of my favorite tools. It's compact, feels extremely well-balanced and weighted, is quite powerful, has two speeds (for screws or drill bits), and is reversible. Changing the maximum torque by rotating the ring under the chuck produces a series of satisfying clicks. The included charger will bring the dead lithium ion batteries back to life in about half an hour. And there are two included so you never have to stop working. It's a fantastic all-round tool that's handy for just about everything.

The Morningside Sofa Set

I've been an illustrator for the last 18 years. I actually have an industrial design degree, so, recently I thought it would be interesting and satisfying to get back to my industrial design roots and build furniture. I designed this sofa set and it's called the Morningside. This sofa set has fold-back rests that fold down and the cushions on the backrest cushions are kinda of loose so you can take them off. By virtue of having these folding back rests, the pieces can be configured as a sofa or you push the two together and fold all the back rests down except for two, which you leave horizontal and then you have queen beds with nightstands, or you can push them against each other and leave one side of the back rest up and fold the other ones down and then you have a lounger. For us, it just seemed like the most versatile piece of furniture that we could have.

Titan Tools Ratcheting Wire Terminal Crimper

This tool crimps terminals onto wires. I use it for 12V electrical projects on cars and boats. It has a ratcheting jaw. One click of the lever will hold a terminal in place, making it easy to insert a wire. Then just ratchet all the way through to finish the crimp and you'll never drop the terminal. They make a perfect double crimp with the correct amount of force every time. They even sell a version with

Terri Schweitzer
Editor of Better Humans

Terrie Schweitzer is the editor of Better Humans for Coach.me, and on the weekend she's a professional bubble entertainer with Big Top Bubbles. She loves unconventional adventures and spent two years working with cashew farmers in Ghana, has been a goat milker, and counts hawks with Golden Gate Raptor Observatory. (Published 4/12/19)

Soap Bubble Wiki

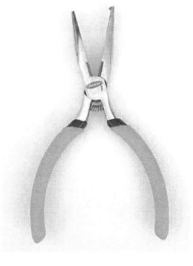

This is a sort of giant open source encyclopedia to the world of soap bubbles. Everything from the giant soap bubbles you might have seen us doing at Maker Faire to foams and films and fog-filled bubbles and all sorts of things. This resource is developed by the community of bubblers worldwide and people really share a lot of information. We like to say "We don't have a secret ingredient." We share information freely; we help teach each other. I learned myself from mentors in this space. So, this is the go-to place for information if you want to make some great bubble juice of your own. My favorite bubble juice, and the one that we use for performance, is called Brian's competition mix and that recipe is available on the wiki. It's a little complicated and time consuming to make; I learned it from Brian Lawrence who runs the giant bubble booth at Maker Faire every year. That would be my go-to juice, but he also has a very simplified version and he shares this at Maker Faire, which is a lot of fun because it's basically just water, dish detergent, and personal lube.

Berkley Chrome Split Ring Pliers

Split ring pliers are for opening the kind of split rings that you find on key chains. You can find them in fishing tackle stores or in the fishing tackle aisle, but sometimes beaders and jewelry makers use them too. It's just a pair of pliers with a notch on the end that you slip in between the rings and it pries the ring open. This is related to the work I do in making bubble tools. For our wands, we make giant wands with fishing poles and then we rig leaders on to the ends of the poles to connect the wicks. And so, we use small split rings to connect up our wicks and our poles together. If you have to connect something, split rings are super useful because they're utterly reliable.

Early Retirement Extreme

This is a book by Jacob Lund Fisker who is an early-retired astrophysicists. There's also an associated website and a really cool discussion forum. It's sort of an extreme frugality or anti-consumerist type of movement. The hook is that if you're smart about how you spend money, you can retire in your thirties, and then have the rest of your life to do whatever you want with. So, I mean, obviously I'm way beyond that age, and I think a lot of other people that are drawn to this also are. Early Retirement Extreme is just sort of the hook to get

you interested. He describes it as "a combination of simple living, anti-consumerism, DIY ethics, self-reliance, resilience, and applied capitalism." It's really more about a way to be an independent free-thinking person and always question, from the standpoint of money, how you spend your money, how you spend your time. And in the forums you'll see everything from permaculture, to sort of this modern nomadism and van dwelling, to people who are living in really unconventional spaces doing unconventional things. There's a thread that I love called the Something From Nothing Log, and it's people finding something that somebody has thrown out and they fix it up and then they sell it or they put it to use.

Quetext Plagiarism Checker

We found Quetext because in my work as an editor of Better Humans, we get a lot of articles pitched to us, and the first couple times I noticed we were getting

articles that made me think this text doesn't match up with who I perceive this author to be, and I would Google a section and I could often find a match. I could pinpoint where they had copied from and it would confirm that this is just somebody that's kind of doing a content farm thing, and trying to piece together articles up out of other articles. But, we found Quetext, and with this, we can just upload a document or paste it in, and it does a search and it tells you if it finds matching text from other sources. The pro version is just $10 a month. We pay for that. You can check up to 500 words at a time on the free version. This will give you a full report so that you can see how many hits are in the document at one point, and sort of a percentage of how much is found on other sites, and it'll give you a citation. One of the uses of it is evidently for students who need to create citations out of things they've written, so it will find the original source of what they're citing.

BetterHumans: Self Improvement Advice that Works

Better Humans is a publication of Coach.me, which is the company I work with Tony Stubblebine on. We're basically all about self improvement advice that really works. So, we publish articles mostly by authors who have done something themselves, and can now teach other people how to do. Sometimes we also publish advice from coaches, and once in a while, by an academic who's done some type of deep research. For example, we've done some articles along those lines on procrastination. What is procrastination, why do we do it, and how do you overcome it? But, we cover everything from productivity advice to diet and fitness advice. We've done some great relationship articles, and we love even some sort of edge-case topics—we kind of like to experiment and see where those edges of self-improvement are. We did a great edge-topic article, for example, on how to be a good neighbor to homeless people.

Dan Shapiro
Founder of Glowforge

Dan Shapiro is the founder of Glowforge, the 3D laser printer. He's also the creator of Robot Turtles, the board game that teaches programming to preschoolers. He wrote Hot Seat: The CEO Guidebook, and his latest hobby is throwing his wife and twin 10-year-olds in dungeons with dragons. You can find him on Twitter @danshapiro. (Published 07/26/19)

Cast Iron Skillet and Random Orbital Sander

I love cooking for the family and my favorite cooking tool is something that my wife got me for my birthday. She went on eBay and she got a 1950-something 12-inch vintage cast iron skillet. You say, "Okay, vintage cast iron. What's the fuss?" I wound up super geeking out on this. It turns out that nowadays cast iron skillets come directly out of the cast and they have this rough bottom. So you read about cast iron being the ultimate nonstick cookware, but you've got this grating surface on the bottom of your cast iron. Modern cast iron has this, but the old stuff didn't. The old stuff they actually ground down so it was smooth on the bottom. I wanted to figure out, is this something you could replicate today? And I found a really cheap achievable way of doing this. Because it turns out, if you take a modern cast iron skillet and you sand it flat, which takes about a half an hour, you can get

almost as good as the old vintage stuff that's really hard to get ahold of. So what you do is use a random orbital sander and put on the coarsest sandpaper that you have laying around, and you just sand the bottom of the pan. You go around and around until it is smooth to the touch. Then you follow any of the good "how to season your cast iron skillet" how-tos on the internet, and you wind up with a cast iron skillet that works like nonstick cookware, but doesn't flake carcinogens and you can use metal spatulas in it and all that good stuff that cast iron is wonderful for, and will last another century. It is kitchen magic.

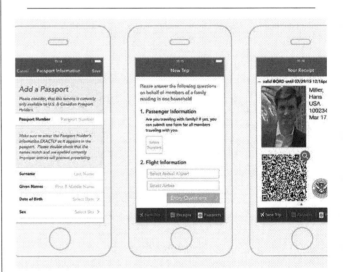

Mobile Passport App

I have to travel internationally for my job, and nowadays I go through these lines and I see, "Okay, here's the forever line of chumps with paper, and here's the Global

Entry of people who planned ahead, or you can install this app," and you think to yourself, "Surely this cannot be this simple," but in my experience you can install the app before you leave, or you can do it when you touch down, you fill out everything in the app and you can do it while you're walking to customs, and then they let you right through. It is the shortest line. It's shorter than Global Entry, which you have to pay for. I've had friends who are not U.S. citizens who used it successfully. So I think it's the intersection of it's streamlined and quick because you can enter all the data there, and people don't know about it that just makes it really fast.

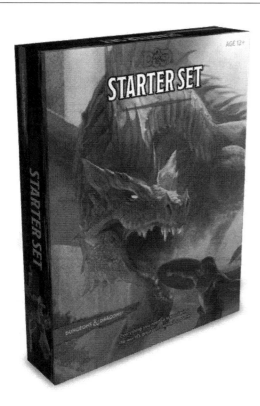

Dungeons & Dragons Starter Set

For those who may have touched Dungeons & Dragons at some point in their life, Wizards of the Coast released a new version, a new set of rules that they call 5e, the fifth edition. They're widely regarded as one of the most friendly and approachable versions.They did an amazing job with the starter kit because they put together everything you need for a group of three to eight people to play probably 20 to 40 hours of wonderful game time in a box for about 20 bucks. The starter kit is two books: one that's read by the dungeon master, who's sort of the head storyteller and who guides the story, and one that is read by everybody. Or, as is often the case, that's also read by the dungeon master

who just sort of tells people what they need to know as they play, depending on your audience. It comes with a set of dice and it comes with some character sheets. Besides a pencil and either extra dice or a dice rolling app, that's really all you need. My wife, who didn't grow up with it at all, was a little skeptical at first, and then it was like, "Oh my gosh, we're spending four hours at the table with our kids talking to each other. This is amazing!"

Glowforge

The Glowforge 3D laser printer is something that founded the company now almost five years ago. We did a crowdfunding campaign, but now we've actually been shipping them for a couple of years. We got people building businesses on them, we've got people building their woodworking hobbies and fundraisers around them, we've got schools who are using them for prototyping and for art class and for engineering and for STEM, and it is basically a desktop CNC laser cutter engraver that can engrave and cut and sculpt surfaces with a ton of precision pretty fast. It's really easy to use. It fits on a desktop. It's about the size of a bag you'd check. It's like 38 inches wide and I want to say 18, 20 inches deep. You can cut 18 by 10.5 inches. I have it in the basement. There's no ventilation there. We have a product called the Compact Filter, which sits underneath the Glowforge. Glowforge starts at $2,500, and you can connect it to a window or you can put it in the basement like me and put in a Compact Filter, which is another $995, and that does all the filtering so you can run it anywhere with wifi and a power plug.

M.G. Siegler
General Partner at GV

M.G. Siegler is a general partner at GV — Google's venture capital arm. Before that, he helped start a seed fund called CrunchFund. And before that, he was a tech reporter for a number of years at publications such as TechCrunch and VentureBeat. Way back when, he was a front-end web developer.
(Published 12/21/18)

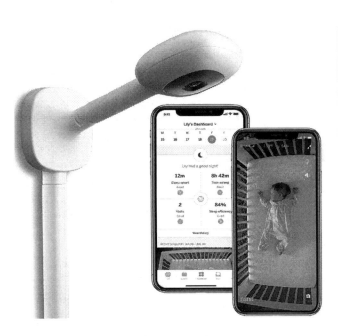

Nanit Smart Baby Monitor

There's been a lot of baby monitors out there that are connected to the internet and have various different functionality. This one was highly recommended by a number of people sort of in my cohort that have had children recently. And so it's a newer device. It basically overlooks a crib. So you set it up, and it's sort of overhanging right on top of a crib for a top-down view. You set it up so you can see, obviously, the entire baby, but also the crib and also the surrounding area. So if someone's coming in to either pick up the baby, to comfort the baby, to feed the baby, you can see that all within sort of line of sight. And a couple of cool features about it is that it also does real-time alerts. There's an app that's associated with it and when the baby either wakes up after sleeping for a bit or is crying, it'll send you a push notification about those two things. It can sort of distinguish between just other noises and knowing when you should probably be alerted. And in our experience it's been pretty good with that. And then obviously you can look in in real-time. But one of the cooler things, I think, that it does is they give you a summary of the entire day for the baby in the crib.

Voice Dream

Read It Later apps like Pocket and Instapaper now have functionality to be able to sort of read back to you articles that you've saved and whatnot. Voice Dream is sort of that on steroids, because it can do it for anything. Once you download this app — you can either do it in a browser or you can have the extension within the app — you'll be able to save anything you want, any webpage or PDF. It even has integrations with things like Pocket and Instapaper. You can create a playlist of things that you want to listen to throughout a day or a commute. You can do all different sorts of speeds. I'm a big proponent of sort of listening to things, including podcasts at 1.5 to 2X speed. It's definitely a time saver, of course, to be able to do that. It also has some really nice voices. The one that I use is a British gentleman.

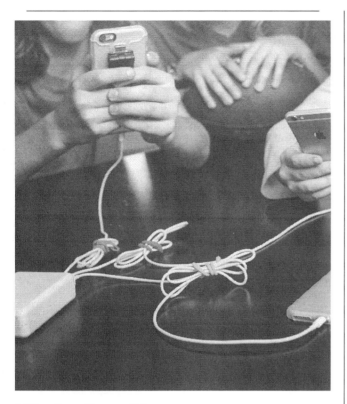

Nite Ize Gear Ties

This one is definitely the lowest of low-tech things. But basically all of us, of course, have so many cables in our bags for different things — USB, USB-C, lightning cables — that you have to carry around. And so I had just basically been throwing them in my bag, and it's just a tangle of wires, a giant mess. So I started using these ties. Actually, my wife got them for me one day. And it's basically great. They're super malleable tie-up cables and they come in all different sort of shapes and sizes. Some of them are massive. I think I saw on their website, some people use them to tie piping together. They have a wide range of uses. But obviously I use the smaller variety for these cable ties. But even for larger cables — I have a few giant HDMI cables in my TV room — you could just tie them up and make sure that there's no loose cables hanging down. I find they're very useful, very easy to put on and very easy to get off.

Logitech Keys-to-Go Portable Keyboard

The reason I like this, is first of all, it's super light. It's very, very easy to carry around. It is a full-size keyboard. It's a little bit smaller on some of the side keys,

but it is technically a full-size keyboard and pretty easy to type on. It's also covered in a sort of fabric material that makes it spill-proof. So if you take it to a café you can spill coffee on it, and it's no big deal. It's Bluetooth so you can use with a wide variety of iOS devices. They even sort of talk up the notion that you can use it for an Apple TV if you wanted to type in passwords or do searches if you are using that. I also use it with the iPhone, which is great because sometimes when I'm out and about and I want to do a bit of writing, and if I don't happen to have my computer or the iPad with me, you can actually use it and it's great with the iPhone. There's no lag or anything. You just connect via Bluetooth and then you basically have a full-sized keyboard and you can either obviously keep your phone in regular mode or you can switch over to landscape mode and just start typing. And while there might be a little bit of a stigma attached to that, it works great just having that little screen and having a keyboard to be able to type anywhere you want.

5ish

I've been running this newsletter as an experiment of sorts. I use the newsletter almost like a link blog in a way, like the old school link blogs being able to just link to things that I find interesting throughout a given week that I think are worthy of people's time either for them to read various articles, or for things that are just sort of interesting in different ways that I think are worth linking to from around the web.

Star Simpson
Electronics Designer

Star Simpson is an electronics designer whose greatest joy is designing objects and tools that are useful to others, which inspire and delight. Her previous work includes research on robotics and work in drones, and an electronics reference card PCB designed for Octopart, now carried in the wallets of electrical engineers everywhere. She is also the creator of Circuit Classics — printed circuit boards that bring to life Forrest Mims' vintage designs from Getting Started in Electronics. (Published 08/4/16)

Metcal MX-500S Soldering System

This is a tool for electrical engineers who want to solder things. Metcal does this really great engineering for their soldering irons. You choose a particular soldering tool to go with the temperature that you want to solder at, I really love that. One other thing that's great about it is it also heats up extremely quickly because it uses RF, it uses radio frequency heating to heat the tip of the soldering iron instead of normal resistive heating, so it's much faster to heat up. The Metcal is the industrial one, because it heats so quickly that if you're doing industrial line soldering, you don't wait around for it to warm up. Whereas I think a Weller station is a really good, solid, reliable desk tool for an engineer during more occasional soldering.

Specialized Globe 08 Bicycle

I love bicycle engineering and I really love this bike. The one I have has a built-in cargo rack that I find just imminently useful. I think it's the perfect compromise between everything I've seen in bicycle design for a great bike to get around in a city, great gear ratio, great for carrying things from time to time, but still fun and fast and lightweight. This line was made by Specialized for a very short time, but just as like a throw to people who really care about bicycle design.

How to Read a Book

How to Read a Book, I believe it was written in the '40s. I consider it a tool because it is a book about, as it says, different techniques and strategies for really extracting the content of books. You'd think it was a lot simpler than that based on the title, but it really teaches you strategies that I think are great. I wish I had read it when I was in my first year of high school, I think it's a great accelerant. It's also an amazingly, amazingly fun book to read in public. I was on the London Tube and I found people will actually look you in your eyes from over 10 feet away to find out what's going on over there, when you're reading a book about how to read a book. If you really want to have fun in that moment, you can just suddenly turn the book upside down. I was having too much fun and I love that book.

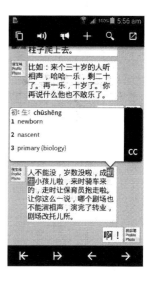

Pleco

Pleco is a great tool because it's an English-Chinese dictionary that I ended up using plenty. The most common use is like, "What exactly does this menu say?" And the other is if you're in a conversation with someone and something's not clear, you can ask if they would write the word into Pleco, or you can write the English word in Pleco, and get a pretty good translation to convey your meaning through it. So I would recommend everyone, everyone, everyone, who's not fluent in speaking Chinese, if you're traveling to a country that is primarily Chinese-speaking, to have that app.

Scott Smith
Founder of Changeist

Scott Smith is a critical futurist and founder of Changeist, where he leads strategy and research. His work taps over 20 years' experience tracking social, tech and economic trends. He works with brands and organizations to find new futures. He's also a writer and frequent speaker, and on Twitter @changeist.
(Published 03/8/18)

iA Writer

This is a very, very basic multi-platform text processing editor. I've thrown Microsoft Office overboard, even getting out of Google Docs, and just use this incredibly simple, very low-feature text editor to spend a lot of my time with and make a lot of notes. It's a proxy for a blank piece of paper. It seems to work quite similar to Notational Velocity. It's on my phone, it's on my iPad, it's on my laptop. I travel a lot for work, I have to do a lot of talks, and I'm also constantly making lists of notes and ideas and workshops. Everything has come down to these really simple 10 bullets, five bullets, three lines of text and then move on. I can see all of it from one screen so it makes it really simple.

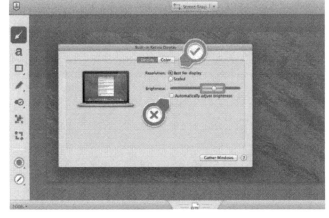

Skitch

I use Skitch because there's such a high velocity of stuff going through my desktop. I use it to catch articles, images, ads, to grab visuals for talks if I'm putting together a presentation or a talk really quickly. And you can grab screenshots of various products or headlines from newspapers, that kind of thing. It's integrated into Evernote so when I snap something on Skitch it shows up in my Evernote library. That's really helpful. Part of it's habit, but part of the attraction is that you can either time a screen, if there were images rotating through for example, and you wanted to catch a certain ad showing up, as an example of something, or it's just got an elastic drag and click so instead of getting your entire desktop, I can just catch the thing I want. I can collect them, and if I'm going to do a talk in a month and I want to go ahead and start building visuals, I'll just grab quick snapshots of them and have them all in one folder somewhere so that's helpful.

Tweetdeck

TweetDeck is basically a Twitter client that sits on the desktop and allows you to run multiple columns so you can have your regular feed, your notifications, your DMs. I'm usually running three or four accounts for different projects, so to be able to run them left to right and see different feeds simultaneously is important. And then another element of it is the work that I do is very heavily tilted toward horizon scanning, toward constant collection of new information and intelligence to feed our research. Some days for me it's this big, almost a war room screen in front of me. With a lot of different messages coming in, a lot of different people in different places of the world talking about what they're seeing. Papers they've read, conferences they're live tweeting, and it just becomes a big board for me to pay attention to during the day.

Minitel

Minitel is France's pre-Internet online platform that survived from 1978 to 2012. It's now coming up on its 40th anniversary of initial development. I've started collecting working models as part of research for a personal project, and also to reconsider the idea of creating a centralized, free network utility in the public interest.

Will Smith
CEO at FOO VR

Will Smith is a journalist turned entrepreneur. He was the editor-in-chief of Maximum PC magazine, founder of Tested.com, and is currently working on VR software. He has stood atop a running nuclear reactor, eaten unreconstituted freeze-dried shrimp, and once played astronaut in the Space Shuttle simulator at Johnson Space Center. (Published 07/12/17)

Gerber Shard Keychain Tool

This is ridiculously useful and is probably interesting enough on its own. I stopped carrying a multi-tool after donating several to the TSA, and got the Shard because I broke the electronics in my car key by using it as a pry bar once. The Shard is $7, lives on all my keychains, and does almost everything I used to use a multi-tool for (pliers are really the only thing I miss). It can go through airport security, and while it isn't great or even very good at anything, it's good enough in a pinch. It has a pair of terrible screwdriver heads (that have saved me a couple of times), a wire stripper, a pry bar, and a bottle opener. I've used the wire stripper to pry up nails a couple of times, and a few minutes with a file made it sharp enough that it's great for cutting tape on packages.

AirStick Microsuction Tape by Sewell

This stuff is amazing, it's better than Velcro for sticking small-to-medium-sized objects to things. It looks like tape but it has loads of tiny micro suction cups on one side. Basically you can use it to stick any flatish, smoothish surface to anything you don't mind sticking adhesive to. The suction cup side holds without leaving any residue behind, and can be used in vertical or even inverted instances, if your materials are smooth enough and the object is pretty light. If you want to stick a tablet on your kitchen cabinet or tiles, this is a great way to do it. You can buy it in tiny quantities on Amazon too, but Inventables has the best bulk pricing I've seen from a reputable vendor.

Zojirushi Stainless Steel Mug

This is the best thermos-type bottle I've ever owned. It's designed to be used as a mug, it holds your hot drink hot for much longer than you'll ever need, keeps a cold drink cold on the hottest day, and the lid has never leaked. I trust it to the point that I regularly put a full bottle in a bag with $5-10k worth of computer gear.

Field Notes

I used to be a Moleskin guy, but they got too expensive and almost always broke apart before I could fill a notebook. Now I just get these Field Notes books and devote one to each project I'm working on. They're cheap enough ($4 each in a 3-pack, less if you subscribe) that I don't feel bad if they get banged up, wet, or if I need to tear out a page for someone else. And, they fit in jeans pockets, shirt pockets, jacket pockets — pretty much any pocket except for that tiny pocket in the front of your jeans.

Robert Stephens
Founder of The Geek Squad

Robert Stephens is the founder of The Geek Squad and former CTO of Best Buy. The Geek Squad turns 25 this year, employing over 24,000 people. A native of Chicago, he now lives in the Bay Area. He has read the Cool Tools book back-to-back at least five times. (Published 04/5/19)

Mark One Pen

This one is from the folks at Studio Neat in Austin, Texas. They just come up with the best handmade design stuff. This one is the Mark One pen. It's a custom-machined, all-metal, retractable pen with a ceramic-based exterior coating. I get most people might think 99% of all of communication now is electronic. It makes sense to throw everything out of your kitchen drawer, but maybe keep one pen, and this is that pen. They put a lot of care into it, and if you go to the website with the link, you'll see them tell the story of this. They really tried to think, "What are you looking for in a pen?" Number one, you're looking for good ink and quality, and they designed this specifically to fit everybody's favorite Schmidt P812 ink refill, which you can get on Amazon pretty inexpensively. It's got a really nice feel to it. So it's designed to be easy to refill, which is key. Number two, they spent months machining some special alloys for a satisfying click. It's a nice audible click. It's a little bit thicker than a pen you're used to, which gives it a nice hand feel. And lastly, the length is just longer than about the length of your hand,

so it's got a nice balance in your hand. What I love about this product is it's such a basic thing we take for granted, and if you want to make an impression, a handwritten note will go a lot longer in this day and age, and this is the pen I recommend, either for yourself or for someone you know that needs to be sending more letters.

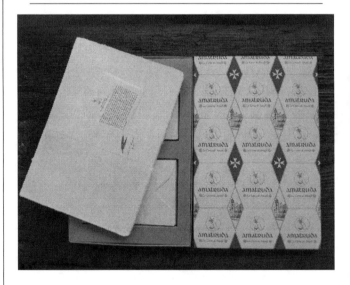

Amatruda writing papers

If we're going to have a pen, you better send some letters. I'm a big fan of paper, just the textile quality. And a company near Salerno, Italy, Amatruda, has been making paper in this area of Italy for probably over 1,000 years. Amatruda you can get inexpensively on Amazon for 15 bucks. You can probably find it in your local bookstore. It's this little pack of like 10 sheets folded. It's that deckled rough edge. Just a beautiful quality with a nice watermark. The quality of the paper is real cotton rag, and that's the mark of the best paper. I recommend that you skip the Amazon click and you go to Salerno, and you go to Amatruda, have a custom order made and have a custom watermark made. Four hundred meters from their place is the Museo della Carta, which is the paper museum that has the original equipment that's hundreds of years old. When you're down there, you can write a letter to all your friends and rub it in.

Occupancy Sensor Light Switch

So you're in Italy, in a castle, writing letters with your pen, and you've just lit that fire, and you're thinking, "Did I leave the lights on at home?" Well, you would think, as the founder of Geek Squad, that I would recommend some newfangled Amazon or Google Home switch. No, that smart-home stuff is dumb, okay? The software updates, I can't recommend it. The smart home is a mess right now. This is an occupancy sensor. It's a simple motion switch with a push button, and it's got two little dials in it that you can adjust the length of time the light is on and the sensitivity and depth. I've got five of these, and they're great all over the place, even in the laundry room. And my wife even said that she liked this thing, and she doesn't like anything I install in the house. You know why? Because she's always complaining like, "The TV turned itself on and off. The front porch light is blinking." This thing is guaranteed to work even if the internet disappears.

Wand Fire Starter

This one is a breakthrough. This is one of my favorites because it's the easiest. Everybody can use it. When you're writing your love letters from that abandoned castle you rented on Airbnb at Salerno to go buy your paper, you're going to need fire and some light to see what kind of poetry you're composing. And a friend of mine gave me this as a gift because I built him a clay oven. And this is a wand fire-starter. It's basically a metal rod. At the end of it is some kind of a pumice ceramic stone, and it's a bit porous. You keep it in a vessel of lamp oil; odorless, smokeless lamp oil. Whether you're

lighting a grill out back or your fireplace, sometimes if you don't have the right kindling, it doesn't get going right away, and this is safer than newspaper because sometimes the newspaper can fly up into the chimney. So this thing, what you do is after you shake it out of the lamp oil a little bit, you roll it in the last fireplace ashes, in a little bit of ashes. And what happens is the lamp oil soaks into that and becomes like a torch, like in the old Frankenstein movies. And you light it, and it'll stay lit for about 20 minutes, and then it becomes easy to fish out of the fire because you leave that little metal rod hanging out. They can run as high as 200 bucks with the ceramic vessel, but I found one for $18, and you can get lamp oil at any hardware store.

TouchNote: Cards & Gifts

This is the use case for everybody. You've just had an amazing weekend or a great dinner with friends, and we're all filling up our camera roll with stuff. And I don't even have a photo printer because it's too much of a pain in the butt. This is an app that simply will let you select any photo on your phone in the moment before you even get home that night, and you can send a postcard or a nice greeting card with that photo with different fonts, and they'll do postage. And I think, all in, it's $3 to $5, and you prepay five or 10 cards at a time, but you can send a card to anybody. I just spent a great weekend with friends out of town, and we took some amazing photos, and all 10 people are getting a card in about three days from me.

Becky Stern
Content Creator at Instructables

Becky Stern is a Content Creator at Instructables, and part-time faculty member at New York's School of Visual Arts Products of Design grad program. Making and sharing are her two biggest passions, and she's created hundreds of free online DIY tutorials and videos, mostly about technology and its intersection with crafts. (Published 06/15/18)

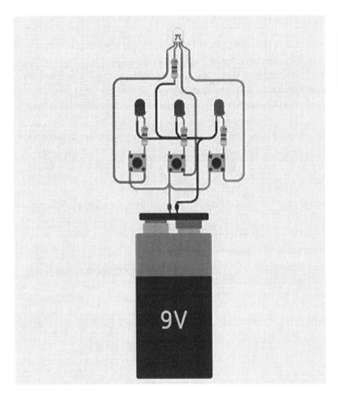

Circuits on Tinkercad

In addition to its free 3D modeling tools, Tinkercad now has a circuit simulator for prototyping with parts and code. I've been working with the Tinkercad team recently to help create and organize their Arduino curriculum, and I'm impressed with how useful it is as a teaching tool and how fun and fast it is to "wire up" a quick idea. Once you're logged in to Tinkercad, you can also follow along with my interactive lessons which guide you through using the editor and learning Arduino at the same time.

Parrot Teleprompter with Bluetooth Remote

This thing attaches to the end of your camera lens and holds a phone running a teleprompter app. I drag my video scripts into a dropbox folder and they are automatically slurped into the Parrot app. The Bluetooth remote makes it easy to redo a take or adjust the speed of the playback myself while recording. This dramatically decreases the time it takes to both film and edit scripted tutorial videos.

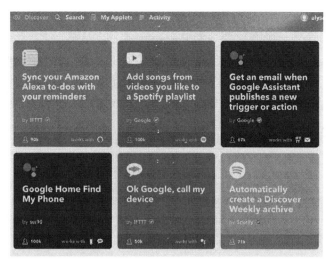

button" devices you can find if you scroll through the expanded list of services on IFTTT's site.

Engineer SS-02 Solder Sucker

When I worked at Adafruit, I got to try out and show off new products of theirs all the time. One of my favorite new tools that I still use today is this Japanese solder sucker. I remember struggling to undo big soldering mistakes when I was first learning, melting the tips off the cheap RadioShack solder suckers and burning myself on copper braid. This sucker's got a heat-resistant silicone tip that you can press right up against the hot soldering iron tip to get a good seal to slurp the solder once it's molten. Also the sounds it makes are very satisfying. It may be more expensive than its alternatives, but provides a big boost in performance and luxury handling. In that way it feels like driving a fancy car.

IFTTT

Many of my design grad students are able to catapult their single semester of simple Arduino into complex product prototype functionality by integrating IFTTT. I teach folks online how to use it with an ESP8266 microcontroller board and adafruit.io in my free Instructables Internet of Things class, but you can also use it with hardware from Particle, littleBits, and Raspberry Pi as well as a handful of "single

Becky Stern's Maker videos on Youtube

I've been doing my own personal channel since I left Adafruit in 2016, so not all that long when you compare it to the amount of time I've been making videos both for Adafruit and before that for MAKE magazine. I would say you can find anything I'm passionate about or currently working on, which includes more than just electronics. I recently made a leather wallet, a foot pedal shutter remote for my camera, a humidity-controlled storage and dispenser box for 3D printer filament, and a bluetooth device for coaching your knife sharpening angle.

Mark Stramaglia
Experimental Musician and Digital Artist

Mark Stramaglia is an experimental musician and digital artist. He creates games and audio software under the name Bludgeonsoft, and produces and performs music and art as Wizard Master and Operation Re-Information. His current project is Vilmonic, an artificial life, evolution, and genetics sandbox game and virtual world. Vilmonic is available now, on Steam and Itch. io. (Published 3/15/19)

Chrome Kursk Sneaker

I've had this one pair for probably over eight years. They're only slightly looking worn. They're just the most durable, indestructible shoes I've ever owned. They're made for cycling mostly, but these are a kind of street pair. I have photos of the same pair from eight years ago, and they really don't look very different. It's military-grade, nylon-reinforced, vulcanized rubber — who knows what this stuff is, but they're not worn down. I rarely use the car, so I'm pretty much biking and walking. So, they do get a bunch of wear, but I'm mostly comparing them to other shoes I've had and there's no comparison. They're the best. They're really practical. They're completely stripped down, just utilitarian. I love that look.

BIC 4-Color Ballpoint Pen

Everyone has used this and has them seen around, but I think they don't get the props that they deserve and it's the BIC 4-color ballpoint pens. This is great

because it's got the four colors in it, but really my main thing is that I love ballpoint pens. The difference between these and gel pens is that this oil-based ink is fairly viscous, and you can get a really amazing range of a texture and tone out of it by writing lightly or writing heavily. So they're really great for drawing. There are two main uses that I have. One is I take my sketchbook all around Oakland and I bike around and I do these kind of representational, or non-representational representational drawings. They're just blind contour drawings, but not of people; they're of places, and things, and textures to try to take my eyes off of what they would kind of land on and find the kind of least significant thing around, and then zoom in and do these drawings on them. These pens allow me to get so much kind of variation and texture and weight. Another cool thing is that if you draw hard with them, they really impress the paper. So, you get this kind of embossed look to your sketches, too, which I love, especially if you use heavier weight paper. It totally is retro, and if you look at these pens, these are like simple, completely utilitarian design. They're really minimal and they're beautiful.

Hemingway Editor

I was looking for something to simplify the technical explanations that I was doing for the complexities in the game, and this editor — their goal is to kind of simplify your writing as much as possible based on the styles and the concepts that Hemingway would use in his writing. I've found that you just put your text in the webpage, and it instantly highlights complex sentences, kind of unnecessary bulk. And it was great. I would kind of play it as a game almost and try to get my reading level as low as possible. It starts to change the character of your writing, which is not necessarily the best thing, but it's really great. What I would do is, I would take these tech heavy explanations of how artificial life works, and genetics, and evolution, and natural selection — which are bulky and for a game where I want as broad an audience as possible. I really needed a way to simplify that. So this tool was indispensable. They have a web browser version and you can just go there and it's free, and they have a downloadable version also for the desktop. It has more features and I haven't gotten that yet. It's $20.

VMware on macOS

I have this Mac laptop that I was able to get from work years ago and keep it, so it's a pretty old Mac laptop, but Macs seem to run VMS, virtual machines really well. I've got VMware and so this is really using my Mac as a hypervisor, meaning that I'm using it to run my macOS, plus a bunch of virtual machines of different operating systems. That process is amazing for me. I actually do most of my

development in Linux. I've got this laptop that runs all three operating systems. My setup is normally KDE Neon Linux in one VM, and Windows 7 or 10 in the other. The great thing is, macOS allows you to use gestures. So I have four finger swipe set up so that I can just kind of slide back and forth between different spaces and I have a different OS on each space. The main desktop that I have is macOS. I have my browser running in there, and I have one version of my game running there. And then I just four finger swipe, and I'm instantly in Linux, and that's where I do all of my coding. My coding apps are on there, my text editors, code editors, and then I four finger swipe again and there, I'm in Windows. I can test the 64 bit version of the Windows app immediately. They're all accessing the Mac hard drive. So, I have the same code base that I can access it. It's pretty amazing. It's a great way to develop for multiple platforms.

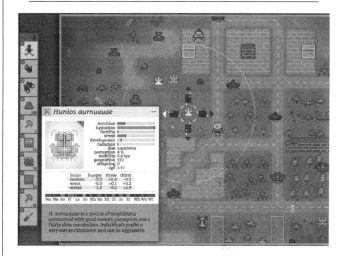

Vilmonic

This game is called Vilmonic, and it's an artificial life, a simulator, and a virtual world. So the idea behind it was to create a world where you exist within it. There's no God mode in this game. It's just its own kind of biology and physics that you have to work with. This game is all interesting, because it's all pixel arts. The pixel art in this game all has meaning. So the number of pixels on the screen and the color of the pixels all determine the life forms and how much nutrients or hydration they use, and how they're going to exist within their environments. So all of it is generated. It's all generative life forms based on genetic code for these creatures. You protect and breed generative pixel-art life forms whose genes, pixels, shape and color determine their physiology and behavior.

Zach Supalla
CEO of Particle

Zach Supalla is the CEO and one of the founders of Particle, the most widely-used IoT platform. Particle is used by more than 140,000 developers and 8,500 companies to build IoT products ranging from the smart home to industrial equipment.
(Published 03/16/18)

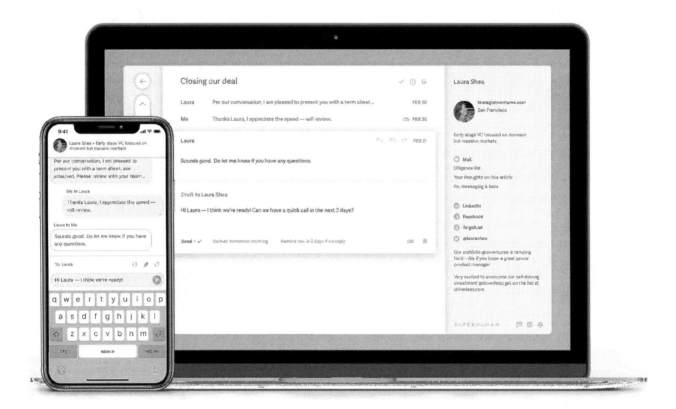

Superhuman

Superhuman is brand new email software — still in private beta — that is all designed around keyboard shortcuts. Extremely low-friction email software, and besides being super well-designed, the team there has been incredibly hands-on during the private beta and super open to feedback. It's very fast, very responsive, so as you're clicking around things just happen immediately, which I think when you're working through emails quickly is important. It has some other great features that I think are now becoming standard in good email clients, like snoozing and some cool macro things, so if you send out a lot of emails that are kind of the same, you can create a macro — a template, and then just automatically create that email. I feel like if you are into keyboard shortcuts, it's either because once upon a time you did a lot of Excel work, or once upon a time you did a lot of work in Vim. So, at which point you're like, "I don't want my hands to ever leave the keyboard." It has to be possible to navigate the entire piece of software without ever lifting your hands from the keys, and that's what they really nailed with Superhuman. You can spend a half an hour going through your email and never take your hands off the keyboard.

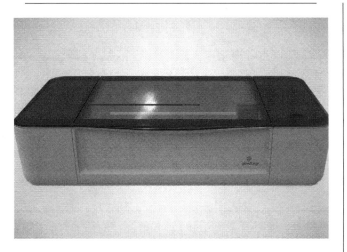

Glowforge

Glowforge laser cutter is a desktop, consumer-friendly laser cutter. It's got a web application that you use to interact with it. It comes with tons of templates for designs that are already sort of built in, and they send you a set of materials that are designed to work with it that it can automatically recognize and adjust the laser strength accordingly. So it comes with cuts of leather, it comes with cuts of acrylic, it comes with wood and wood veneer, and all that stuff just works right out of the box. I got it up and running in probably 20 minutes and learned how to use it in 15, and had cut out my first thing in about half an hour after setting it up, which was super cool.

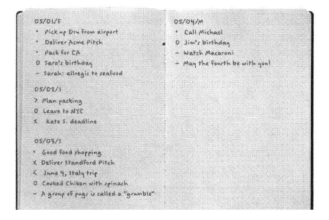

Bullet journal

Bullet Journal is a system for using a notebook to keep track of things. I have tried every piece of task management software ever created (Asana, Trello, Wunderlist, etc. etc.) and a good notebook with this system trumps them all.

AeroPress Coffee Maker and Porlex Coffee Grinder

I love great coffee, and I have a whole complicated setup at home. But when I'm traveling, I carry an Aeropress coffeemaker with a Porlex coffee grinder, which somehow perfectly fits inside the Aeropress, a la "things fitting perfectly into other things." With the two you can make delicious coffee anywhere, even on a plane.

Talin
Recovering game programmer

Talin is a "recovering game programmer" whose career spans 25 years, stretching from the early years of personal computing to more recent games like Sim City 4 and The Sims 2. He's also a writer, artist, cosplayer, musician, and web developer.
(Published 05/4/18)

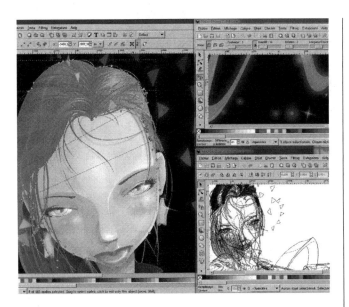

Inkscape SVG editor

Inkscape is an editor for SVG files, Scalable Vector Graphics, which is a web standard. Most images are made out of pixels, little square blocks, but vector images are made out of lines and points and geometric shapes. That means they can be scaled up and scaled down without any loss of quality. All the major browsers support them, so SVGs are very efficient. Most websites use SVGs for their icons now, because SVG is a web standard. It can be embedded in the web page directly, without having to do a separate download, which you would have to do with an image. That makes for much fewer network connections. This is one of the most polished and professional opensource apps out there. It's better than GIMP in many ways, in terms of its overall level of quality of the user interface.

ResMed AirSense CPAP Machine

I suffered from sleep apnea, like many people do, and I didn't know this until about 20 years ago, and somebody told me, "Hey, by the way, do you know that you choke when you're sleeping?" Sleep apnea is essentially an extreme form of snoring, where your nasal passages get blocked up and you start to choke. This has all kinds of negative effects. It means you're tired all the time. You don't get enough sleep, and also because you're at a reduced oxygen level, it has other health impacts. So they recommended that I get a CPAP machine. CPAP stands for Continuous Positive Air Pressure. It's kind of like a miniature iron lung. It's basically a little mask that fits over your face and provides a gentle air pressure to inflate your nasal tissues so that you get a clear airflow. It takes a little getting used to at first, but now that I've been using it for 10

years, I don't think I could sleep without it. Well I can, but it's actually more comfortable now, to be able to breathe freely when I'm lying down like that. I've tried a couple ones, and the thing is, every one I get is better than the last, because the technology keeps improving. The machine I've got right now is about a year old. It's a ResMed AirSense. It's actually a BiPAP machine. Which means that it actually senses. It's got a computer system that senses that you're breathing, and that adjusts the pressure for your inhale and exhale, so that it's actually easier. You don't have to breathe against the pressure as you're breathing out.

Forbidden Desert Board Game

First of all, I really like cooperative board games. I find winning is not that interesting. I like collaboration and cooperation. The thing I love about cooperative board games is that every turn becomes this kind of creative brainstorming session. Forbidden Desert is a very interesting cooperative game. It has an interesting play mechanic, where the board is changing its configuration as you're playing. The desert consists of a bunch of tiles, and each turn there's a new storm card that comes up, and it moves the storm around. Every time the storm moves, it shifts the tiles, and so as you're playing it's like you're playing on shifting sands. The goal of the game is you're working together to find all of the hidden pieces of the lost airship, so that you can escape the desert

before you run out of water, because every time a sun-beats-down card comes up, you all lose one unit worth of water, and if you run out of water the game ends.

The Captain is Dead Board Game

The Captain is Dead is kind of a parody of classic Star Trek. The basic premise is that you are all crewmen on a star-ship where the captain has died, and you're being attacked by aliens, and all these things are going wrong. Each crewman has a different role. There's a dozen different crewmen you can choose from, and usually you have four or five players, each with a different role. It's like, the doctor, and the hologram, and the alien. There's even one that's called crewman, which wears a red shirt, and every time he dies he respawns on the bridge as a new character. Every turn there's a new disaster that you have to cope with, like the systems are going down, or you have a weird anomaly that's changing the crew behavior. A lot of it is trading resources. It's like, I'll have three engineering skill cards, and I'll use the communication system to give you three of my engineering skills so that next turn you can fix the warp core, and then you can use the teleporter to move me over to the armory so I can attack the aliens. It's a very challenging game.

Brad Templeton
Futurist

Brad Templeton is founding faculty for Computing & Networks at Singularity University, and Chairman Emeritus and futurist of the Electronic Frontier Foundation (EFF), the leading cyberspace civil rights foundation. He is on the board of the Foresight Institute. He also advised Google's team developing self-driving cars, and writes about such cars at robocars.com. He also advises Starship on delivery robots and Quanergy in the LIDAR space. He founded ClariNet Communications Corp (the world's first "dot-com" company.) He also created rec.humor.funny, the world's longest running blog. (Published 07/19/17)

4K TVs as Computer Monitors

I have a 50-inch 4K television as my monitor, and you may think, "Wow, that's really big, how far away do you sit from it?'" I sit the same distance I sat from the 30-inch and the 24-inch that so many people use. In fact, if you think about it, the typical 24-inch HD monitor, that is the most common sort of monitor sold today or a few years ago, is one quarter of a 4K and it's 24 inches, which means it's basically half of the 50-inch screen. The great thing though is, they're selling these TVs really cheap. They're selling them down to 500, 600 bucks, even less. They didn't want you to use these as monitors, they designed them to be TVs. So there's a few tricks to pull, but if you do you can get something that's just amazing.

Sony Cameras

I like the fact that my cameras keep getting smaller. I've got the Sony a7RII; that's about the best of the digital SLRs for image quality right now. Now, Sony just came out with their A9 which is possibly better. And then in their line I have their APS-C size, that's the sensor that's about half the size of a full 35-millimeter frame. That drops a lot of weight. I also have one of the nicest little point-and-shoots that fits in your pocket, and it's the DSC-RX100 IV, and that guy does get some great images, and it just has a point-and-shoot zoom lens on it.

Fire TV Stick

I brought my Amazon Fire Stick overseas. I have the first generation one, that was my mistake. The second generation one can be programmed to do what you need

to do here, which is use a VPN, a virtual private network. Why? Because you want to cheat all these global content controls that are telling me — even though I have an American Netflix account and I'm paying money into it right now —Netflix will not show me the things that I pay for in the US, because I'm in France. The old Fire Stick won't bypass this, but if you buy any of the various little TV devices and you hook them up to use a VPN, then you can get it to appear like it's in the United States.

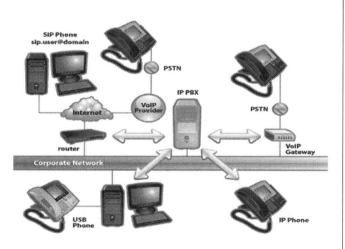

VoIP PBX

I run a voice over IP PBX in my home, that's a little unusual. You may not need to do that, but there are lots of voice over IP services now, so you can get even your

landline phone to travel with you. No matter where you are in the world, even on your cell phone or on your computer, or if you want to bring a small phone with you because you like that landline experience, which I happen to. I like the voice quality and the physicality of it for a real conversation. You can get that and proxy it up so that my phone in California, you can call it, and it's gonna ring at my desk in Paris and I can call you back. It's gonna look like I'm there. A lot of people are doing that.

Starship Technologies

My favorite tool I'm working on right now is with a company that's based in Estonia, and it's called Starship Technologies. We're making a delivery robot. It's a little robot the size of a big beer cooler, and it's got six wheels, and it's not fully autonomous yet, but it's going to be. It's going to bring you everything that you want to order in 30 minutes, and it's gonna cost under a dollar to do it. Like so many things these days, you won't be able to get one. You'll be able to get one to bring you something, or if you're a delivery company you might be able to buy them. What is interesting about this is thinking about goods being able to move like data. Do we even need to own things? Imagine I'm walking down that Paris street and I can pick up my phone and say, "Hey, could someone send me a really good camera that I'm gonna rent for an hour because I'm walking around with just my iPhone?" I think that's gonna be really interesting in terms of what tools we carry on our body, what we have as well as all the things you'd think about in terms of delivering food, and flowers, and all that stuff.

Grant Thompson
The King of Random

Grant Thompson was an airline pilot when he started posting videos of his crazy science experiments and DIY projects. His channel became wildly popular for making science fun, and he's become home to nearly 10 million subscribers. As "The King of Random," Grant's mission has been to share the joy of experimenting and hands-on learning. Through constant experimenting and undying persistence, he's become one of the most-subscribed YouTubers in the world. (Published 04/27/18)
Note: Since this interview was conducted Grant Thompson passed away in a hang-gliding accident.

DEWALT 20V MAX XR Drill Driver

My number one tool that I love the most is a DEWALT drill driver. I got a 20-volt MAX XR. I don't know why I chose that. I just went to Home Depot and tested a

few, and I really liked that one, the way that it fit in my hand. It's got a lot of torque, a lot of power, some really cool settings so you don't strip out the screw if you don't want to. Probably like most drill drivers, honestly. They're probably all the same. But the reason I like the drill driver the most is because it's so versatile. I used to do a lot of handyman work. I used to build properties, and I do everything from framing to electrical and everything between. And then to have that much power just right at your trigger finger is a really satisfying feeling. I was just using it this morning while assembling some new office furniture.

Hack Saw

The thing about a hacksaw is it's just versatile. You can use it to cut wood, you can use it to cut metal. You can basically cut anything. I cut PVC pipe with it all the time. I put a hacksaw on the list just because so many of the projects that I do involve cutting things, and hacksaw will just cut basically anything. And it's not so much about the hacksaw that you have, it's more about the blade that you have, and they do come in different blades. Some were made for metal. They have different teeth per inch. I honestly don't worry about that too much. I just get the one that's kind of in the middle. I don't know what that is, like 25 teeth per inch, somewhere around there. And I just find myself using it all the time. We went through a series of metal casting projects where we were melting down pop cans and making our own tools in the backyard, and having a

I can share on the internet wouldn't b[...] without a computer. I would say if yo[...] a computer, something that's portab[...] take with you, is a great way to go. T[...] Pro has served me well. I love it. I got t[...] older model, so I don't have to get the don[...] everything into. It's still got all the ports and[...] jacks, and I personally prefer that. And it's ru[...] like a charm. So, I'm really happy with my 2014 MacBook Pro.

Electrical Tape

Electrical tape is a staple. It's like you need bread and rice to survive, and you need electrical tape in your workshop to survive. You know how MacGyver's always associated with duct tape because he could do anything with duct tape, and I feel like I've tried using duct tape — it has its place — but there's nothing that I use more often than electrical tape. I use it for decorating. If I make nunchucks or blowguns, I can use it for decoration on the outside. I use it for patching things together. I've had a vacuum pump that was falling apart, and I used electrical tape to tie that back together. And the reason I love the electrical tape is because it's got that stretchy vinyl quality to it. If you stretch it a little bit harder, it kind of pulls back on itself, so you get a little bit of elastic property, which duct tape just doesn't have.

hacksaw was just really handy to have to clean that up. I've since upgraded that to a reciprocal saw, which is basically like a hacksaw on steroids.

MacBook Pro

Everybody had different opinions. I was always a PC guy, but I decided to pull the trigger and go to a Mac, and it's worked really well for me. Now, I guess a couple years ago I got this MacBook Pro, and the reason I love it is because it's got amazing processing power — it's even better than my desktop computer — and traveling around the country I can take it with me anywhere, I can work anywhere, and turning my projects into digital that

Carol Tilley
Information Science Professor

Disguised as a mild-mannered Midwestern library and information science professor, Carol Tilley is actually the Comics Crusader, whose 2013 research debunked evidence used by 1950s anti-comics advocate Fredric Wertham. A 2016 Eisner Award judge, Carol is also president-elect of the Comics Studies Society and an in-demand speaker on comics history. (Published 12/15/17)

Instant Pot

I'm not a big kitchen gadget person. I sort of operate under the idea that if you have a good pan, and a good knife, that's more or less all you need. I fell under the sway of the Instant Pot marketing about a year ago, and some friends of mine convinced me that it was a miracle. I was a little bit hesitant, but I thought for 100 bucks I would give it a try. It really is something very cool. I sometimes joke that it's the "one pot," sort of like the "one ring," except in a good way. We make yogurt, rice, dry beans; everything that we've tried so far has been pretty magical in terms of cutting down the time and cutting down the mess of making set up.

Antsy Labs Fidget Cube

I was one of the Kickstarter backers for the original Fidget Cubes from Antsy Labs. I am so happy and so impressed. I've always been one of those folks who even as a kid, I twiddled my thumbs, which was kind of a joke at times. I cannot sit still. I've never been able to sit still. The Fidget Cube, even though it doesn't keep me from tapping my legs, or crossing or uncrossing my legs, it does keep my hands occupied. I really love that there are six different things that I can do with this. I think probably the glide side is my favorite, but also the spinner side, and the side that looks like the five on a die where you can punch the little buttons in and out. It's just very satisfying.

Pilot Varsity Disposable Fountain Pens

Like a lot of people, I love to sort of glam on to pens, but I also lose them frequently. I like to be able to write with something that feels good when the tip touches the paper. With the Varsity, I found that the nib is really nice and smooth. I think the ink flow is good. I feel like I can write elegantly with it. If I lose it, it's not the end of the world. I haven't spent $500 or $1,000 on a month-long pen and then feel guilty when it disappears out of my bag. I keep a box of the black ones and a box of the purple ink handy, pretty much all the time.

Library Card

I'm a librarian by training. I teach people who are going to be librarians. I have been a library user since age three. I'm lucky to live in a community that has two extraordinarily good public library systems; Champaign Public and Urbana Free Library. Our university library system here at University of Illinois is one of the best in the world. I can't imagine being without that access. I think that whether you are a kid, or a senior, or a college student, or a parent, an entrepreneur, I think there's something at your local library that can really make a difference in your life.

Maggie Tokuda-Hall
Children's Author

Maggie Tokuda-Hall is the author of the Parent's Choice Gold Medal winning picture book, Also an Octopus. Her debut young adult novel, "The Mermaid, The Witch, and The Sea" is due out in Fall 2019. She is the host of the Drunk Safari podcast.
(Published 12/14/18)

ARB Awning

This is ARB's two-meter-by-two-meter awning. It clips onto the sides of cars for camping and for travel. My husband and I spent about a year driving down the west coast of South America and living in our Toyota 4Runner. The awning is just what it sounds like, but it's attached to the car permanently. When you're in a bunch of different environments over the course of a couple of months, it's the best for providing shelter from the rain and from sun, which was a much bigger deal than I'd anticipated. I don't know what we would've done if we hadn't had that. It's also really easy to pack up and to put back out.

Autohome Columbus Rooftop Tent

Our AutoHome Columbus Rooftop Tent was our bedroom for a year. For this, we did have to have a special, additional rack added and drilled into our car to have it mounted correctly. That was expensive,

and the product itself is pretty expensive. The reason I'm such an advocate for it is because it is shockingly comfortable. The actual mattress inside of the tent is really comfortable. It's about the size of a slightly large full bed, but for camping in North America, it's awesome because it can get pretty cold. You zip close all the windows and it can retain a certain amount of heat pretty well. You still need a good sleeping bag with it. When it gets really, really hot, you can open up all the windows and there's screens so that you can have fresh air all night.

Scrivener

I recently turned in the edited draft of my young adult novel that'll come out next year. Scrivener has a bunch of different tools within it that make it really easy to do revision and track changes and things like that. It also does things at the beginning of a project for you, like give you prompts for characters and settings, and different kinds of things you might want to think about with your book so that you can spend a little bit of time walking around your story before you get going on it. It's very handy to have

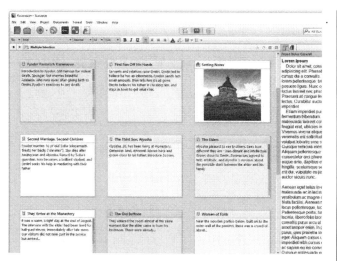

that all in one place, so you can refer back to it as you're writing. You can also write scripts in it. I just wrote a graphic novel script using it, and I couldn't believe how much easier it made that, as well. Right at the beginning, you can select script as your format. Then it helps you format it for the rest of the time. That was just so exciting because that was my first graphic novel script.

Literaticast podcast

I've written children's books for my entire career. On the editorial side, reading for agents, and now writing but I also have done marketing and a lot of book-selling. Literaticast is hosted by Jennifer Laughran, who's an agent at the Andrea Brown Literary Agency. She's also my agent, which is why I started listening to it in the first place. She's also a career children's book professional, and she has different people from different parts of the industry on every episode. Her most recent episode had an editor on talking about revision. She's had publicists on talking about what tools an author should be able to provide their publicist. I've just been really pleased by how much I've learned from listening to it, even though my entire career

has been in children's books. I just feel like anyone who's ever thought, even casually, about writing a children's book should listen to a couple episodes of this because she gets amazing guests, and every episode, I learn something new about the industry or some sort of better practice that I'm really grateful for.

Drunk Safari podcast

This podcast is dilettantes talking about their favorite animals — with a few cocktails. Every episode, we talk about either one or two animals and we get into the important questions like, "How do they mate?" "Could you beat it in a fist fight?" "How would describe it to an alien?" along with some of its most pertinent details.

iOverlander

A mapping project to find your next camping location.

Ziya Tong
Author of The Reality Bubble

Ziya Tong is an award-winning science broadcaster, best known for her work with Discovery's flagship show, Daily Planet, as well as NOVA ScienceNow and Wired Science on PBS. She is the author of the forthcoming book The Reality Bubble, the Vice Chair of the World Wildlife Fund Canada, and a supporter of the Extinction Rebellion. (Published 5/24/19)

Case of Bass

There's this guy named Ezra who works out of Portland, and several years ago I ended up getting a speaker system through him and it is just an absolute work of art. Basically, it looks like one of those 1980s boomboxes that he has photographed and placed inside of a sort of ornate frame. But inside and behind this frame is an actual boombox. So, it's a little bit meta in the sense that you've got an image of a boombox that is sort of outfitted with a boombox behind it. But what's really cool is he's developed painting skins of these boomboxes. You can change your art so you'll have different boomboxes or different images and you'll still have the physical boombox right there. Another thing that he has been doing lately is he's been going to vintage stores and picking up old suitcases and old luggage to make boomboxes. He just really likes repurposing things that people have kind of given up on and giving them a purpose again.

AFP FactCheck Twitter Feed

This Twitter feed is by AFP the news organization, and it comes in French, in Spanish, and in Portuguese. What I love about it is, we live in the era of fake news of course as we all know. But not all of us have time when we come across something to immediately

go to Snopes, unless we're super keener nerds which some of us are, but at the same time, it's nice to have this through your feed. In this instance, you have AFP using reverse Google Image search to look at a lot of the postings that are going through and going viral on all these Facebook news sites that are patently false. There's an image that I saw the other day and it was of a pig that is in Hungary. It says, "Here's how Hungarian border police keep Muslims from crossing their borders." And they

276

have a giant pig there and a cop holding the pig and a whole bunch of refugees fleeing the border. And it's just bullshit. And so, right next to it, they've got the image and it's actually a doctored image from the Philippines of just somebody who's with their pig and some piglets and some people playing in the background.

The Extinction Logo

I think we've all said for a long time that the revolution will not be televised. But I think the revolution is certainly happening for us right now on the internet. We're in the middle of the sixth mass extinction right now. We're seeing loss of animals and vertebrate species around the world. At the same time, we're battling a real planetary emergency. A lot of people are starting to protest in the streets. It's a real form of joyful resistance and joyful rebellion. And a lot of this sort of emerged around this symbol and this was an extinction symbol that was developed a little while ago. It's very simple. It's being called the new peace symbol of our era. The circle represents the planet. In the inside, it looks like two triangles that kind of kiss and that's the hourglass signifying that we are running out of time. And there are rebellions that are planned and taking place all around the world. People can go to the xrebellion.org website and sign up and find out what's happening locally or start their own local chapter. And they can go to extinctionsymbol.info and that's where you can actually download the graphic. And you can make anything you want out of it so long as it's not for commercial purposes. People are making flags out of the symbol. I have a old sweatshirt that I put the extinction logo graphic on. It's a lot like the peace symbol of yore but with a modern twist to it.

Signal

Signal is a wonderful messaging app that has end-to-end encryption on it. It's just a really great tool if you're talking to other activists because it gives you an opportunity to feel safe and free, and it's a free space with which to speak. A long time ago, I think it was Hakim Bey who came up with the term

TAZ or Temporary Autonomous Zones, and this notion of free space. And we live in a time now where there's very, very little free space in the world. We're not very aware of how little space there really is for us to freely communicate. In places around the world, of course, censorship is increasing, places like America, places like Asia. And so being able to communicate around the world with a tool like this is really wonderful.

The Reality Bubble: Blind Spots, Hidden Truths, and the Dangerous Illusions that Shape Our World

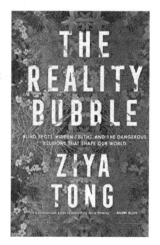

This book has kind of been described as a cross between Cosmos and The Matrix in the sense that I've been a science journalist and broadcaster for 15 years. So it's been really wonderful getting to work with scientists and seeing so many different sort of realities that they're able to see with the scientific lens. But at the same time, what I kind of started realizing was in the 21st century, we have cameras everywhere, everywhere except where our food comes from, where our energy comes from, and where our waste goes. It's really strange that fundamentally our society is completely blind when it comes to how it survives. So, I really wanted to get to the bottom of how we became the most powerful species on earth when we don't know how we survive. That was the initial sort of thing that got me on this journey, and it's trippy and I hope illuminating. And I'm just very, very excited for people to read it.

Gever Tulley
Founder of Tinkering School

Gever Tulley is founder of Tinkering School, an internationally famous summer camp where kids build amazing things from rollercoasters to wind-powered trains. He is also the founder of SF Brightworks, a K-12 school where the student is the co-author of their education, with an emphasis on learning by doing. He is also co-author of 50 Dangerous Things (you should let your children do), a book to help children and families learn to assess and mitigate risk by doing dangerous things together. He speaks and hosts workshops internationally on education and the empowerment of children, and he is constantly fooling around in the shop, building things with kids. (Published 12/7/18)

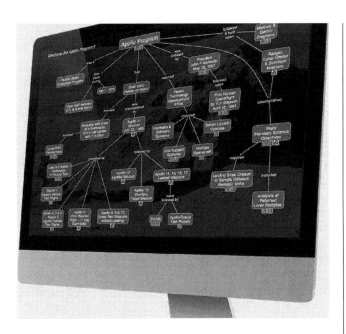

CmapTools (Concept Mapping)

I think everybody these days is familiar with a practice called mind mapping, which is trying to tease out of your own brain the connections that you make to a central concept. And then, those can get hierarchical in complexity, and they branch, and you create this map of what you know. And, years ago, a very young educator introduced me to the concept of concept mapping. This is a very distinct dialect of a mind map. You construct a model of what you know about something. And that consists of the nodes that you're familiar with in a mind map, where you've got a central concept, but it highlights the relationship between those nodes. By distinctly elevating the importance of the relationship between the concepts, we start to, very accurately, capture

what it is we know about a topic — a domain of knowledge. And, what I found in practice, especially when I was working in technology is, I would have a development team in the room, and we would start to use one of these maps as a way to make sure that we were all working on the same thing. And, as we built these maps, both interactively in software, or on a whiteboard, what I realized is that it really starts to highlight those places where you say, "Well, I don't actually know why this component is here. I don't know why we have this module. I don't know why we're doing it this way." And that would highlight the gaps, so that we could really focus our attention on closing unknown, missing knowledge gaps. It helps you find the unknown unknowns.

Highland 2

Highland 2 is developed by John August, and he developed this out of frustration, which is often where I think some of the best tools come from. He felt like there was a tyranny in the industry of people bullying screenwriters about format, and, he felt like format is the least interesting part of a screenplay. He presented such a beautifully clean and crisp writing interface, and it's built around a version of the Courier font that he cleaned up and developed at his company, which, it somehow makes me feel more like writing when I see the letters coming out in this simple, clean Courier. It simplifies everything. I'm not distracted by little blinky lights or wavy underlines, and the writing comes out. The other thing that I love is it stores all of the data as a plain text file with a variation on markdown, like clear text formatting, that is just unique combinations of simple ASCII characters. When I need to, I can jump into them, and use my familiar search tools to do global restructuring, or replace somebody's name, and then jump right back into Highland, and see it formatted as a document again.

Irwin Vice-Grip Self-Adjusting Wire Stripper

Just recently, I've fallen in love with this self-adjusting wire stripper. It is the most reliable tool I've ever put in my hand. We have yet to have it fail to perfectly strip the end of a wire. And, it requires no finesse. Even the youngest kids, who are still struggling with their motor skills, are able to set the wire in the right place, squeeze the handle, and have a perfectly stripped wire.

Trinket.io

Trinket is a terrific online browser-based Python environment, where students at our school have really had a good time doing Turtle graphics and TextAdventures, and it presents a really comfortable on-ramp where you can start with a Block-style programming environment, and then jump over into Python as they're comfortable with algorithmic thinking, and ability to express themselves. We needed a place where kids could be playful with code, but also be serious and write some real code. Unlike a lot of the online systems for kids getting into code, this supports doing a project that has multiple files, or multiple Python modules. It's a great place to develop those skills, and I can go in and look at their code, and co-edit with them. I can be sick at home and talking over the phone while they

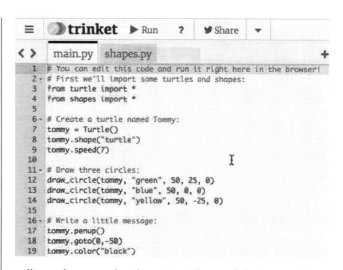

```
# You can edit this code and run it right here in the browser!
# First we'll import some turtles and shapes:
from turtle import *
from shapes import *

# Create a turtle named Tommy:
tommy = Turtle()
tommy.shape("turtle")
tommy.speed(7)

# Draw three circles:
draw_circle(tommy, "green", 50, 25, 0)
draw_circle(tommy, "blue", 50, 0, 0)
draw_circle(tommy, "yellow", 50, -25, 0)

# Write a little message:
tommy.penup()
tommy.goto(0,-50)
tommy.color("black")
```

edit, and we can be there together solving a problem, which I've done more than once.

Tinkering Labs Motor Catalyst

It's a open-ended, play-based, or discovery-based learning environment, for understanding how electric motors work, building physical contraptions to do curious and interesting things. You can build almost anything out of it. We're constantly getting pictures from kids who've built egg beaters, and somebody made a saw that could cut through a piece of paper; all kinds of little robotic creatures that scurry around on the floor. And it's all held together with rubber bands. It's very forgiving. It doesn't require precision. In fact, what it emphasizes is iteration, and that really supports a work mode of kids setting themselves a goal: "Can I make something that runs around on the floor?," and then suddenly they're like, "It's just going in circles. Can I get it to go straight?" And then they get it to go straight. And then it runs into a wall. "Oh, I know how to build it, so it stays together once it hits the wall," and it self-feeds and self-stimulates a really productive learning process that's self-directed.

Matt Velderman
Black+Decker Tool Designer

Matt Velderman is a DYIer, an engineer, inventor, and he leads Stanley Black+Decker's Breakthrough Innovation Group. (Published 11/16/17)

FlexVolt Miter Saw

This is a new product for DEWALT as of June of last year, I think. In DEWALT we have a platform called 20-volt max, and it's a very large platform. There's 130 tools or something like that that run off a 20 volt, but we wanted to make more powerful tools and ones that were more efficient. One of the ways to do that is to make a higher voltage, so we made a battery that actually converts between 20- and 60-volt mode. That's a world's first. What's really cool about it is you could take two 60-volt batteries and put them in series and get 120 volts. If you know anything about the power grid here, it's 120-volts AC coming out of your wall. We made a miter saw that runs both off two 60-volt batteries, 120-volts DC, and it will also run off of 120-volts AC coming out of your wall with safe performance, whether it's corded or cordless.

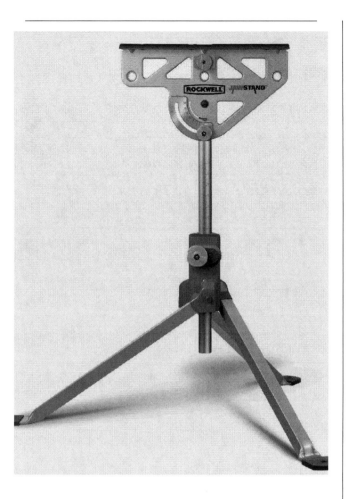

I just have not found a better way to modify things. Tools like a Dremel or any of the kind of power tool that rotates just doesn't have the precision to mate stuff together and make these clean cuts.

Rockwell JawStand

This is a clamp/stand combination that allows me to do a variety of work solo that would otherwise require another set of hands. I use it for holding doors, outfeed for a table saw or surface planer, as a support for long boards in the bench vise, to hold a deadman for installing hanging cabinets, etc.

Honda Electronics Ultrasonic Cutter

This is probably one of my favorite tools in the lab at work. We do a lot of modification of plastic. We have to make very quick prototypes and usually hacking up something that already exists. This gives me super precision to make precise, clean cuts off existing prototypes or production parts. It's like a penknife that has a small ultrasonic motor, for lack of a better word, inside of it, and it oscillates at a very high frequency with very minute movements and more or less melts the plastic as it cuts through the prototype or whatever you're trying to hack up.

Stanley Removable Compartment Professional Organizer

This is a great way to store random small parts. The real value of this system is when you commit to the system, get a bunch of them, and create a DIY storage cabinet. This an alternative to Adam Savage's sortimo recommendation. It's basically the same thing, but at a lower cost and more available. I recommend both Stanley and Harbor Freight varieties.

Jake von Slatt
Hardware Hacker

Jake von Slatt is someone that delights in making things. Hours spent in the workshop are a meditation, an end unto themselves. This results in adventures that Jake has coined "toolchain journeys," the most recent of which started with a desire to learn blacksmithing and lead to 3D printing a model to cast in aluminum to make a pulley to drive an alternator converted to a welder with a 1946 car engine to weld a pile of scrap steel into a serviceable anvil. The process is the thing. (Published 06/29/18)

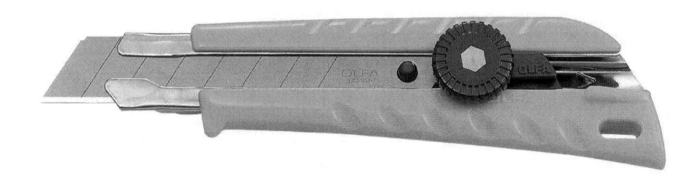

OLFA Heavy Duty Utility Knife

This was a surprise to me as I've been using regular utility knives for years and I had no idea that these existed. I've seen snap-off knives but always thought of them as disposable because the quality of what you find was so cheap. But OLFA's come from the art world, you find them in art supply store and they're especially great for cutting and any sort of foam. It's much more rigid, the blade is held really firmly, and they're just that awesome, especially for cutting things like foam, and plastics, and trimming. If you use that filler foam to fill in the areas around windows when you're installing it into the studs, the OLFA is the perfect tool for trimming that back after it hardens.

CamBam

CamBam is software for creating toolpaths for CNC machines, be they mills, routers, or plasma cutters. It is basically a two-dimensional CAD drawing tool that knows about a third dimension. So sort of like we know about three dimensions, and we live in three dimensions, but we know about the fourth dimension. This tool only lives in two dimensions, but it knows about a third dimension — up and down. Because, of course, a milling machine can move up and down, but it can't undercut, it can't get underneath something. So that's why we say it's two-and-a-half dimensions. This package lets you draw shapes and then create the code for milling operations. Those are things like drilling an array of holes, or carving out the inside of a defined space, which is called pocketing, or carving out a shape out of a plate of metal, with is called profiling, So of all of the different software packages I saw there, this was the one that allowed me to go from an idea to a finished part the quickest and the least expensively.

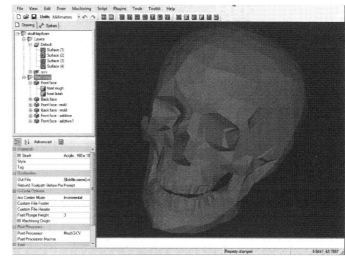

Anvil or any big chunk of metal

There is something about hitting something with a hammer that is backed up by a significant mass of steel that is so pleasurable. It's surprising how little effort it takes to accurately center punch, or flatten, or straighten something on an anvil. I use it all the time for backing things up when I center punch them, or if I'm using the little letter punch set, or I try to tap out a pin. Anytime I'm trying to carefully hammer on something, I find that I can always be much more precise and effective if I back up whatever I'm hammering on with that big chunk of steel. Just find the biggest junk of scrap iron you can lift and keep it on your workbench. You'll be amazed how often you'll use it.

BLACK+DECKER Portable Project Center

This is a very, very clever folding table made out of stamped steel. My parents gave it to me about 35 years ago and I still use it today. The split table sort of forms a vise. But it's super rigid and has a step so you can hold it down with your foot and a host of other features you won't even notice until you need them, and then you'll think to yourself, "Damn! That's genius!"

Rob Walker
The Art of Noticing

Rob Walker is the Human Resource Columnist for Lifehacker.com, and a longtime contributor to The New York Times and many other publications. He's on the faculty of Products of Design graduate program at the School of Visual Arts, and his new book from Knopf is The Art of Noticing: 131 Ways to Spark Creativity, Find Inspiration and Discover Joy in the Everyday. You can find him on Twitter and Medium at @notrobwalker. (Published 09/13/19)

Bienfang Notesketch Pad with Horizontal Lines

This is a notebook that I've used for a long time. I know that people have such strong opinions about notebooks. But what I like about it is on each page, the bottom half is ruled and the top half is blank. I like that to be able to either write things, or sketch things, or whatever. And that's what drew me to these notebooks in the beginning. I get the 8 1/2 x 5 1/2 size — the small size. I've been using them I realize now, since college. The other thing I like about these notebooks is that they're not too precious. They're actually cheap. I went through a Moleskine phase, but I never felt like I had anything worth saying to it, to ruin this beautiful object. This is spiral bound, but it's not too precious. It's not this object that you feel like you're spoiling every time you write down some dumb observations.

Switchmate for Toggle Light Switches

We happen to have these front lights that are on a standard toggle switch and I was always forgetting to turn them on at night or turn them off in the morning. I'd leave them on until noon or something, because I would just forget. And I didn't want to go through the whole rigmarole of rigging up, getting an electrician. I didn't want a problem and I randomly discovered this thing and I thought that looks perfect. It's a little box that has magnets in it that you can put over a standard toggle switch, and there's a mechanism inside that literally, physically just flips the switch up or down. Clunk, clunk. So it's a dumb smart home product, you hook it up to an app and put it on a timer. You don't need to worry about the wiring.

Decibel X Noise Meter

Decibel X is an app tells you what the decibel reading is. And that's it. That's the whole story. I get such pleasure out of it and it's kind of like junior-high-school-dork pleasure of just like, I wonder what the decibel level is in here. There's one tab that you can poke on that'll say like analogous to a quiet room or a noisy street for whatever. I have no point to this, but I find that it's one of the apps that I check the most frequently. I bet I open it as much as I open Instagram. For no good reason. I've never crosschecked it, but its answers seem intuitively right in the sense of it's loud in here now, so it's in the red zone. The red zone is considered harmful and that's like 90 to 100. A subway is 100. A jet engine is 140, 150.

In Our Time Podcast

I'm a huge fan of this podcast. I've been listening to it for some years now. The host is Melvyn Bragg. The premise is that every week he gets in three academics to talk briskly for an hour through one topic, which can be anything from Frankenstein to Ulysses Grant. It's sort of like those Great Courses, except it's all just boiled down to one hour, and it's just lightning fast. It's quite impressive.

The Art of Noticing: 131 Ways to Spark Creativity, Find Inspiration, and Discover Joy in the Everyday

This my new book. It's designed as a series of exercises and prompts and games and things you can actually do (or reflect upon) to build attention muscles or just get off your phone and enjoy noticing stuff that everyone else missed. Prompts such as:

Look Slowly. Discover the Big Within the Small. Sketch a Room You Just Left. Follow the Quiet. Review the Everyday. Hunt the Infrathin. Get There the Hard Way. Eat Somewhere Dubious. Trespass. Make a Field Guide. Talk To a Stranger. Listen to an Elder. Be Alone in Public. Make a Personal Map. Interview An Object. Care for Something.

Laura Welcher
Director of Operations at Long Now Foundation

Laura Welcher is a Linguist, Director of Operations for the Long Now Foundation, and volunteer at the Global Lives Project. (Published 02/18/15)

Yaesu VX-8DR

A lot of people think that ham radios are really big. The one that I've had for several years, is called a Yaesu VX-8DR. It's quite small. I'm a small person, I have a small hand and it fits really well in my hand, and you don't need this crazy long antenna if you're doing local communications. One of the things that I think is really great about it is, if you get your license, you can start using a couple of the popular

bands, which is, it's usually called 144 and 440, and that allows you to talk to people who have other ham radios using a set of designated frequencies. I use it to talk with people around the Bay Area. My husband and I both have ham radios and we've established frequencies that we would call each other on in case of an emergency because we work across the bay from each other, so if there was an earthquake or something like that it would be tough for us to be able to get to each other quickly and you kind of want to make sure that somebody is okay in that kind of a circumstance. Actually, ham radios have a really important function in emergencies as well because there are all of these informal groups that practice what are called directed nets. A directed net uses an agreed upon frequency, it can be simplex, so just you know, we're talking sort of point to point, or it can be using a repeater, and there's lots of repeaters set up all over the country. That allows you to communicate over farther distances. A directed net is a verbal protocol for people using a ham radio, where one person is in control of the net, and they handle all traffic that goes on between the net and the net can cover a large area. For example, where I got my license was in Marin County, and they have a set of linked repeaters all throughout the county that's used for a lot of purposes, but also emergency coordination. If they operate a directed net on those linked repeaters, they can handle emergency communications all across Marin County.

The Family Piano Doctor

When I was younger and I didn't have much of any money to spend on an instrument, I found a very cheap piano. It was an upright and it was so unremarkable I could not even tell you

light, ready to paint at a moment's notice and under-the-radar painter. A stealth, ready-to-jump-into-action painter would carry one of these. The design of this box is really great. I use it for pastels so I have dividers in it and I have a way to cushion the pastels so that they don't break. There's a way of carrying your canvases in so that they don't get messed up.

Sennelier Oil Pastels

I have a variety of different types of pastels, but the soft, super buttery ones are Sennelier. They are a French pastel. They're nice for those finishing effects because you can either do an underpainting or you can lay down the harder pastel. If you scrape one of the softer pastels over it, it just looks like shimmering light. You're laying down pure pigment. It's a wonderful, sensual experience and these colors are just so saturated. You can't really blend them like oils so you juxtapose colors to get these interesting effects. Anyways, I love them. I've enjoyed using them for a very long time.

what the make of it was. I managed to get it home. I think the deal was basically if I could move it I could have it. I got it into my house and it looked like it was in good shape, but the person hadn't maintained the tuning in about 10 years. I got myself this book, which I currently don't have a copy of. It's such a great book I loaned it out to a friend of mine after. You know, once you learn it you don't really need the book anymore. I learned how to tune a piano using that book, and as far as I know you can't even get it in digital. The book isn't available as a Kindle book or anything. It's still paper, which seems very appropriate for it.

Guerilla Painter French Resistance Pochade

This art case is for the plein air painter traveling

April Wilkerson
Creator of Wilker Do's

April Wilkerson is a maker who started building stuff out of necessity, but then it turned into a passion, and now it's her full-time job. Anything she needs, she figures out how to build, so nothing is off-limits. Woodworking, metalworking, construction, renovation. She does it all. (Published 10/26/18)

ISOtunes Bluetooth Earplug Headphones

This is a really great tool, because I'm constantly in the shop, since it's my job. I also use them pretty much any other time I'm outside of the shop. Whenever I'm doing any sort of yard work, traveling, or going to the gym. They're also, of course, noise-canceling. So I use them if I'm traveling, and I just want to block out the people next to me. The ISO is really breaking the market with reducing the cost but not reducing the quality. So these are gonna be the highest quality hearing protection that you can get on the market that are Bluetooth, outside of the Bose. And they're very affordable. You can listen to music, you can listen to podcasts, anything that you're listening to on your phone you then listen to in your ears. I have a shop full of woodworking tools and metalworking tools, yard full of a tractor, a chainsaw, weed eater, and I've never once encountered a tool that can overpower the ISOtunes.

Fairwin Nylon Web Belt

Being a female, my clothes are typically form-fitting, and I cannot stand wearing big, bulky leather belts. I discovered this nylon, it's called a military tactical belt, and it's very low-profile. They come in multiple different colors: black, gray, green. It's a game-changer belt, which is silly, but it really does make me happy. It's something that I can wear without anything else, like out in the shop, but then also it fits very nicely under my tool belt. So I can wear my belt to hold my pants up but then also not get in the way of rocking a tool belt around my waist as well. One thing that I really like about it is not only is it durable, but it doesn't have holes in it. So it has this clasping mechanism that you can cinch around your waist as much as you need it to without being constricted to a position where a pre-drilled hole is, and then having to pick between too tight or too loose. Wherever you need it, you clasp it down and that's where it stays.

Triton SuperJaws Portable Clamping System

This is a clamp that is also a vise. I use it in a variety of different ways. I have a shelf full of tools, a woodworking side and a metalworking side, and this is the most versatile tool in my shop. Regardless of what sort of project, whether it be inside my shop or outside on my job site, this tool is always used. There's a pedal on it so that you can suck up the material with the jaw, turn the Super Jaws into a locking position, and then press down with your foot, and then you can just put as much pressure on whatever it is that you're clamping that you want to. So it's essentially a vise that you clamp down with your foot. But it's as big as a sawhorse. They do fold up so that you can put them away, but I use them on every single project and it's just a daily-used tool for me.

SketchUp

SketchUp is a 3D modeling software package that I use. There is a free version and a website version. I'm dyslexic, and so my brain has a hard time keeping things straight whenever I'm just trying to think about it in my head. I discovered modeling, and this way, it gives me a way to design and visualize things before I ever step foot into my workshop and waste a bunch of time and material trying to figure it out as I go. I utilize this tool anytime I want to build something or anytime I want to pick out colors. Anytime I want to do some math that I don't want to do in my head or by longhand, I end up using this program. This is something that I definitely recommend to anybody who's thinking about designing — I mean, you can remodel your

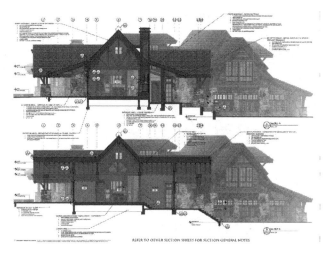

kitchen, you can design a desk. I just recently built a 4000-square-foot shop and I couldn't figure out what paint scheme I wanted. So I modeled it up, just so I can simply have a visual aid on playing around with different paint colors before going and buying 15 samples at the store.

Uni Jetstream 4&1 Pen

This one is one of those small things in my life that I absolutely love and I don't go anywhere without. It's a 4-in-1 pen almost like what you had as a child. I use a manual day planner because I just want to write, I wanna see my whole month and I don't want it digitally, and this allows me to very quickly glance at things that I use different colors for. I bought like five of them, I always carry one with me, and I have one in about every room of my house and in my shop. It's just one of those small things in life that I'm like, "Everybody should know about this."

Cameo Wood
Filmmaker

Cameo Wood is an Emmy-nominated filmmaker. She is also a former tech founder, founded an urban beekeeping store, was the first to perform Turing's Original Imitation Game experiment, and has completed grad programs in Egyptology and Medical Neuroscience. (Published 06/7/19)

Moment Anamorphic Lens

There's a company called Moment and what they do is they create incredibly high-quality lenses for photography or for filmmaking. They have this new one called an anamorphic lens which has incredibly high-quality glass, and you can just pop this right on your iPhone, and capture beautiful images. An anamorphic lens is a very high-quality type of lens. Whenever you see a film and you see this beautiful, incredibly in-depth, sort of rich looking video, and horizontal lens flares in like this widescreen letterbox look, that's indicative of being an anamorphic lens. With this you can get all the lens flares that you want and this beautiful widescreen letterbox look. They have their own app, the Moment filmmaking app, so you can control aperture, and all different kinds of frame rates to really create cinematic looking video just from your iPhone, and it's just absolutely beautiful.

Peak Design Black Slide Camera Strap

I really like Peak Design's other products like their backpacks and bags. They're very popular here in the Bay area, and I found this thing called the Slide. It looks like a regular camera strap, and where you would connect the strap to the camera, instead of having something that is permanently attached, it just has these clips. The clips are basically strings of incredibly strong material that attach to your camera using these little circular dongles hanging off your camera. When I was recently in Egypt, I was bringing my iPhone, and a mirror, this camera, and a DSLR. So rather than just having numerous camera straps which I've done in the past, I decided instead to just have one strap, and all of my cameras have these little dongle clips attached to them, so that I could just pull the camera out of my bag, snap it into my strap, and go. It only takes 10 seconds or so to just clip them in, and I found the entire system incredibly easy to use. I never had any problems with being able to get the clips on, or off, and I never had any failures where the clip failed. So, I found this incredibly useful.

myCharge 10050mAh Portable Charger

I understand that everyone has their favorite charger. I just happened to randomly get this charger while I was in an airport, and I had forgotten whichever one I usually had at that time, and now I have two or three of these. So, this particular charger looks sort of like a small silver brick that we've sort of become familiar with. It's silver, it sort of has the shape of a book, and it is 4.6 inches by 2.8 inches by around one inch, and it weighs about one pound. I love this thing because I don't need to find a plug, it doesn't have anything extra, it just has a little flip down wall plug. I just plug it into any wall, it has two cables built into it, so it has an iPhone cable — I use an iPhone — and it also has a micro USB, so I can charge other people's stuff, and in the bottom of it, it has just a regular USB plug, so I can plug any kind of USB device into it. It's 10,050 milliamp hours, so it can charge my iPhone and my iPad fully, multiple times. I've been in film festivals where I've been waiting for the next film, and everyone's phone is dying, and so I've been able to charge like three phones at a time on this while we're all waiting in line. So, especially on things like international flights where sometimes the in-seat charging isn't working,

I'm able to watch movies, and do all kinds of work just using one, or two of these. I find them just massively useful, especially when I'm traveling in the outback.

Planet E Reusable Grocery Shopping Bags

I've been using these folding heavy-duty bags for about three years now, and these are super low tech, but they are amazing. They're sort of almost cubes, they fold incredibly small, they have a solid piece of plastic built into the bottom that folds down, so that it has a solid bottom. They can carry up to about 45, 50 pounds in each. I can use these for carrying heavy liquids around. I use them at home, because they're rectangular enough that you can sort of stack them, and whenever I have donations, I can load those in and fill them with cans. I can use them for absolutely anything. Every time I go to the grocery store, all the packers are like, "These are amazing. These are the best bags I've ever seen."

Real Artists Short Film

I made a film about two years ago now called Real Artists. Real Artists is a film about a young woman who is interviewing at her dream job at an animation studio and finds that films are no longer made entirely by people. It touches on artificial intelligence and memory-erasing drugs.

Tool Index

Made in the USA
Monee, IL
28 November 2019